Let Me Enjoy

Essays, partly geographical

O. H. K. SPATE

Let me enjoy the earth no less
Because the all-enacting Might
That fashioned forth its loveliness
Had other aims than my delight.
THOMAS HARDY, *Minor Key*

METHUEN & CO. LTD

First published in Great Britain 1966
by Methuen & Co. Ltd, 11 New Fetter Lane, London EC4

© *O. H. K. Spate, 1966*

Printed in Australia

Let Me Enjoy

G
59
S6
1966

TO MY WIFE

Um encolhido ousar; uma brandura;
um mêdo sem ter culpa; um ar sereno;
um longo e obediente sofrimento:

Esta foi a celeste formosura
da minha Circe, e o mágico veneno
que pôde transformar meu pensamento.

Preface

IN view of the propensity of *Festschriften* to become memorial volumes, one is tempted to take no chances and to 'do it oneself'; and I have never been very good at resisting temptation. After all, this volume will be out of print or remaindered by 1976, so that any loyal disciples who may be left to me by then will have another chance.

All except one of these essays were written since I joined the Australian National University in 1951; and I should like here to express my heartfelt gratitude to whatever quirk of destiny led me into so pleasant a place. They represent, then, a selection from the work of thirteen years; and this selection is designed with three main purposes. Firstly, as the title of the book implies, to attempt some reflection of the joy—intellectual, moral, and emotional—which any sensitive mind must feel in contact with the inconsequential variety of human experience, and this is the unifying thread of Part I; secondly, to try to explain what it is that the craft of the geographer can bring to the understanding and generalizing of this experience, and this is the theme of Part II; and thirdly, to assert that it is not necessary to be always solemn to be serious, and this, I hope, informs the whole, including the more specialized sections on Toynbee and on Australian discovery.

The essays have been reprinted as they first appeared, with the silent adjustment of a few infelicities of phrase. In no case has any substantive expression of fact or opinion been tampered with, despite the temptation to smooth over the follies or brashness of earlier years. In only one essay—'Geography and Racism'—is there any material difference between first printing and reprint, and here the additional matter in the reprint is a faithful reproduction, from my contemporaneous notes, of what was actually said in the delivery of the paper. The temptation to revision was particularly strong here, since I must add, with deep regret, that I was unduly optimistic on the problem of the aborigines in Australia; I hope to redress the balance in a future book.

Apart from this, an effort, in the nature of the case not wholly successful, has been made to reduce (to eliminate would be impossible) the rigorous documentation which is appropriate to 'learned journals' (a rather quaint phrase, when one comes to think of it) but is just a nuisance to the wider readership which I hope to attain or seduce.

O. H. K. SPATE

The Australian National University
Canberra
August 1964

Acknowledgements

FIRST, in the pleasurable task of the acknowledgements, should come thanks to my secretary, Miss Joan Binns, for the meticulous typing of multigenic copy. I am also grateful to the editors of journals, mentioned below, for their courtesy in extending permission to reprint.

Association of American Geographers, for 'Quantity and Quality in Geography' from their *Annals*;

Australian Institute of Political Science, for 'Finis Coronat Opus?' from *Australian Outlook*;

British Broadcasting Corporation, for 'Fossils of Forgotten Empire' (published as 'Monuments of Imperial Rule in India') from *The Listener*;

Department of Geography, Aligarh Muslim University, for 'Geography and Racism' from the *Proceedings of the International Geography Seminar*;

Foreign Policy Research Institute of the University of Pennsylvania, for ' "Region" as a Term of Art' from *Orbis*, the quarterly journal of world affairs published by the Institute;

Historical Studies Australia and New Zealand, for 'Reflections on *A Study of History*' and 'Terra Australis—Cognita?';

Meanjin Quarterly, Melbourne, for 'Konarak and Sindri', 'Under Two Laws', and 'Manuel Godinho de Erédia';

Quadrant, Sydney, for 'On Being an Expert' and 'Westwards the Course';

Royal Geographical Society, London, for 'Toynbee and Huntington' from *The Geographical Journal*; and to

Yale University Press, for the extract from Huntington's *Civilization and Climate*.

Acknowledgements

Thanks are also due to Nancy Parker for the half-title illustrations on pages 1 and 183, and to Messrs B. T. Batsford Ltd for permission to reproduce the engraving on page 89 from *Maps and Map-Makers*, by R. V. Tooley, published by them in 1949.

The half-title illustration on page 247 is a self-portrait from Erédia's *Declaracam de Malaca*; the end-papers are an adaptation of his original map referred to on page 263.

Contents

Contents

People and Places

On Being an Expert

I

ALL you District Officers, whatever your Colony, know him. He comes into your office, brisk and immaculate, usually an hour before or an hour after the arranged time, and consequently just as you are beginning to fathom which of those two litigants has a slight lead in perjury, or where that five pounds to which Audit has been drawing such pointed attention had got to. Another ten minutes would do the trick, and with nice condescension ('I know you officials are always at it, my job can wait a few minutes . . .') he grants you them. But at the end of two he is fidgeting, at four he is moving in a very marked manner to the wall-map, at six he has worn you down and you wearily close the file, your concentration gone, and knowing you will have to begin the job all over again.

Then the two of you fix his itinerary. It is now—perhaps —that he displays his worst colours. You have been given only the vaguest idea of what he wants to see, but you have worked out a very nice little programme which anyone really interested in the progress of your District would accept at sight. But he is finicky to the point of sheer obstruction.

That pet little Village Improvement scheme that is going so well, and is not really so difficult to reach—well, he is sure that it is interesting, most interesting, but unfortunately it's not *quite* what he's after; and then his tour with your neighbour, an admirable fellow, was *very* successful, but it *was* rather exhausting, he's feeling the strain a bit, he's flying back tomorrow and *must* be fresh for his talk with His Excellency. . . . (Your neighbour, naturally, is a

Reprinted from *Quadrant*, Vol. 5 Pt 2, 1961.

slick type who always manages to pass his District off as a model of ordered progress, whereas you know for a fact, only you mustn't say so, that it's all whitewash . . .)

Alternatively, he has got wind (probably from the same neighbour, blast him) of that really nasty little fiasco you thought you had covered up in the Annual Report; however thick you lay on the difficulties, he gives you to understand that from youth up he has simply revelled in mud, monsoons, and mosquitoes, and nothing on earth will stop him: he'll get there if it kills him, and if he dies on your hands it will be in the very last ditch in the entire Commonwealth to which you wish official, or any, attention to be drawn.

After that he tells you how to run the District. Somehow or other he has ferreted out some fact about it that you have never heard of—something obscure, obsolete, probably obscene and certainly trivial and irrelevant. He doesn't say anything outright, of course, but he lets you see what he thinks of District Officers who don't know their Districts. That pet scheme—from his vast experience he is able to point out, with indecent gusto, the slight but fatal flaw which, he implies, ought to have been obvious to ι child. The fiasco—well, what else can be expected in an Administration so archaic as to employ the likes of you? That momentary hesitation while you are seeking the right word, one that won't be misleading—he doesn't press you, that would be bad tactics as well as bad form, he just gives a horrible knowing look and switches to another point, delighted to find something he can pass off as evasion. You can sense the pleasure with which he is mentally chewing over those well-worn phrases of his Report: 'It is regrettable that many District Officers seem far from active in ascertaining the most essential facts in the life of the people under their charge . . . a deplorable tendency to evade or minimize the consequences of misdirected official action. . . .' You just can't win.

Off duty it's as bad. He is an *ex officio* guest in your house, where he monopolizes your bathroom, upsets your servants, keeps your children up long past bedtime in clumsy attempts to make himself agreeable, drinks your whisky with no thought of the morrow (*your* morrow—his will be with the Colonial Secretary), and either pointedly neglects or even more pointedly plays up to your wife.

Yes, definitely, a low type. But, like so many of the more loathly forms of modern life, powerful and dangerous. One has to humour the beast, in the faint hope of making it relatively innocuous. Also of course it is seeing H.E. to-morrow. . . .

II

But there is another aspect to the creature, almost human; indeed, if you could see all that goes to the making of his damned Report (he damns it quite as much as you do) you might even be a little sorry for him. That brisk manner, for example—may it not at times conceal a nervous diffidence before the practical administrator, who from his experience may instantly see the slight but fatal flaw which ought to be obvious to a child but which he, the theoretic man, may miss?

Let us reverse the roles for a short course in Expertise: from now on *you* are the Expert. We will assume—and it is not always a too generous assumption—that all those qualities which mark you as a District Officer are carried over into your new role: keenness, devotion to your duty, integrity, industry, intelligence, flair for getting on with other races. . . .

Begin then by putting yourself into that neat tropical suit. Since you are by hypothesis a very junior Expert, it has quite possibly been bought with the last thirty in the bank: it ought to have been held for emergencies, but one must look decent, one might even meet H.E., and your wife has said 'you must go, it's your big chance, we'll manage somehow, don't worry'. But you do, and most of all on those parts of your travels which are otherwise amongst the most pleasant, when after days of high-pressure 'seeing people' you are journeying leisurely and alone, but for a jeep or boat crew who (thank Heaven!) have little conversation and less English; though efforts at intercommunica-

B

tion afford much unaffected merriment to both parties. Those are good hours, but liable to be stabbed by a sudden guilt-feeling.

The mere mechanics of experting are the least of it, though they have pains and penalties enough. The schedule itself and the staff-work, relying so much (it seems) on telepathy for intercom, a medium favoured doubtless for its cheapness and simplicity of operation, but with a high failure rate. The innate genius of local airways to ditch you for a couple of days on some field surrounded by all too vast open spaces long forsaken of God and man but not mosquitoes. The endless round of visits to treeless fields and throbbing oily-aired factories, when all peanut fields look alike to your untutored eyes and anything more mechanical than a pushbike has always defeated you; yet though head and feet are dull aches connected by an aching spine you must still seem alertly appreciative of the finer points dear to the hearts of your guides. The parties, invariably just after or just before such a round of visits, so that there is a chain-reaction of the hangover. The inner unease which comes from trying to keep up with the locals in the consumption of ceremonial drinks and a diet which consists substantially (and that's the word) of repulsive roots and the more terrifying and disgusting products of river or ocean, which (remembering dyspeptic Caesar and the peasant's pickles) you must appear to enjoy lest feelings be hurt—never mind your tum! *Expertise oblige*: and all this (which your friends at home are thinking is a pleasant working holiday) is as nothing to the more refined mental torments.

These amount to controlled schizophrenia: the primary professional qualification of the visiting Expert. The control is as essential as the schizophrenia, and much more difficult to attain. Yet the capacity to induce in yourself such a state of mind, and to operate effectively within it, is necessary to success. For the Expert is supposed to be impartial, which means that when he meets them he has to appear equally partial to all interested parties, who are legion.

There are degrees of suffering. At the lowest level, after

years of research, you are probably inured to the aridity of Annual Reports; but you must listen and not talk too much. If, as is most likely, you come from a University, this is in itself a difficult and a painful thing.

Doubly so, however, when it is listening to the most arrant nonsense while displaying every appearance of gaining new and exciting knowledge. Then at a party you meet the man you have long wanted to meet: he is of course going on leave tomorrow, but your hostess descends and you are carried off to lend an unwilling ear to troubles with the storekeeper or the housegirl—and this to the interruption of the marriage, or at least the love at first sight, of true minds. Or you are locked in a ring of alcoholic bawdy, while from behind your shoulder come snatches of a really vital talk. And there is also the excruciating frustration of trying to converse with those who are too suspicious, too frightened, or just too dumb to tell what they know.

It goes without saying that a large proportion of those you meet will regard you with amused tolerance (they have had Experts before) and another large fraction with perhaps well-founded suspicion of what you are up to. The minority which seems really enthusiastic (you in turn shrewdly suspect) are relying on you to say with explosive effect what they have been whispering, but dare not proclaim aloud, for years. You are the radical Forlorn Hope to mount their breach for them; tough luck if you get shot to pieces, but then as an outsider you are expendable. After all, you have your getaway ready and won't have to live years with the other party, and it's all in a good cause.

The multiplication of your personalities goes on. You readily assume the part of the modest eager questioner; but you must also accept (striking the difficult mean between over-humility and over-assurance) that queer mixture of contempt and homage with which so many Practical Men regard the academic type. Many of those you meet will not be able to understand that you are not an Expert in everything, able to meet offhand any question under or even not under the sun, such as: How can good Muslims who happen to be wintering at the North Pole, when and where there is no sun, know in which direction to turn for Mecca? An improbable situation, one might think, but one Expert had to cope with it (and he had forgotten the schoolbook diagrams) when he was publicly referred to, by a Syrian *moulvi*, as a Specialist in All Things. When the eager young student takes you for an omniscientist, all that need be done is to put on some easy donmanship and stifle the conscience; but you must also recognize when the question is tendentious or tactical, coming from the man who will say 'That fellow was here last year, and when I asked him he didn't know the difference between millet and sorghum.' On such occasions you must demand, suavely but firmly, the deference due to your expertise . . . a little difficult if you don't know the difference.

Then there are the normal hazards of the chase. Protocol: you have just got used to calling on the Chief first and the District officials second when you find yourself unawares in a Province where this is a deadly affront to Government. So often the man who really knows is on leave, and you must pretend—it is difficult—that the Acting Stooge sitting in his chair is just as good. Or you know that the second-in-command has the real *nous*, but his Departmental Head knows it too, and has been looking forward to a long talk—and your schedule has been fixed (by whom?) to allow of only one long talk. The man you have revered from afar turns out, now you know a bit about the facts, to be a pompous ass; on the other hand, that other fellow you have scornfully judged by some misquotation out of context is actually the best informed and most thoughtful of the lot—and of course by some fantastically indirect and crooked way that bright remark of yours in the Senior Common Room has filtered back to him.

But always, always, the strain and stress of being all things to all men, entering into everybody's enthusiasms and sharing everybody's gravest misgivings: earnest and idealist with the Mission and the Young Men in a Hurry; sober and precise with the technicians; worldly and broadly statesmanlike with Kings or at least Colonial Secretaries; coarsely cynical in club or pub—this last at any rate is likely to come easy! And you must watch your step in these deep waters veiled with thin ice. Irony may often come to your aid, but then it is not always safe to rely on the other chap being as thick-witted as he looks.

It is the only way to do it: you must take a back-sight to every bearing or you will go hopelessly astray. But this means balancing delicately between informant and informant; you may very likely be the only person in the confidence of both sides, and if there is a leak they'll know just where. Yet the leak may be needed to prime the pump.

So you must treat the most vulgar gossip as if it were vitally impressive Top Secret information; conversely (everything in your trade has its converse) you must assume an air of knowing all about it when tantalizing scraps of really confidential stuff come out, making a rapid mental note—a paper one would be fatal. You must deplore (according to present company, and without ever going too far) the incurable laziness of the native labourer and the unspeakable greed of the European employer; must be suitably denigratory (but always remembering to put in a saving clause, just in case) with X when discussing Y, and *vice versa*; be prepared to discover unlikely virtues in a man whom you know to be a scoundrel, and listen calmly while the base revile the good—and this last is a hard test indeed.

Finally—or more accurately penultimately—you must accept with outward equanimity the things they will by now be saying about you. Being equally partial to all parties—that is how you must get your data; but you must remember Harold Nicolson's dictum about the Irish North and South: people so often do not want you to love them, they want you to hate their enemies. If you have really passed yourself off as all things to all men, you must not be surprised if in the end you appear in as many shifting guises as Proteus; and since on comparing notes each side will naturally concede to the other your vices and refuse your virtues, you cannot justly complain if at one and the same time you are written off as a long-haired very brash young man, a balding middle-aged fossil, a violent reactionary, and a violent revolutionary.

Supposing that you have surmounted all these hazards and endurances, beside which the demands of Kipling's *If* may well seem child's play, there remains one stern trial more: the agonies of composition, the Report itself. You will, of course, hold ever before you the awful warning of Dr Endorn Weltsz.

That unfortunate and misguided man, the lasting disgrace of his University, turned in an Absolutely Honest Report, in which he said exactly what he thought about everybody: his schizophrenia broke loose from control. In itself this was merely a quixotic aberration; he was quietly removed to a Home for the Maladjusted, and there the matter should have rested. But somehow he leaked it to *Time*. HMG were gravely concerned; Dean Rusk and Mr Khrushchev were for once agreed in their object of denunciation; and several Latin American, United Arab, and Southeast Asian Republics began to talk of withdrawing from UNO. The situation was saved only by the prompt action of UNESCO, which forthwith launched a Major Project for Expert Reports on the Ethical Stylistic and Technical Standards of Expert Reports. Dr Weltsz was forgotten in one world-wide United National yawn. . . .

However: all your facts, ideas and conclusions—at least all that are fit to print—must now go down on paper. They don't look so good as they did, somehow; and even those epigrams which retain some sparkle had better stay locked up in your filing cabinet, though if you fancy yourself as a stylist this will be a bitter wrench (you can use them all up in the seminar when you get back). But all those gaps and loose ends, those notes indicating (illegibly) a brilliant train of thought you will never catch again, those doubtful bits you never got round to verify—how in Heaven's name to check them *now*? Out they go, even though they would have helped the argument along so nicely at a tricky point: for you are well aware that there are plenty of people who, if you make a bit of a bloomer on the production of colza oil in the Lower Septik, will loudly deduce that your views on the more important problem of land tenure in Upper Drongoland are hopelessly unsound and dangerous.

The attempt to please everybody will only result in *'Another* of those smooth wishy-washy official Reports . . .' And you cannot in honesty disguise your convictions, formed after all from patient enquiry by a man trained in enquiry, free (he hopes) from doctrinaire preconceptions and (to begin with anyhow) from local prejudice, and devoting his whole powers continuously for some months to seeing as a whole a problem which those who know the country much better can rarely think about except from their own particular angle and in a scanty fatigued leisure.

So you come to the most delicate task of all: to put what is in you into argument sufficiently well-knit to withstand criticism (not all of which will play fair), presented forcibly enough to command attention yet not so provocatively as to set up an instant defence reaction; to balance with utmost nicety between your ideal and what you can hope to get away with; to take calculated risks with those half-known factors in high places which may spell acceptance or rejection.

But at last the Report is in. You have typed yourself, with loving care, the covering letter to H.E., taking a Gibbonian pleasure in the high formalism of its language. One last and best party with the brighter spirits, and through the alcoholic haze you are airborne, to face the quite impossible academic arrears you know will have overflowed from desk to floor, the bills which have been mounting up, and a wife who will be glad to see you but somehow will never quite allow for the fact that you were sixty miles from a telegraph office on the baby's birthday.

III

Still, it wasn't so bad as all that really. Nobody was rude, hardly anybody what you could call non-co-operative even, you kept your end up quite well. You met a lot of fools, but then you met quite a few wonderful people, white, black, and inbetween, whose talk and whose hospitality will glow in your heart for a long time. Some wonderful places, too, a fine bag of colour slides, and a lot of stories which will go down very well in the Common Room. Your list of publications in the University Calendar will be the envy of your Department and will look fine when you apply for a Chair —not so long now, after this. Your wife is sufficiently modernist and functional in her taste to be delighted with the more archaic and clumsy pieces of craftwork you have picked up. Yes, decidedly it was worthwhile.

Decidedly. And above all you have done a good job of work, used your God-given brain and the skills your society has taught you to help simple people less fortunate than yourself.

Or have you?

For there are sharper discomforts yet. Even when he is dealing with a world of shared experience expressed in a common language, there are traps enough, nice points of tactics and ethics; but there is another side to the Expert's work, from which he may be lucky to escape with an unscarred conscience—that is, if he has a conscience and is not blinded by cocksure pride in his own expertise. Perched up on the only chair, with notebook and pen, the too-obtrusive tools of his trade, he must wrestle in his loneliness to break through the dark curtains of diversity of tongues and of life experienced. The ancient curse of Babel is upon him; he must fumble with concepts from another world, transmitted through another mind—the mind of the interpreter, who, just because of his intermediate position, may not be truly at home in either the old world or the new.

His own system of thought is likely to be impersonal, abstract, generalizing; it is a normal condition of his job that he must take long views; at whatever cost to his feelings, he must refuse to be seduced from his main objective by local sympathies and indignations. But those whose experience and thinking he must unravel are most at home in the personal, the local, the particularized; tomorrow is more important than next year, let alone next decade; often they cannot see much beyond the local exaction, the shifting boundary-pegs, the petty tyrants of their fields. They express themselves in the halting language of earthy experience, articulate only in concrete fact or a dry salty peasant image or a laconic, gnomic summation of the eternal commonplaces.

From these innumerable but incomplete facets of an alien world the Expert must try to capture the feeling and the general form of life, and to construct some generality which shall be at once manageable in the world of affairs and yet not too neglectful or distorting of human facts—of the pride of men who own little but their pride in an identity stemming from ancient ways, who would not willingly lose that nor should be robbed of it, but who yet reach out for new values in the strange new world before them. They long to master that perilous navigation from the old to the new, yet fear to lose sight of their ancestral shores. It is for the Expert to help them chart their course; and how can he be sure of his own plotting amidst so many shifting variables?

He cannot be sure. However convinced he may be of the rightness of his recommendations in the abstract, their working out will be far from abstract and will not be his, even were he skilled to *do* as well as to *say*. 'Implementation' will be at the mercy of a thousand unforeseeable shifting factors of the market, of personality in rulers and ruled, of politics local and world-wide. That lucky phrase which catches the eye of Authority—what if it be the wrong phrase after all? For those with whom he talked in those nights around the bowl, what he writes in some distant office may mean more taxes for no visible return, or it may bless their fields with increase, their children with new heart for a new life; he simply cannot be sure. Even if it will spell a better life for thousands unborn, those tens or scores who have held his hand in theirs may never know this—and may remember him as the man after whom life became tougher, lost some of its colour and savour: the man who let them down.

The Expert is one of the figures of fun of our day, and often doubtless deservedly: there are simple problems and simple-minded Experts content (not always wrongly) with the good intentions and facile recommendations of our improving age. But often he may have in his hands not just the 'progress' but the real happiness of thousands or tens of thousands; and that is not so funny. Often his heart must go out, in that strange disquiet which is love but not an equal love, to people not without sense or shrewdness, but caught up in the world of the market, so infinitely stronger, so often less humane, than their own, with which they must *somehow* come to terms. Yet the heart alone is quite as treacherous a guide as the mind alone; peoples have been wrecked by kind but uncandid friends as well as by base exploiters.

So the questions must be faced: who am I that I should take this responsibility for the ordering of other men's lives? Yet if I do not take it, do not use my God-given brain and the skills my society has taught me, am I not wasting that one Talent which is death to hide? One cannot, in honesty to oneself as to others, fall back on the vaguely benevolent statement of nothing much. The problem must be followed even if it leads to the sapping of cherished habits of thought and feeling, certainly to the forgoing of the delights of mental brilliance; it must be given all that one has both of intellectual passion and of human feeling—and yet these two must be disciplined into strict balance. And who but an expert fool would be sure he had done that?

Konarak and Sindri

Fertility Ancient and Modern

20 m. N.E. from Puri is *Kanarak* (P.W.D. Inspection Bungalow: permit from Executive Engineer, S. Divn., Cuttack: supplies to be taken), celebrated for its *Black Pagoda*. From January (perhaps earlier) to June a car can approach close to the temple, via Pipli on the Cuttack road and Gop, 53 m. (3 hr.). The shore route along the beach takes 10-12 hours by bullock cart by night . . . but much of the decoration is licentious . . .

A Handbook for Travellers in India, Pakistan, Burma and Ceylon (London: John Murray, 17th ed., 1955), pp. 334-5.

Introduction to Konarak

The incurious masters of sailing ships standing close in to the flat coast of the Bay of Bengal, on this last lap of the dreary voyage from the Cape to Hooghly or Chinsura or Fort William, had little use for the niceties of local nomenclature, but were not unobservant of good landmarks. Long before *Juggernaut* became a hackneyed metaphor of bad journalism, the Great Temple of Jagannatha, Lord of the World, at Puri was succinctly noted on the charts as the White Pagoda. Some twenty miles further on a darker tower rose behind the low dunes, to become, inevitably if inaccurately, the Black Pagoda. These captains, Portuguese or Dutch or English, would have been mightily unimpressed had they been told that this Sun Temple at Konarak represented the finest flowering of the rich and overflowingly vital culture of medieval Orissa, a monument which could at least jolt the scepticism (in general perhaps well-founded)

Reprinted from *Meanjin*, Vol. 16 No. 4, 1957.

of hard-boiled Western materialists regarding a Golden Age of Hindu society. But one may suspect that had they landed and inspected its outer walls, these 'rude and bourgeois seamen' would have felt a startled but appreciative interest in the uninhibited realism there displayed. How is it that a building in which a large proportion of the sculptures simply cannot be reproduced in even the most academic publication can yet be a joyous aesthetic experience, even spiritually exhilarating?

That this paradox is fact is evidenced by a long record of impressions: Konarak has been called the only Hindu temple 'which has wrung an unwilling tribute even from the Mohammedans'—though it must be admitted that this tribute comes from Akbar's devoted disciple Abu-l-Fazl, and the Islam of Akbar's court was so sophisticated and eclectic as to deviate eventually into plain heresy. But perhaps the best introduction to Konarak comes from the first description of it (at least in any detail) in English, in Stirling's *An Account, Statistical and Historical, of Orissa Proper,* published in 1825:

> The Black Pagoda even in its present imperfect and dilapidated condition presents a highly curious and beautiful specimen of ancient Hindu temple architecture. . . . If the style of the Black Pagoda, in the rude and clumsy expedients, apparent in its construction, reveals a primitive state of some of the arts, and a deficiency of architectural skill, at the period of its erection, one cannot but wonder at the ease with which the architects seem to have welded and managed the cumbrous masses of iron and stone used for the work. . . . It must be allowed that there is an air of elegance, combined with massiveness, in the whole structure which entitles it to no small share of imagination. There is much, however, in this remarkable building which it is difficult either to describe or to comprehend. . . . The human figures are generally male and female, in the most lewd and obscene attitudes, frequently in the very act of sexual intercourse. . . . The skill and labour of the best artists seems to have been reserved for the finely polished slabs of chlorite, which line and decorate the outer faces of the doorways. The whole of the sculptures on these

figures, comprising men and animals, foliage, and arabesque patterns, is executed with a degree of taste, propriety, and freedom which would stand a comparison with some of our best specimens of Gothic architectural ornaments. . . .

Stirling's is naturally a very average and outside view, coming from an age in which, despite the already existing vogue of Kalidasa's lyrical drama *Sakuntala* (which called forth a perhaps too laudatory epigram from Goethe), the cultural heritage of India was scarcely known, still less understood or appreciated. There had in fact been a sharp decline from the liberal and humanistic quasi-acceptance of Sir William Jones in the 1780s to Macaulay's instantaneous scorn, so brutally complete in its incomprehension as to recall the stock response of the Duchess in Alice: 'Off with his head!' (This is not to say that Macaulay's cold utilitarian douche was not useful in its way and age: one must never forget that he looked forward to the greatest triumph of British rule—its abdication when its mission was done.)

With better lights, derived from a century of Indic studies, than were available to Stirling, I may perhaps try to record something of what Konarak seemed to say to me:

I

So leans this Titan shape against the dawn:
the massy chariot of the quickening Sun
honours its Lord beside the Eastern Sea,
rearing, a mountain wave, its towering flanks
rippling with subtle shifting patterns, caught
a frozen moment of the world's restless dance,
a moment snatched from out the eternal flux
and intricate exquisite tracery of Time.
Almost it seems the straining stallions heave
and the great wheels begin their cyclic path;
almost I hear the drums, the cymbals' clash,
and the rejoicing multitude that hails
with one tumultuous shout the Father of Life;
while in a rapt and quivering ecstasy
Earth, Mother of All Living, waits her Lord.

II

Its porches are of music, and their stone
transmute to lyric; like battalions thrown
in wild yet disciplined escalade, ascend
in sinuous legions dances without end
to cadences unending of the flutes
conches, drums, cymbals, till the very brutes,
those winding files of elephants and horse,
partake the rapture, and their native force
is tamed and tuned to festal gaiety:
regal, processional, yet spontaneous, free
the twining rhythms.
          On the further wall,
the massive fabric of the cyclic hall,
where the great wheels tell the revolving hours,
their fretted spokes wreathed as a bride with flowers,
strange rampant beasts their tireless watches keep,
lion and leogryph, and never sleep
the guardian Planets.
          In the panels curled
lies all man's life, his rich abundant world
wrought to a microcosm: under the sign
of genial Polity arts and arms entwine
in joyous pageant—rioting above
all else, the multitudinous forms of love,
that natural lust of life, our living's root,
the seed, the sowing, and the ripening fruit,
caress and consummation and the flame
of procreant Joy by which all Being became:
and as their children candent with desire
the Mother of All Life and All Life's Sire
relight eternally the engendering fire.

III

But pass the threshold. In these solemn shades
The music dwindles and the pageant fades;
Silent and reverend this court austere
Peopled by other forms. The God is here.

Obviously such an all-embracing work, as it were an
equivalent in stone of Shakespeare or *Faust*, will say different things to different men, and will speak far more clearly

to a perhaps pantheist Hindu than to an agnostic. Yet it does speak a universal language; and one need not, indeed cannot, be cynic enough to say that it is simply the language of sex. For standard Victorians such as Hunter and Fergusson discerned clearly, behind what must have seemed to them a repulsive garment of eroticism, the purity and nobility of its aesthetic appeal. I think, then, that my interpretation is an entirely possible one, and is perhaps the answer to the question posed at the beginning of this essay: how is it that a work so heavily laden with the most unrestrained eroticism can yet seem so healthy and right? But the interpretation so far is simply individual impressionism, and to make the case more generally valid some gloss is needed.

Konarak: the setting and the structure

The great age of Orissan architecture corresponds fairly closely with that of the earlier Gothic cathedrals. The new capital of the State at Bhubaneswar shows some very interesting adaptations of traditional motifs to modern styling, and has a certain rawness and raggedness strongly reminiscent of early Canberra; but around it lie some of the classics of the Orissan style. This reached maturity in the Lingaraj temple of A.D. 1000 and the exquisite little Raja-rani, which is contemporary with the Norman Conquest; the huge Jagannath at Puri belongs to the later twelfth century. Konarak itself, the supreme achievement of a great school, was built by King Narasimha who reigned from 1238 to 1264. This is significant, for about this time the first serious Muslim threat to Orissa was decisively defeated, and Konarak is probably to some extent a monument of victory. It is clear that Orissan society was then at its highest pitch, and this is reflected in the superb vitality shown alike by the massive planning of the structure as a whole and by the abounding social detail of its sculpture.

Siting, plan, elevation, decoration in the Hindu temple are all determined by an intricate cosmic symbolism, worked out in far greater detail than the analogous symbolism of orientation, cruciform shape, and emphasis on the

19

spire in the Gothic cathedral. In Orissa (and elsewhere) this resulted in a standard pattern of three major elements: porch, ceremonial hall, sanctuary; and the general proportions of these are constant. So also, to a great extent, are the placing and nature of the sculptural ornament; but in detailed execution there is room for subtle and almost infinite variety; much as the almost uniform design of the seventeenth century houses along the great canals encircling central Amsterdam is diversified by varying treatment of entrances and gables.

Although Konarak is incomplete in that there is no sanctuary—it is not clear that it was ever finished—the planned proportions can be worked out from surviving complete temples; and they were impressive indeed. The porch is a small building about 50 feet square, which probably had a stepped pyramidal roof like that of the next component, the *jagmohan* (ceremonial or audience hall), which is the major surviving structure, nearly 100 feet square and rising to 128 feet. Beyond it the great *sikhara* or spire of the sanctuary would probably have towered to some 225 feet, a huge sky-pointing cone, strongly ribbed both vertically and horizontally and surmounted by an umbrella-shaped capping—a gigantic lotus—carrying a finial. This tripartite elevation produces a singularly bold and harmonious massing, yet set off by minor structural motifs which give an elegant lifting effect, as in the helicopter-like kiosks of Mogul architecture. All this is carried out in a sandstone which has weathered to a predominantly rusty gold colour, and by the unsophisticated technique of corbelled vaulting.

Such are the bones of the structure, which amply bear out Bishop Heber's dictum that the Indians 'planned like Titans'. But the detail goes far beyond the criticism implied in his rider 'and finished like jewellers'—a criticism which after all could be applied to the Milton whom the Bishop probably loved. Certainly much of the sculpture, especially the foliate ornament, is as delicate as filigree; but much is cast in heroic mould. More especially is this true of the caryatid-like figures on the roof and of the great free-standing horses in the courtyard, monumental in the highest

degree and fully equal to the noble steeds of the Parthenon
or the Han tombs, symbols at once of power and of control.

The porch, which seems to correspond to the *nata-mandir*
or dancing-hall of a royal palace, carries on its walls figures
of dancers and musicians, generally female, literally in hundreds, in rows of niches or panels separated horizontally
by friezes, only a few inches high, of birds, marching
soldiers, and elephants. The little elephants are particularly
attractive: there must be thousands of them, in unending
jolly procession. It is in a sense mass-production: this is and
must be craftsman's work, not that of an 'individual creative
artist', and indeed legend has it that 1,200 masons and sculp-
tors were employed for twelve years, at the cost of twelve
years' revenue of the kingdom. Yet, though very similar or
identical poses recur again and again, the total impression
is of remarkable spontaneity, worlds apart from the com-
mercialized factory-production of Graeco-Buddhist figures
in the Gandharan sites of northwest India, the rococo fantasies of the Hoysala school in the Deccan, or the mechanical virtuosity of the later Dravidian temples of the south,
sophisticated to a harsh dry spikiness, despite the superb
harmony of their massive towers. The walls of the *nata-
mandir* at Konarak are crowded with a disciplined tumult
of gaiety.

Approaching the *jagmohan*, the first things to strike the
eye are likely to be the great stone wheels, about eight feet
high, placed around its base. There are twenty-four of
these: the whole structure is conceived as a gigantic Chariot
of the Sun. The richness of the décor is astounding. The
wheels themselves are fretted with intricate foliate designs,
and each of their eight major spokes (as well as each hub)
carries a roundel with tiny but deeply-carved human figures.
Like the walls of the *nata-mandir*, the basement tier, against
which the wheels are placed, has a cellular texture, formed
by the strong horizontals of mouldings and friezes (with
more hosts of delightfully Disneyish elephants) and the ver-
ticals of niches and pilasters crowded with figures. These
include mythological beasts, lions, griffins, and their cross
the leogryph; *nagas* and *naginis* (serpents with male and

21

c

female human torsos); panels of genre pictures of considerable social realism; and scores of *mithunas,* couples (or indeed triads) engaged in a wide variety of amorous activities.

Above this basement tier rise the main walls, with much more restrained but correspondingly more massive decoration, which consists mainly of figures, more than life-size, of riders on lions or leogryphs trampling prostrate elephants, and of *mithunas.* It is important to note that these are clearly placed according to strict rules, the various subjects succeeding each other in a regular order; and here too we are moving out of the domain of the craftsman into that of the individual master. This is still more obvious on the roof, which recedes in three great steps separated by two tiers of colossal statues of female cymbalists, drummers, flautists, and other musicians. Although the figures conform to the normal canons of medieval India in the emphasis on the bosom, the erotic element has disappeared: instinct with grace and rhythm as they are, their general effect is of a monumental dignity.

Finally there are the statues of the Sun God, Surya, himself, and his attendants—the nine Planets, his charioteer son, and the horses of the dawn. These are not in the sandstone of the other sculptures, but in green chlorite, as if to emphasize separation from the mundane (if at times fantastic) atmosphere of the décor. For not alone has eroticism vanished, but even sensuousness: the details of jewellery and of finely-patterned drapery are rendered with incredible finesse, but the attendants display nothing but a chaste devotion, the God stands in a formal hieratic pose, statuesque and immobile, severe, serene.

Konarak: the problems

What sort of society was it that could move from a wild erotic to austerity on the walls of the same building, what lies behind this strange juxtaposition, and how is it that these two extremes yet seem in keeping?

For a suggestion at least of an answer to the first question (on which the others largely depend) we may look at some of the small genre reliefs. These represent Goethe's 'the little

world, and then the great': domestic and state affairs, private
and public life; and they are very varied. Merely listing
the titles of those few reproduced in Sudhanshu Chowdury's
lovely volume *Konarak*, we have: military supply; pro-
cessions of horses and elephants; boar and tiger hunting;
trapping of wild elephants; the camp of a trading caravan;
a mother and child on a palanquin; a tug of war, for all the
world as at a modern school sports day. Some of the details
can be seen in India to this day, the little vignettes which
stand out in memories of dusty roadsides: the woman
pounding rice in a mortar; the heavy bullock car; the crude
pots on the earthen fireplace; the servants squatting and
chatting until their master arrives. Two of the most famous
represent an indubitable giraffe—a reminder of the widespread trade connections of the Orissa and Coromandel
coasts—and a charming scene in a royal nursery, where the
king, about to go on a journey, is playing with a child on
his lap, while an older child leans from behind over his
shoulder. To me, one of the most significant is a battle
scene: there is some very spirited sword-play at one end,
while at the other a group of prisoners, submissive but not
abject, are approaching the king. In a space about four feet
by eight inches the artist has managed to convey a very
distinct impression that everything is under control: the
war is conducted by Officers and Gentlemen, and the rules
will be observed.

The general picture cannot be mistaken: it is that of a
society well-ordered, civil, healthy, happy, self-confident.
Such a society can of course consist with institutions highly
undemocratic to modern eyes. It must be remembered that
deltaic Orissa is agriculturally rich, and was then probably
more fertile and certainly less over-populated than it is now;
so long as warfare was kept on the borders life could be
easy enough, even were rulers capriciously despotic, as indeed it was under the better and more pacific monarchs of
Burma in quite recent days, in a not dissimilar geographical
and human setting. One does not of course have to assume
that everything in the Orissan garden was lovely, that it was
happy all through; but I do not think that a society which

was not by and large in a thoroughly sound state could have produced such a wide range of pictures of itself without something ugly creeping in: think for example of the naked poverty which breaks into some Egyptian art, the sheer sadism of the reliefs executed to their own greater glory by the Assyrians, the Nazis of the ancient world.

To come to the particular point of the eroticism, it is important to be clear both as to its extent and its place in the general scheme. The placing of the larger *mithunas* is clear as to the latter: they have an explicit role, and not a minor one. As to the extent, phrases such as 'amorous dalliance' are very weak euphemisms indeed: few holds are barred. *Mithunas* are not uncommon in earlier Hindu temples, but except at Khajuraho (to be discussed later) they are rarely if ever as prominent as at Konarak.

It can of course be assumed, by that sort of person, that they are simply advertisements for temple courtesans; at the other end of the scale they can be explained away by highly portentous symbolism. In between, perhaps, is Zimmer's reference to 'the sensuous delights . . . of the sun-god's celestial realm, where "bhoga is yoga", "delight is religion" '.

It is, indeed, perfectly true that Hindu art is very heavily charged with significant gestures and attributes; true also that, as C. P. Fitzgerald puts it in *China: A Short Cultural History*, *yin* and *yang*, 'negative and positive, female and male, dark and light, powers typified in the Earth and the Sky, the great dual forces which control the universe'—this is one of the greatest archetypal patterns of mythology. But the more high-flying metaphysical symbolists carry matters to extremes: it is absurd to think that great artists are at all times, like the Hogarth of *The Rake's Progress*, obsessed with a ruthless determination to ensure that every detail, even a scrap of paper, carries a heavy moral load. In overt reaction to this all-out orientalizing some Indian scholars, including one of the greatest authorities on Orissan art, have gone so far as to suggest that much of the *mithuna* sculpture is simply the personal expression of the artist; almost, as it was put to me, 'having fun'—and the analogy

24

was made with the expressions of a very secular attitude to life, that of *l'homme moyen sensuel*, found here and there in Gothic art. Undoubtedly when religion has had almost a monopoly of aesthetic patronage, artists have now and then taken advantage of opportunities and as it were captured the Church to their own ends: but this really cannot explain an emphasis so deliberate, so explicit, as exists at Konarak. There is simply too much eroticism, too openly displayed and too formal in its placing, for it to be regarded as other than an integral part of the grand design; it is no mere by-product. This openness, the obvious normality of it, also militates against the naïve suggestion (attractive to the ghastly sentimentality so prevalent in the middle reaches of modern Indian life) that the erotic sculptures were placed on the outer walls as a psychological test: if you could put them out of your mind when you reached the real sanctum, you were a fit worshipper of the God! Konarak has no truck with this furtive prurience.

The architectural and iconographic expression of Hindu cosmology and theogony is a highly technical subject, and my own view is that of the merest novice. Yet it seems logical, and consistent with the authorities, to adopt a position between the mystic and the earthy. The temple is after all to the glory of the Sun, the Father of Life: therefore fertility symbolism is appropriate. But it is not directly to Earth, Mother of All Living: therefore this symbolism is phallic, not yonic.* This is after all not incompatible with the *mithuna* as emblem of the unity of Essence and Substance, humanity and divinity (or any number of such pairs); but if, as seems implied by some, this coupling is the supreme moment of realization (and of the melting away of all external accident), then one might expect it to be reserved for the culminating sanctuary or rite, and not so liberally displayed on the outer bounds. And indeed where the sexual act is most directly pressed into the service of self-realization in union with the Godhead, as in the Tantric

* *Yoni*: among Hindus, the female power in nature, or a symbol of it.

sects, it seems distinctly esoteric. But Konarak is not at all esoteric, and it has been suggested, with much plausibility, that the Sun cult included orgiastic festivals. This should not be too shocking: as Zimmer points out in *Philosophies of India*, 'among most of the peoples known to anthropologists and historians there has been an institutionalized system of festivals—festivals of the gods and of genii of vegetation—whereby, without danger to the community, the conventional fiction of good and evil could be suspended for a moment'. We may see a last faint flicker of this genial polity in the Christmas mistletoe. . . .

This then appears to be the answer, or at least a rational answer, to the major problem with which we began: that all this coupling is not in its own right merely, nor yet merely a metaphysical symbolism abstracted entirely from the real life of man. Either way it could topple over the narrow edge between eroticism and pornography, as we may perhaps see by comparison with the temples of Khajuraho in central India. Here (judging by photographs only) the peril has not been avoided; a very competent judge, O. C. Gangoly, speaks of a 'conscious and aggressive vulgarity'. The general massing of the Khajuraho temples has broad affinities with the Orissan style and may have influenced it; in some cases it is perhaps superior in its harmony. At its best the Khajuraho sculpture is very beautiful indeed; but taken as a whole, it seems to have a dryness and harshness of line in comparison with the warmth and fluidity of Konarak, and this in itself contributes to that aggressiveness of which Gangoly speaks. But more important is the actual nature of the *mithunas*: if few holds are barred at Konarak, none at all, even impossible ones, are barred at Khajuraho, and the Citragupta temple reproduces the most absurd acrobatics of the *Kama-sutra* (that miscalled 'Art of Love' which is really a pedantic classification as dry and dull as Kinsey) until it ends in the coldest and most inhuman fantasies. 'Perverse' Konarak may now and then be; but it is nothing if not human, and as a rule its sculptures are suffused by a saving grace, which perhaps springs from the obvious healthy normality of the society depicted in the reliefs of ordinary life, and issues in a sensuous, even sensual, but yet holy joy.

Joyousness: that is indeed the overwhelmingly dominant note of Konarak. And so it is not only acceptable as a great work of art—the Khajuraho temples, however alien, are that—but is actually exhilarating as an expression of the mysterious alchemy of love by which a word or a gesture evokes 'a wonder and a wild desire', of the procreant joy by which all life much beyond the amoeba sustains itself, of the spirit of the great Lucretian invocation (in the opposite phase) of Venus Genetrix—

> delight of Deity and mortal man,
> engendering Venus, breathing yourself through all
> under the heavens and their gliding stars,
> ship-laden seas and fruit-encumbered lands;
> for every living thing only by you
> conceived, can rise to look upon the sun:
> you, Goddess, you the winds, the darkling clouds
> flee, and avoid your advent; for you alone
> the manifold earth spreads out its store of flowers,
> the plains of ocean laugh, and the calmed skies
> gleam in wide radiance of flowing light . . .
> you thrill the breasts of all created beings
> with genial love, the passionate quickening heat
> to renew the generations of each kind.
> Since you alone control the fabric of things
> and without you the shining shores of day
> unvisited of all life must remain
> nor aught of joy or loveliness be made. . . .

New times, new pilgrimages

Today 'the prime needs of India are more fertility in the fields and less in the home'. The places of pilgrimage of the new India are designed to the former end.

At many of these the visitor of any imagination may well feel an analogous excitement to that evoked by the massive planning and exquisite detail of Konarak, and its underlying rhythm of pulsating life. The great thermal power station at Bokaro in the Damodar, for example, a bold and clean-cut building with an admirable use of external colour, enshrines a multitudinous gadgetry as meticulous and in its precise functioning as beautiful as the legions of dancers and gay elephants on the *nata-mandir* at Konarak; there is an elemental feeling by the penstocks of a big hydro plant, vast weights of water perpetually thrusting through the flanged steel; and through the halls and crypts throbs the perpetual hum of the turbo-generators ensconced in their pits like gigantic whirling *lingams*.

Impressive too are the great dams such as Bhakra on the Sutlej, where the atmosphere is positively American or Russian: the highest straight concrete dam in the world, where even the upper coffer-dam, a mere temporary convenience, is over 200 feet high. Bhakra indeed prides itself on not only borrowing but devising new techniques, such as pre-cooling of the aggregate; and it is also magnificent aesthetically, as when one looks down from the flanks of the 700-foot deep gorge onto the huge cranes gleaming like the skeletons of pterodactyls bigger than the biggest airliner. Bhakra alone will irrigate over 3,500,000 acres: well over twice the entire irrigated area of Australia, or as much as the total arable land of South Australia. And the submergence of Adaminaby and Jindabyne sinks into insignificance beside the 63 villages, many probably with more people than the Snowy pair put together, which lie beneath the waters impounded by the 23 miles of dyke and dam at Hirakud on the Mahanadi, the great river in whose delta Konarak stands.

Orissa indeed has fallen on evil days since Narasimha's time: built piecemeal in the past twenty years from the extremities of three British Provinces (and distance from the State capital is at least as genuine a grievance in India as in Australia) plus a mosaic of tiny and incredibly backward princely statelets, its levels of administration, education, and social services are still well below those of a State like Madras or Mysore. But now, with the new million-ton steelworks being built at Rourkela and the irrigation and power to come from Hirakud, Orissa feels itself on the edge of a renaissance, a social revolution. It was needed: the 'basic wage' for unskilled navvy labour on government contract at Hirakud was several times as much as sufficed, only a few years back, to buy a man as general drudge for some petty chief in the zone of fragmented statelets.

All these things of course are to be found in other countries, East and West, and a power station is much the same in Tasmania, Brazil, or the Ukraine. But they have a mystique of their own in an India newly free to build for its own ends. At some of them the government has built temples or mosques for the increasing number of visitors; one might indeed say pilgrims, for at all of them are resthouses with visitors' books, the study of which is both entertaining and instructive. Glowing testimonials from foreign VIPs (some perhaps as much convinced of their own importance as of that of what they saw); diplomatic politenesses, cool and tactful (from the West), or dead flowery rhetoric (from the East); naïve criticisms and naïve enthusiasms—these there are in plenty. But from Indian visitors one note recurs again and again: 'This will be one of the great shrines of our country'; 'this for me has been as a pilgrimage.'

And this is as it should be. For every age, if it is not to be sterile, must create its own places of pilgrimage. And in this age when Asia is increasingly free of alien domination, but increasingly overshadowed by the spectres of its fatal unborn millions, what fitter place for devotion than one itself devoted to fertility: to the impregnation of a rejuvenated Mother Earth? That is why, of all these new shrines, Sindri seems to me the most significant.

Sindri: the new fertility

Sindri lies in the coal-bearing Damodar valley, the heart of India's newly developing heavy industry. You will not find it in Murray's *Handbook*, nor in the *Imperial Gazetteer*, where you will find almost everything else. It is too young for that; young, and very lusty.

With a daily output of about 1,000 tons of ammonium sulphate, Sindri is the largest fertilizer factory in Asia—that is the simple main fact about it; that, and the further fact that India stands more in need of a bold fertilizer policy than perhaps any other country in the world. For in many regions her fields have been tilled with little rest for fifteen to twenty centuries at least, while immemorial social habits, not to be lightly scorned, inhibit the Chinese use of every scrap of organic refuse. Despite the possession of the largest cattle population in the world, ordinary animal manures are in short supply: it is not generally realized that about 40 per cent of cow-dung is in fact used as manure, and that there is simply no alternative in sight to replace much at least of the further 40 per cent which falls into the housewife's hands as domestic fuel; while unless a small boy is permanently attached to the tail of each cow, the wastage of the remaining 20 per cent can scarcely be avoided. Even with the great irrigation projects, the amount of extra food which can be produced by winning new ground is not likely to exceed nor even to equal the demand of new mouths, and the unused cultivable area, except in Assam, is very limited in quantity and very marginal in quality. It follows that better techniques are essential, and among them an increased use of artificials.

Before the war the situation was simply grotesque: an annual application of about 90,000 tons, most of which went to plantation and cash crops covering less than two per cent of a total sown area of over 200 million acres; Japan used about four million tons on a cultivated area of 16 million acres. It can hardly be said that even the programme of the Second Five Year Plan is excessive: sulphate and superphosphate output together will amount to under 2·2 million tons by 1961. But at least Sindri is giving a new vision of what can be done in Indian fields.

This is the converse of the other need: less fertility in the home. No reasonably well-informed student of Indian affairs, unless blinded by prejudice Catholic or Communist (for pseudo-science makes one lie with strange bedfellows), doubts the need for family limitation, and this has indeed been formally recognized in the Plan. There are strange tales of the misadventures of Family Planning, in itself an ambiguous term; it is said, for example, that the rosaries distributed for calculating the 'safe period', being unluckily in colours already traditionally sacred or at least lucky, have been found adorning the necks of cows; which in India doubtless need some measure of birth control (they are getting artificial insemination). But, though prejudice against anything 'artificial' is perhaps stronger in circles influenced by Gandhian or straight Brahminical ideology than in most societies, there is no definite sanction against birth control in Hindu scriptures: the sanction is for male progeny. And it has long been suspected that if not the Indian villager, then at least his wife would not be unresponsive to anything which promised to relieve her of the almost annual round of births and the almost triennial round of deaths. . . . Informal advice given by 'village workers' at the right time (after the unwanted baby has just been born or just died) seems already to be having an effect on the vital statistics. The simple methods indicated are available in almost any village and are no doubt frightfully unhygienic; but then nothing can be nearly so unhygienic as childbirth in a village hut.

But it is not a mere play upon words to say that this policy, essential as it is, is also essentially sterile. Acceptance, yes; enthusiasm, no. But enthusiasm, and mass enthusiasm, there must be if the vicious circles which enmesh Indian rural life as in concertina wire are to be broken. And here the Community Development Project, with its co-ordinated and continuous drive to enlist the villagers themselves to work out their own salvation by better farming and better living, can be very powerfully aided by a positive emphasis on the new fertility which could be attained if every State in India had its Sindri.

A few years ago there was only an obscure village where are now a pervasive smell of ammonia and a vast clutter of ironmongery; coke-ovens, huge retorts, miles of giant piping, and the rest. To me, two things above all stand out. First, the huge storage hall: 220 yards long, pillarless, just a huge paraboloid roof and outside the ribbed and curving concrete walls, lines which in their naked simplicity recalled Edna St Vincent Millay's verse: 'Euclid alone has looked on beauty bare.' It was almost empty; only at the far end a few heaps of dirty-white powder and a travelling crane, tiny at that vast distance, under that superb arch; it is difficult to keep pace with demand. Yet once the crane was jammed up against the near end, there was no out-take, and production had to be suspended for lack of stor-age. Then the tide turned, and has never turned back again.

And again, leaving in the rapid tropical darkness, the great clouds of steam from the coke-ovens lit up by a huge jet of burning waste gas, and against this turbulent lurid background the towering chimney with the two bright red eyes of its aircraft warning lights; a symbol of Titan potency. It may be that the surrounding jungly tribes, Santals and Hos, already worship it: even to a sophisticate Westerner, it seemed luridly alive, a magic, no less. And so it is: a white magic which shall bless the fields with in-crease. Earth remains, the Mother of All Living; and in her profuse womb mingle the quickening Sun of Konarak, the quickening dust of Sindri, and tirelessly she bears the gen-erations of every living thing, each after its kind. . . .

Note: Illustrations of Konarak will be found in most books on Indian art, though it is badly under-represented in what is perhaps the best-known of them, Stella Kramrisch's *The Art of India through the Ages* (Phaidon Press, London, 1954). The balance is to some extent redressed in Benjamin Rowland, *The Art and Architecture of India* (Pelican History of Art, 1953). But, apart from Indian publications, by far the finest selection of photographs and by far the most useful text is Heinrich Zimmer, *The Art of Indian Asia* (Pantheon Books, New York, 1955).

Fossils of Forgotten Empire

To all of us, I suppose, archaeology is a study concerned solely with the remote and dusty past; but of course the archaeological method can be applied to history as well as pre-history. The preparations for the defence of Britain against the expected invasion of 1940 littered the island with potential raw material for archaeologists of the future; only it is hardly economic to employ this painful and often conjectural method of reconstruction to ages for which we have ample historical documents. But it is sometimes entertaining to wander among the material relics of past phases of our own civilization, and to see how far our impressions of their culture square with what we know from the history books. When I was in India last I was able to take a little time off from Science Congresses and Planning Boards, and I found the monuments of European rule a fascinating field for this modestly intellectual exercise.

It was perhaps the greatest glory of Lord Curzon as Viceroy that he did more than any other ruler of India to preserve the material monuments of her past. Now his empire in its turn is history and has gone to join its predecessors, the dynasties which have left their fossil imprints in palace and fort, temple and tomb, crowning rocky scarps or hidden in the jungle and the marsh. The most ambitious memorial of British rule is still alive and active: New Delhi is not yet on the road to ruins. I found the Secretariat even more bustling and bureaucratic than when I worked in it in 1944; only the names on the office doors were different. But already I feel a sort of melancholy piety in seeking out the relics of the great days of European expansion in the East. It is ironic that the earliest of the European

Reprinted from *The Listener*, 26 July 1956.

dominions is the last to retain, however precariously, a territorial holding in India. Goa hangs almost by a thread; but the faith which the Portuguese brought with them retains a stronger hold, even where Portuguese power was displaced more than two centuries ago.

Thirty miles north of Bombay, for instance, commanding the great estuary which separates Salsette Island from the mainland, the Portuguese ramparts of Bassein stand up massively from the mangroves. The whole circuit of the walls, which in the seventeenth century sheltered perhaps 35,000 people, is intact; within them now live a handful of Hindu peasants, and two Franciscan fathers and a couple of dozen orphans in their charge. On the citadel the arms of Portugal look almost as if they had been cut yesterday, but all around are the mere shells of what were once fine Baroque churches, roofless, with broken walls half split asunder and half held together by the roots and creepers of the jungle; in the stillness of the afternoon the only movement in the lifeless air is the effortless slow swing of the great kites circling overhead.

The Portuguese had a more than British capacity for military unpreparedness, redeemed morally though not materially by the most gallant last-ditch defences. When in 1739 Bassein fell to the Marathas after a stout defence, the victors promptly built a temple in the middle of the conquered town. But the people of the little fishing village which lies outside the walls are still in large part Christian, churches are more prominent than temples in the otherwise completely Indian town of Bassein a couple of miles away, and the little wayside shrines dotted over the countryside do not harbour Hindu gods, Hanuman or Ganesha or more local deities, but boldly carry the Cross. On Sundays one can still see the girls going to Mass in blouses and skirts of seventeenth-century cut, or even in saris topped by little mantillas of black lace.

It seems likely that this intimate impress of the Portuguese springs in the last resort from the fact that they fitted more naturally into the Asian society of their day than did their supplanters. Where the Dutch and British pioneers in Asia, coming a scant century later, were definitely early moderns, the Portuguese were late medievals. They ran their business through a royal monopoly, cumbrous and creaking, as an instrument of commercial penetration and exploitation far inferior to the business-like chartered companies of Holland and England. Their leaders were soldiers, nobles or at least gentry: this can be read in their monuments. The armorial blazons on their gravestones have more of a flourish than the grander but more stolid tombs of the merchant princes who succeeded them. Then again the Portuguese were theocratic, always conscious of the duty of winning souls for Christ. The Church was bitterly hostile to heathendom, and especially Islam, but this was in a sense more intelligible to non-secular Asian societies than the clear-cut separation of the spiritual and the mundane life, the neutralism in matters of religion, which marked the Dutch and English commercial companies. We might guess this from the little wayside crosses of Bassein.

So even where the Portuguese early lost or never possessed a legal and territorial base, their cultural influence rooted more deeply and subtly than that of the Dutch, perhaps even than that of the British, although of course with a far more restricted range. Even when both are nominally nineteenth century Gothic, you cannot mistake an Anglican and a Roman Catholic church in India, even from some distance: the Anglican seems always to be standing at attention, the Catholic betrays its origins, quite apart from a clutter of minor statuary, by its Iberian Baroque detail.

I was enormously impressed by this contrast in Ceylon, where first the Portuguese and then the Dutch ruled, both for just 150 years. There is one perfect relic of Holland in Ceylon, but it is curiously aloof and isolated. At Galle on the south coast a rock-bound, flat-topped headland is still girdled by the Dutch fortifications, formal bastions and curtains in the manner of Vauban and his Dutch compeer Cohorn—in themselves a marked contrast with the vertical, almost medieval, walls of Bassein, pierced for the lighter guns of the sixteenth century. Unlike Old Bassein, Old

Galle is not a deserted city: on the grassy plateau within the walls sleeps a charming little town, entirely devoted to administration and residence, a town of clean narrow streets still with their Dutch names—the old ropewalk is still Leynbaan Street, and so on. Here and there you come across the house of some solid burgher: one has its classical doorway surmounted by a splendid red cock and the date: Anno 1683. But the picture is very different from the dreamy, half-feudal, romanticism of Bassein. Within its girdle of sea and rampart, Old Galle gives the impression of being locked away safely, neatly folded like some Dutch girl's household linen laid away in her dower-chest.

Below, separated by the broad gardens on the old glacis, is an altogether different town: the bazaar town, dirty but alive. It has its own fossils, of another kind, though: I was astonished to find the Hotel Sydney, complete with bar and billiards, a survivor of the days before Colombo Harbour was built, when ships on the Australian and Far East runs coaled at Galle. Coaling being what it was, those passengers who could afford it slept ashore, and many a returning squatter must have hailed the Southern Cross in the Hotel Sydney's beer. But the only visible sign of Dutch influence outside the Fort is a locked graveyard: the Portuguese church, built in the later nineteenth century, still dominates part of the bazaar town.

Protestant or Catholic, both were strangers in a strange land, and in one place they came together in a strange and moving manner. Hidden away in the unspeakably chaotic and filthy northern suburbs of Agra is a walled garden: the Old Cemetery on ground granted in 1604 to the Jesuits by Akbar, that seeker for the truths behind religion. For some two centuries every European of any rank or fortune who died in northern India saw to it that he was buried in that only spot of consecrated ground away from the trading factories scattered along the coast. Beside humble and forgotten martyrs and Jesuit missionaries who gave their lives in heroic travels and labours lie more worldly characters: merchants, freelance adventurers, ambassadors. The martyrs and the missionaries have simple, almost anonymous, gravestones; some of their successors were interred with an almost imperial splendour.

The most prominent of these is perhaps John Hessing, a Dutch soldier of fortune who died in 1803 and is buried in a splendid miniature of one of the greater Mogul tombs. Despite its rhetorical flourishes his epitaph has a good business-like note befitting a Dutchman: in the service of the Maratha war-lord Scindia, his gallantry 'in the several Engagements leading to the Aggrandisement of that Prince' earned him 'the Esteem and Approbation of his Employer'; also, to judge by his mortuary magnificence, many lakhs of rupees. Not far away lies John Mildenhall, self-styled English ambassador to the Mogul, who died at Ajmer in 1614. The good Portuguese Fathers, unable to spell his outlandish name, above all unable to conceive of an ambassador who was not entitled to the noble prefix, have turned him into perfect Portuguese: the slab of red sandstone bears the name João de Menendal, Ingles. And was the João Alemão who lies beside him a French Jean Allemand, or simply a German named Johann?

Now we too have our monuments, our stones which tell of the grandeur of empire and of the innumerable private lives which sustained it and were sustained by it. At Madras the Anglican Cathedral of St George, nobly reminiscent of St Martin's in the Fields, may have but a handful of European worshippers even at Christmas: but on the walls are English names and an English piety. Among them is a memorial which seems to me one of the most moving I have ever seen. It begins in formal Latin, the stilted manner of the eighteenth century: to the memory of one who was loved by his friends, esteemed by all who knew him, and was 'the Perfect first of Canara and then of Madura in these Oriental Regions'. Then the Roman pose breaks down and we are left with the simple heartbreak of the girl who had waited for him in England, and now mourned him 'not as a wife but as an espoused bride, not as a widow yet sorrowing as a widow' . . . Such are the fossils of faith and empire, a record as fragmentary and yet as imperishable as the fossils of the rock.

D

Westwards the Course

Impressions of Portugal and Brazil

MOTHER and daughter have a clear family likeness, and much the same emotional and rhetorical temperament; but they live in different worlds. The mother can never forget her past, the leap from medieval modesty to leading lady on the theatre of the world, when both the Indias of spice and mine were her playthings. Since then she has had her troubles, penury even, but now, *en secondes noces*, she has settled down to a neat bourgeois existence. But the daughter—what a wench! young as she is, she has had some lively times, but they are nothing to the future she promises herself. . . . She is sentimental about the old home, now and then, but of course it always was poky. As for what Mother thinks, naturally she is proud of her splendid if unpredictable daughter's dazzling prospects, but looks a little askance at her manners—at bottom perhaps

> In the little country cottage
> Where her aged parents live
> Though they drink champagne she sends them
> Yet they never can forgive.

Most of this, after all, would apply also to Britain and the United States. . . .

It is of course rash and unfair to generalize after a fortnight or so in each country. I can only plead that training as a human geographer fosters a lively eye for significant detail; and, more specifically, that a long devotion to Lusian culture had given me a reasonably full background for the

Reprinted from *Quadrant*, Vol. 2 Pt 1, 1957-8.

montage of these detached impressionistic *Reisebilder* of two countries which share a great cultural tradition, but whose physical and social environments are starkly dissimilar. For what it is worth, the general impression is of a contrast between a vigorous democracy, somewhat turbulent and raffish, and a police state, respectable as police states go, but still not a free country.

The Portugal of the standard British stereotype—scruffy, picturesquely inefficient, in a word 'Dago'—is simply not there: the country is to all appearance nearly as well run as Holland, and one cannot well say more! That is presumably the achievement of Salazar. No doubt there is plenty of poverty in Oporto slums, in isolated little factory towns, in the mountain valleys and the dry plains of the south, and these the casual visitor cannot well see. But I am bound to say that the countryside I did see, the country of vines and pine forests, wool and olives, between Coimbra and the Tagus, bore many tokens of a surprising if modest prosperity. And yet it seems that only the past, whether medieval or Renaissance, has greatness; Portuguese modernity is mediocre.

Medieval Portugal was a well-knit state served by monarchs well above the average in spirit and competence. What other country could produce an Alfred the Great with his hair let down? A strange conception indeed, but incarnated in Dom Diniz, the founder of the Navy and the University, the planter of the waste lands on the old Moorish frontier and of the still-existing pine forest of Leiria, a rampart against shifting dunes and an arsenal of marine stores; and yet in the midst of more than the usual activities of a medieval (and merry) monarch finding time to write the most ravishing love-lyrics. One feels some of the spirit of this Portugal in the serenity of Batalha, the 'Battle Abbey' built (in the loveliest Gothic I have ever seen) to commemorate Aljubarrota, in which John of Gaunt's men helped to maintain independence from Castile; or again in Alcobaça, before the high marble tomb of Dom Pedro and Inez de Castro:

Até o fim do mundo—feet to feet,
not side by side, the lovers lie, to greet
first, when the Last Day dawns, each other's eyes
as caring for no other Paradise.

A hundred years ago the great historian Alexandre Herculano pointed out that the decadence was inherent in the
very nature of the 'Golden Age' of the Discoveries; yet its
expression in Manueline architecture, with its rioting orna-
mentation of marine and patriotic motifs, has undeniable
panache; and there was a last rally in Pombal's replanning
of central Lisbon after the 1755 earthquake. Portugal has
of course some good modern buildings, including the only
church I have seen which was at once absolutely modern
and not self-conscious about it; but the great new quarters
which encircle Lisbon are of a dullness which owes nothing
to tradition but much to official care. And this seems to
run through much of Portuguese cultural life. Perhaps because the modern version of the Philosopher as King is the
Professor (of Economics at that) as Dictator?

One must admit that at no time since the Napoleonic
wars has Portugal managed to combine liberty and order
for more than a few years at a time; that the workers,
though exploited, probably get more social services than
ever before; that Kingsley Martin's statement that Portugal 'enjoyed' civil liberty under the Republic is a desper-
ately unhappy formula for twenty-five years of putsches.
Nevertheless one senses a malaise. Where a dozen or so
Lisbon citizens are gathered together, there seems always
to be a policeman at hand. The newspapers speak with one
monotonous voice: not the democracies (behind which they
shelter) but Portugal and (in a minor role) Spain are the
real defenders of Western civilization; and the best of all
possible states is the corporative state in which ordinary
people need not bother with the responsibilities of running public affairs. Coupled with rhetoric to this effect are
pathetic complaints that nobody does bother to take any
interest in affairs, the interest permitted being voting in
very minor guild elections and the like.

The Church? frankly I do not know. The Portuguese system has been called 'Fascism in the Name of Jesus', a label which seems inaccurate. There is little of the mass apparatus of Fascism proper; the state is highly authoritarian rather than totalitarian in the total sense. It is of course next to impossible for an outsider to be able to assess such intangibles as the extent to which religion enters daily life; but 'Fascism in the Name of Jesus' hardly squares, for example, with the barracks radio playing dance music while the Sunday morning service was still on in the adjacent church. It is true that I was anxiously asked 'Do the Orders play a great part in Australian culture?'; when I recovered I gave a synopsis of that revealing work *Benedictine Pioneers in Australia* and of the current state of the ALP. There are plenty of books of pietistic morality and—literally—Cook's Tours to Fatima; but, paradoxically enough, one gets the impression that the temper of the country is a good old-fashioned belief in bourgeois progress, not far removed from a mediocre materialism.

Bookshops are perhaps as good a rough index of cultural vitality as any. Those of Rio de Janeiro are reasonably well organized, with a very wide range of stock, very lively and very crowded. In Lisbon the better bookshops seemed to have almost more foreign than Portuguese literature—but not always foreign literature of a high order—and the only decent arrangement seemed to be reserved for series of translated French and American thrillers; elsewhere was chaos. I asked in one of the most reputable booksellers in Lisbon for a good history of Portugal 'not, I think Ameal'—this being a work of such intense patriotic feeling that one is rather uneasy (its rhetoric was awarded the Herculano Prize; surely in variance with the spirit of that ruggedly honest and superbly masculine writer). They had nothing in stock, but could get me one if I called next day. It turned out to be four little paperbacks of about 125 pages each, without a trace of documentation or even a reading-list—good in a way, the way of the popular introduction, with here and there a between-the-lines hint of dissatisfaction with the regimen-

tation of thought, a hankering for the days of disorder . . .
and at least some freedom. In Brazil on the other hand
there are many excellent historical and sociological works,
with plenty of pride and faith in the country but also with
acute and far-reaching criticism of the national temper
and polity.

After the bookshops, the walls: slogans, posters, placards.
Despite a wealth of highly eligible sites, in Portugal I saw
only one wall inscription—SALAZAR—and that had been
half scrubbed out. But Central Lisbon was plastered with
broadsheets denouncing the 'backward and adventurous
people' of India—all suspiciously alike in styling, and signally failing to give the impression which it is not unchari-
table to suppose was desired, of a spontaneous upsurge of
popular feeling. (Incidentally, the more outrageous utterances of Nehru, the more firm and dignified statements of
Salazar, had been printed in red ink, which had naturally
faded to produce the appearance of censored blanks.) In
Brazil every wall has its slogan—Down with the President,
Long Live the President, Shoot the Profiteers, Hang the
Reds, Antonio Ferreira for Councillor, Buy at Oliveira's
and (best of all) Abaixo o Golpe—Down with the Coup
d'État (past, present, or future? this was in the sleepy
country town of Ouro Preto, which has however a history
of 'movements' going back to 1721).

As for the Press, no greater contrast with the staid and
regimented Portuguese journals could be imagined; the
Brazilian papers are much more up-to-date technically, full
of supplements and features, most of them agin the Government and quite uninhibited about it. The politics of
Rio seemed not dissimilar to those of Sydney, if more
colourful: one felt quite at home with impending failure
of the city's supplies of milk, water, and bread, due of
course to restrictive producers, conscienceless middlemen,
and municipal mismanagement. The President's morbid
love of publicity had led to a dastardly outrage on the
dignity of the nation—a published photograph of him
shaving (in dressing-gown, admittedly) with a W.C. faintly
visible in the background; juiciest of all scandals, the Vice-

President had been named by the Argentine Commission of Enquiry as having taken hard cash from Peron for electoral purposes. . . . To judge from the Press alone, Brazil is violent, unbalanced, messy, rhetorical, openly corrupt, but blazingly dynamic; Portugal ordered, tidy, still rhetorical, probably covertly corrupt, and intellectually asleep.

In all this of course due regard should be paid to Brazil's enormously greater resources: almost exactly the size of Australia, with a humid desert in Amazonia corresponding to the dry desert in Australia, and with a strikingly similar layout in the developed southeast, where the arrangement of relief and climate and geology is such that some landscapes are almost indistinguishable from say interior Queensland; but with four and a half centuries of a most diversified history and fifty million people of the most diverse stocks and social attributes. Already in 1822 the Prince Regent of Brazil, Dom Pedro, bluntly told his father in Lisbon that since Portugal was a state of the fourth and Brazil of the first class, they could not remain united unless Portugal were to be a dependency of Brazil: a point he sufficiently proved by becoming first Emperor of Brazil, and later abdicating to return to Portugal and lead the constitutional forces to victory in a hard-fought civil war. Incidentally the half-century of the Empire gave Brazil the inestimable gift of stability relative to the other Republics of Latin America: with a Braganza on the throne, it was not open to disgruntled magnates to reflect that they were of as old a family as the President and had as many retainers, so why not seize the Presidency? The Empire fell at last because the emancipation of the slaves alienated really conservative opinion, while ideologically it was too close to its opponents to oppose them with any vigour. With an estimable bourgeois liberal as Emperor, why not have a real Republic and save the expense? a calculation which was not perhaps too well founded.

One need not go into detail over the more familiar features of Brazilian life: the national history and psychology of boom and slump, the incredible physical diversity of the people, the practical absence of a colour bar except in some higher reaches of the Services, the exhilarating architecture, the divertingly overt expression of the sexual instinct (in marked contrast to the—official—prudery of Portugal), the violent contrasts of primitivity and poverty (certainly more obvious than in Portugal) with sophisticated luxury, of *o sertão e a cidade*—a phrase which corresponds exactly to Bush and City. Perhaps the last is best seen in Belo Horizonte, the capital of Minas Gerais State, founded in 1897 and now with over half a million people. Without the magnificence of São Paulo, it is very up-and-coming architecturally—the noise of building fills its mathematically gridded streets, and skyscrapers of the newest brand cluster thickly in its centre. But along these very streets little temporarily rented shops advertise The Champion Faster of Brazil, The Largest Python Ever, The Human-Headed Monster—the bush is not so far away after all. But for twelve or fifteen miles around the scrub is already gridded for the roads of the suburbs to be built in the next boom.

Sixty miles away is the old state capital Ouro Preto, a sleepy little town which has been declared a National Monument in its entirety: a lost gem of eighteenth century Iberia, dotted with lovely little Baroque churches which include some of the masterpieces of O Aleijadinho, a mulatto, born a slave, who in a long life (1738-1814), for much of which he was half-crippled, produced perhaps the finest religious art to come from the New World—statues in steatite and polychrome wood of astonishing realism, raciness, and vivid dramatic temper. Here in 1787 occurred the first movement against Portuguese rule, the Inconfidência, an abortive conspiracy of lawyers and poets with perhaps only one leader of the stuff of which real rebels are made, the Army Ensign Tiradentes. He was hanged, the rest shipped to Angola; and in the memorial hall in the nobly simple Courthouse built by Aleijadinho's father the engaging but often slightly absurd Brazilian exuberance in matters monumental is for once forgotten. The remains of the conspirators rest in plain granite boxes; and behind the empty sarcophagus of Tiradentes hangs the banner of the Inconfidência with its motto: LIBERTAS QUAE SERA TAMEN.

And back to Portugal for the last word: from the disorderly progression of a country not at all certain of where it is going but joyously conscious of being on the move into an exciting future, to ordered, all-too-ordered, Progress. It takes about a day and a half to be completely subjugated by the agreeable Lisbon habit of taking a *cafezinho* —and another and another—under the trees of the broad Avenida da Liberdade. It is all very pleasant; and very depressing to reflect on the absence of liberty. Better, far better, to be back in the chill austerity before Tiradentes' cenotaph, in a country no doubt full of poverty and injustices, but where conflict is open and *Libertas sera tamen*.

Under Two Laws

The Fijian Dilemma

'FIJI is always smiling' proclaims the tourist brochure; and yes, that is what it looks like. On his first day, as we drove from Nadi to Suva, my young son burst out, 'This *is* a lovely country, everybody is friends with everybody. . . .' Those strapping Fijian wenches, broad in hair-style and bosom and hip, with grins to match and a wave and a shout of *Sa bula*—cheerio!—to every passing car; a gang of Fijian men hauling a car out of a ditch as though it were the funniest thing in the world—but salving a capsized dinghy is even funnier; the cheerful colour and chatter of the markets, entrancingly half India and half South Sea; the lithe and active young Indian farmers riding around like cowboys on wiry ponies; the long roadside files of tiny Indians and tiny Fijians, so neat and so full of that engaging seriousness of the very young when they feel they are being business-like; the ever-mobile mouths, the bubbling-over gaiety of little Fijian faces; the wonderful eyes, deep swimming brown yet with an alert glint, of little Indian faces—everything that the pamphlet says is there, and more. To be fair to tourism, it usually is; but there are such a lot of other things. . . . Few places in the world can be such fun on the surface; but underneath?

Undeniably, as things now stand (but how long can they stand?) Fiji is a most pleasant place for a sojourn. By and large relations between the races are remarkably good in a day-to-day give-and-take fashion. All colours (if not quite all classes and creeds) can meet in the Public Bar; Fijian

Reprinted from *Meanjin*, Vol. 19 No. 2, 1960.

villagers 'borrow' the Indian's bullocks for their bit of ploughing, and he grazes them on that patch of village land which somehow will never get entered as a lease on the Native Land Trust's books; in rural offices the big bowl of *yaqona* (kava) is free for all, and one may indeed be served by an Indian who claps his hands Fijian-fashion when one has finished one's drink; conversely, as it was charmingly inverted by a Fijian lass on one of the outer islands, 'The Indians aren't so very different from us really, they even eat curry too!' Yes, cheerful, extrovert, jolly—and underneath the all too actual frustrations, the tensions latent but very real. The Fijian looks overflowing with bright animal spirits, gay and irresponsible; or deeply worried; rarely indeed relaxed.

'Under two laws'

The Fijians are now a decreasing minority in their own homeland: say about 170,000 of them to 200,000 Indians, of whom nearly 90 per cent were born in Fiji. This latter, originally immigrant, community, only about forty years ago scarcely emerged from the status of indentured coolies, is now on the whole distinctly better off than the Fijians, and in many cases—the most obvious and striking to a Fijian—very conspicuously more wealthy. And the Indians are increasing much more rapidly than the Fijians, and beginning to feel cramped between European freehold and Fijian Reserved Lands; they feel insecure, with nothing to live on but leaseholds, for which there is much competition, and their wits. With the loss of their own cohesive Custom in India, and the loss of cultural satisfactions (since Punjabis, Biharis, Madrassis live scattered on isolated homesteads), they have little to do except to make money and have babies, and they are good at both. . . . Conversely the Fijians hold most of the land, but much of this is hilly and infertile, and the good alluvial valleys are largely out of their control, in European hands; and they too are increasing rapidly.

In this situation, a fundamental difficulty of the Fijians

—and this is consciously felt and often clearly expressed in the villages—is that they are 'under two laws'. This is true, firstly, in the sense (common to many peoples at a similar stage) that the old law of Custom, kinship, and status is increasingly difficult to square with the new law of Money, contract, and jobs; but it is also true in the literal sense that, as well as the ordinary courts and laws, the Fijians are subject to a special law of their own, expressed in the very minute Fijian Regulations. In theory, these regulations control pretty well everything that exists or can happen in the villages, down to the size of kitchens and the number of windows therein (this regulation is often met by having one, two, or three sides open to the weather) and the holding of a village dance.

The regulations are administered by the separate Fijian Administration, a form of 'indirect rule' which has set itself the double task of promoting modern economic development and of maintaining intact 'the Fijian Way of Life' based on kinship and hierarchy. It is not unfair to say that the latter and more conservative aim wins out, perhaps inevitably, in the Administration's practice. Since in a subsistence economy the storing of a surplus is practically impossible, once the primary needs of food, shelter, and defence have been met there is nothing left in which to invest spare time and energy, except the elaboration of social ceremony and code. In this view, the Fijian Way of Life was undoubtedly a work of art; it is unfortunate that some British friends of the Fijians (perhaps seeing in their society that squire's Merrie England which allegedly existed before the Reform Bill and the Industrial Revolution) seem to feel that the whole duty of the Fijians, their *raison d'être* almost, is the aesthetic purpose of serving the Way of Life. And indeed one can sympathize to some extent with the stress on Tradition, with the fear that change may mean the loss of the specific values of Fijian society. But those values were called forth by, and beautifully adjusted to, a static environment very different from that which prevails in Fiji today; and the effort to preserve the Fijian Way of Life may not be compatible with the growth of the Fijians as a live people. In fact, the old society did possess some powers of flexibility which were lost when Custom was codified into Regulation; and yet change is there, is yearly more potently insistent, and cannot be gainsaid.

In the old days, for example, Chiefs had vitally important functions: they led in war, they organized the use of the land; and an ineffective Chief could be eliminated by the very direct action of an effective claimant—and often was. With the *pax Britannica*, the Rule of Law, the Native Lands Trust Board, these functions are virtually vanished; but the status remains. Too often traditional status is held to warrant the assumption of leadership in fields which need altogether different qualifications, or the right of sharing in the proceeds of economic endeavour to which nothing has been contributed. Again, in a subsistence economy reciprocal borrowing among kinsmen, the conspicuous display of generous feasting on occasions such as births and marriages, had as it were a self-regulating mechanism, a thermostat, built in: wealth was in the main perishable, so too much of the year's output could not be expended at once. But with the introduction of money, this safeguard has gone: with tinned food, kerosene, soap, cattle, clothing, thus made available, it is possible to squander two years' past savings and mortgage two years' future earnings on a marriage feast. Many customary obligations now represent nothing more nor less than a levy on the energetic at the behest of the shiftless; yet, in the eyes of traditional leaders, they must be preserved lest abandoning them sap the foundations of the Fijian Way of Life.

By and large, the effort to maintain Tradition runs counter to the eternal exhortations to the Fijian people to stand on their own feet economically; not in all respects, but as a general thing. Their village system has been accidentally labelled 'communal', and this gives rise to semantic confusion: in 1944 a European member of the Legislative Council gravely congratulated them on having attained, generations ago, a state of society which the Soviet Union was struggling to reach. . . . Because it is thus assumed that the 'communal system' is collectivist in *pro-duction* (which it is not, and never was except when taxes were produced in kind and communally in the last century—an alien imposition), and because Fijians have a very strong distributist sense among kin-groups, official economic development is wedded to a sort of semi-socialist agrarianism, which meets with very little response from the people.

They have indeed become conditioned to authoritarian (but not always authoritative!) leadership, so that for the most part they tend to do little but what they are told to do; but authority is so minutely regulative that they have developed an art of self-defence—dodging the column—and have become conditioned again to doing as little as possible of what they are told to do, and that is often very little indeed, by reason of the sheer impossibility (except with a truly totalitarian police apparatus) of checking daily life in such minute detail. So much is trivial, unenforced, and unenforceable, that the important things slide too, and passive co-operation can insensibly change into passive resistance. As it was neatly put by Professor Geddes of Sydney: 'In contrast to some of their efforts in their own gardens, the men on communal work never overstrain themselves, stopping periodically to yarn or imbibe *yaqona*. However, it is the tropics; there is still tomorrow, and after all, it is public works.'

All this is of course not simply Administration's fault, and many officials, Chiefs and commoners, work hard and sincerely . . . spinning ropes of sand? Like that of the Country Party in Australia, the villagers' attitude (a world-wide one) is often enough: 'Government interferes with us, Government neglects us'—all in one breath. They feel too, as individuals, as families, as kin-groups, the pull of the old Custom, with its stress on competitive giving: the letter rather than the spirit of 'It is more blessed to give than to receive', since giving is the path to prestige. Increasingly they are aware of this confusing incompatibility between their love of their Custom and their desire for material advance, and between the two official objectives of Tradi-

tion and Development. Small wonder, then, that they feel
deeply and consciously that they are ensnared in the

> wearisome Condition of Humanity,
> Borne under one Law, to another, bound:
> Vainly begot, and yet forbidden vanity,
> Created sicke, commanded to be sound.
> What meaneth Nature by these diverse Laws?
> *Passion* and *Reason*, selfe-division cause . . .

Nights around the bowl

The variety of expressions of this dilemma, the variety
of reactions to it, are amazing. Active discontent is rare, but
forthright impatience with the system is common; sometimes it is rationalized to 'we should live like the Indians'
(an effort, this, reached by what spiritual wrestlings can
only be imagined) or 'we should all become independent
for five years, as an experiment'—naïve, unreflective, yet
surely reflecting a deep malaise in the body politic. Then
there are varying degrees of resignation, until at last a
weary apathetic fatalism is reached, as in parts of the outlying island of Kadavu, where so many men—despite the
efforts of Administration—have emigrated that there is
hardly the man-power to make best use of such scanty resources as there are. Yet only a few miles away from the
dreariest of run-down hamlets may be a village most beautiful to look at, alive, vigorous, reasonably confident in itself.
Very much depends, of course, on social structure; on the
presence or absence (more often the former) of local feuds;
on local opportunity; on the local leadership, be it official,
commoner, or Chiefly. Yet, with all this variety, the pattern
of village discussion is broadly similar, so much so that it
adds up to a definite public opinion: often naïve, muddled,
incoherent, but sometimes (probably more often than is
usually realized) sensible and thoughtful.

The village discussions vary greatly in depth and comprehension; the village receptions vary greatly in scale and
formality, scarcely ever in cordiality. In fifty-two villages,
I met with suspicion—easily explicable—in two. One of

these, on the little island of Moturiki, had been the scene
of a much-publicized Community Development Project,
the failure of which was dismissed—by its main sponsor—
in the laconic words: 'What happened on Moturiki after
the team was withdrawn is secondary.' Such is not the view
of the 600 souls on Moturiki, savouring fully of hopes raised
to a high pitch and then withdrawn, aware that they were
used as pawns in a bureaucratic game, resenting it, and
frightened lest they were again to be cast as guinea-pigs.
For two hours I refrained from even mentioning this sore
point, and then but briefly; several hours (and many rounds
of *yaqona*) later they came back to it of themselves, and
would not come off it. A most revealing session. . . .

The other, Nasomo, was a real 'sport': a scruffy little
hamlet, squatting on the Colonial Sugar Refinery Company's land, inhabited by a bunch of semi-anarchists stemming from an old freelance missionary's experiment in
individualism. The Nasomo folk live in squalor and they
like it, are most reprehensible (never have I seen women
more sluttish) but—unless you are responsible for law and
order—rather likeable. They have repudiated the normal
discipline of the Fijian village (it is possible to contract out
of the system by paying a special tax); but, paradoxically,
many have accepted the very alien discipline of wage labour
in the adjacent gold mines: just because it is so completely
alien, so entirely a new thing that there are no old rules
of living to apply. Here of course I had to swear that I
was nothing to do with Colonial Sugar Refining, Emperor
Gold Mines, or Fijian Administration; after that (and a lot
of *yaqona*) they opened up.

For *yaqona* is the absolutely invariable thing: unhappy
the fieldworker who 'can't take it' (my own record, 26
bowls in a day—never have I refused one—is respectable
even by Fijian standards: but then I *like* it). One has
it all ways: from the domestic version in which the pow-
dered root is squeezed through an old singlet and watered
from a decrepit bucket, to the full *vakaturaga* (Chiefly)
ceremony. This is an art-form of a very high order. The
water is poured from long bamboos and the powder

strained, with formal gesture, through hibiscus fibre; the officiants are dressed in stencilled *tapa* cloth and variegated foliage, there are elaborate chants to a beautifully rhythmic accompaniment of bamboo gongs and the deep resonant Fijian hand-clapping: then the cup-bearer, a young man chosen it seems for his magnificent physique, squats by the cowry-decorated mixing bowl, and slowly rises, to move with exquisitely formal movement to the recipient of the first cup, fixing him with an almost hypnotic gaze. This first round—it goes by complicated precedence which is an elaborate art in itself—must be taken with a deep solemnity, a religious awe. After that everything eases up: one can smoke, chatting goes on on the side-lines, until by two or three in the morning even the girls are wheedling a cup from the master of the bowl.

In the most formal receptions there are other presentations: a whole bush of *yaqona*, root and all; the *tabua*, the sacred whale's tooth, the most indispensable of Fijian cult-objects; perhaps mats and a whole roast pig—and not a sucking pig either. Nor are these merely token gifts; two or three days after leaving one village I tracked down that smell, in the boot of the car. . . . At another some consternation was caused by an inadvertent breech presentation; one felt that in the old days this gaffe might have had to be put right by a presentation of 'long pig'. Then there is the *meke*, usually a very belated sitting-dance by the women, followed by the elephantine scramble, on all fours and with amazing speed, of enormous Fijian matrons to shake hands with the guests—the Fijians have an obsession with hand-shaking. And later still, perhaps, the *taralala*: a simplified fox-trot (the Fijians take their pleasures simply) to a couple of guitars and the 'bush bass', a Malayan importation consisting of a tea-chest as sound-box, to which is attached a string drawn taut with a bow. There must be something in geographical determinism: in my own temperate habitat I dread and detest dancing, in the Pacific I never want to stop, even when in the embrace of a mountain of Fijian womanhood given to disconcerting hisses. All this in the curious glare, harsh and soft alternately, of pressure lan-

53

E

terns, on floors of five or six layers of mats over split bamboo. Around four in the morning, one can curl down: if lucky, on the floor, so much softer than the 'European' beds—hard boards with one thickness of mat—which the Fijians keep for prestige, and (alas) for European guests. . . .

Something of the spirit of the full *yaqona vakaturaga* ceremony remains even in much less formal private parties. Although long night-after-night sessions undoubtedly contribute to a listlessness in daily work—if only the Fijians worked with the energy they put into play!—and far too much day-time is frittered away in 'knocking off for a bowl', there is no question of the socially cohesive value of *yaqona* drinking, the focus, one might say, of Fijian social life. This is an element of Tradition which need not and should not be despised: it is, I think, significant that the most impressive ceremonies I saw were in villages which had really done something for themselves, or at least were most aware of and went deepest into their fundamental problems; the most perfunctory, on the whole, were in those with no special opportunity, no leadership, no hope—which may, paradoxically, mean those where the cash influx is greatest, but in the form of an unearned increment from rents most unequally distributed both between different kin-groups and within a group, Chiefs taking the lion's share. Here indeed there is demoralization by easy money: when the Chief's house is on a high plinth and its roof-tree loaded with cowry shells, that is Custom and acceptable by all; when it is also surrounded by a barbed-wire fence (like many things *vaka Viti*—'Fiji-fashion'—more symbolic than effective), social disintegration has definitely set in.

But one returns in memory to the good villages: Viseisei, where the Chief Adi Mere, a lady of much spirit and sense, who has led her people in a fine housing project, summed up 'but unless the people are truly interested, we can have Report on Report and the position will not be clear'—one for the Expert!; Namacu, with its bright new concrete-block houses built with copra money; Narewa, where fundamental questions—indeed a very shrewd critique of British policy—were put forward, and the heretical suggestion made that Fijians and Indians should go to the same schools from the start, so that they might learn about each other. ... Here, in villages impressive both by Tradition and by Development, there is some hope that the old and the new may be married, not unfruitfully.

It is in the long night sessions, when the ceremonies are put aside and the talk is punctuated with earthy jokes and here and there a bit of flirtation, that the mind of the Fijian village becomes most realistic. The jokes are the simple peasant ones—Viliame who doesn't know how many acres he has (*voice*: 'nor how many kids'), or the leading official who 'came to our village and actually ate and slept on the job here—so *of course* it failed'. But here also fundamental questions, perhaps not asked often enough in the high places of Suva, are brought forward: Are we the *only* people in the world, caught like this between Custom and Money? Do the Indians in India have Custom like we do? Can we live for ever under two laws? *Must we for ever be treated as children?*

And the answers ... they are not always easy. For in one world, the potent world of the market, they *are*, as yet, too often as children: the ambivalence of Fijian life has struck deep. They wish to be free, and are frightened of freedom; to make money, but will throw a fine opening away for a good time or to show how open-handed they are; see clearly that they are crippling themselves by fantastic marriage expenditures, but feel all well lost for Honour. Yet slowly, painfully, wastefully, they are finding answers for themselves.

The answers take many forms: the chequered growth of the co-operatives; Credit Unions; sometimes the traditional head of a kin-group may organize his kin in a petty enterprise, and produce in effect a sort of manorial régime, extending perhaps to the whole village—instead of grinding at the Lord's mill, one dries one's copra in the Turaga-ni-Mataqali's drier. One village took up manganese mining on its own—unluckily it got involved with an overseas firm which may not be content to be a sleeping partner; another runs its own bus service to Suva; in a third a local official, a commoner, has managed to manipulate a very complex local political situation and direct a thoroughly authoritarian banana project, accompanied by a reconstruction of the village on approved modern planning lines. Some Fijians at least, the Independent farmers, are willing to stand on their own feet and to pay the price—a hard price in work, in an un-Fijian thrift, in the consequent loss (to begin with at any rate) of good fellowship and social prestige. These do not have divided minds: they feel that they know where they are going, and that this is the way forward for their people.

But the pity is that time may well be short for the Fijians, who do not value it over-much; and that some of their answers look backward, basing themselves on a Third and Higher Law derived from Scripture and ending in the dreams of millennial enthusiasm. Of these none is more striking than that of Ratu Emosi of Daku, who has made his village the most fascinating—but not therefore the most important—sociological exhibit of Fiji.

New Jerusalem in the mangroves

One had heard vaguely of Daku—'a model village, the best in Fiji, it has electric light'—and of Ratu Emosi—'a fine leader, but fits of religious mania'. And then, at a tiny road-head jetty in the Rewa delta, I met him, quite by chance: a short man, looking taller by virtue of the long white smock he wore, with a fine-modelled head, rather like an Egyptian portrait-sculpture in effect, nervous gestures, nervous bright eyes. I said with vague politeness that I would like to see Daku sometime: he fixed me with a glittering eye, and firmly intimated (I divined the gist before it was interpreted) that he was very busy about the Lord's work, and if my intentions were sincere and honourable, I would name the date . . . like the Wedding Guest, I weakly complied. Yes, undoubtedly a fine leader!

So down by the long winding delta channels, between high alluvial banks with the cane to the very edge, then miles of mangrove, through a fine insinuating drizzle which turned to solid rain as we approached Daku. But first one passes New Anitioki, a mile or so from Daku itself: some new wood-and-iron buildings, some decrepit patched-up sheds, and a number of launches flying a strange but effective flag: yellow with a green cross, a red roundel superimposed on the cross, and a red cross in the upper canton next the staff, Ratu Emosi's personal flag afloat—there is a different version for shore establishments.

Even in the steady rain, Daku itself was impressive. Right by the little stone landing-place, where the reception committee, all in jackets and ties, was drawn up, is a very fine weatherboard church; then a wide village green, and beyond it a very well-designed and spacious white weatherboard house. 'Not mine personally, but the House of the Government of the Village', says Ratu Emosi apologetically: of course the Head of the State must live in befitting dignity. Not a woman to be seen, though, and even allowing for the rain, this is oddly un-Fijian. Ratu Emosi is unmarried —un-Fijian again—and this may count for much.

Ratu Emosi, one had heard, had cut out all the ceremonies; clearly the Establishment was Puritanical. So it was: in the great hall of Government House the followers were marshalled, some fifty of them cross-legged on the floor, all dressed with extreme—and un-Fijian—neatness, all with white shirts. On every face, a broad fixed smile— compulsory spontaneous joy? Not all ceremonies were cut out, but clearly they were cut down: the bowl was brought in, with the *yaqona* ready prepared, a formal round (no chants, no costuming) for the guests, Ratu Emosi, and a few lieutenants, and then it was borne out again. And then Ratu Emosi talked. . . .

The only thing he would not talk about was the flag— a political act; *that* he had explained in writing to the Governor, and this was the answer he had made to the Harbour Master when his launch put into Levuka flying this strange new ensign. For the rest, twenty years ago he had seen his village going downhill, had decided to set aside all personal ambition and build it up; for twenty years—with one gap—he had borne the rule. And I could see the result: the wood-and-iron houses, the dock at New

Anitioki, the electric lights (and the flush toilet in Government House), the launches, the carpentry and metalworking shops where he reconditioned the second-hand launches he picked up (there were seven); and the result yet to come, the College of Anitioki, which is Antioch where the Church was set on a new course. . . . All was built up from a launch and a lighter, bought on hire-purchase from an Indian and used to take mangrove fuel to market. No, there was no banking account, Ratu Emosi handled everything (but, though this is regarded as very mysterious, there has been no hint of financial nor even—more surprisingly—of sexual irregularity). It is obvious, in the workshops, that wherever he got his know-how (self-taught, he claims), Ratu Emosi is not only a good organizer, a dynamic leader, but a very fine improviser with considerable technical capacity—a 'waste-paper basket mechanic'.

It was, of course, very difficult to begin with. At first people spoke ill of him. Indeed, some of the people even withdrew from the village and followed a different faith; but he was firm. This is a magnificent euphemism: in fact, the Catholics left when their houses were burned down, and (according to repute at any rate) their leaders were trussed up to bamboos in traditional fashion and taken over to Bau island, the seat of the old Fijian kings—and Daku in the old days had had the right and duty of looking after prisoners of war until they were needed. When they were deposited before a very startled Paramount Chief of Fiji, with the intimation that they were now at his disposal, enquiries were made. At this point the gap already mentioned occurred: Ratu Emosi retired to the Suva mental hospital for some years. He makes no concealment of this fact; and it is a striking tribute to his leadership that he had no difficulty in taking his place among his people when he came out. Of course this Toynbeean withdrawal-and-return is not an uncommon feature with such charismatic leaders, and Ratu Emosi has all the gifts: a rare combination of personal magnetism, outstanding organizing power, technical competence, religious enthusiasm, and Chiefly standing.

The detail of the material and social achievement need not be gone into, except to note that his success in reducing marriage ceremonies to what one might call a modest civic celebration (there is something oddly reminiscent of the civic marriages in the anti-religious phase of the French Revolution) was attained not by just talking generally, but by turning up to point hard morals on each individual occasion: in fact, the Communist distinction between propaganda and agitation. There was, incidentally, another odd convergence when the question of continuity when he can no longer be the Leader was discussed: he is trying (or so he believes: there is little overt sign of anything so democratic) to make people learn 'to be led by the job they have to do'—very much Lenin's formulation in *State and Revolution*; but will Emosi's State wither away any more than Lenin's? Yet continuity is in his mind: no inscription will be placed on the monument by the church until the work is completed, and to the question 'How is the New Life completed?' he made the superb reply: 'It is like a crop: the harvest is the completion of the work, and then one takes the seed and plants again', until all Fiji has entered the New World.

For this is the path for Fijians. At breakfast the next morning I repeated a question of the night before: do we need as many Emosis as there are villages in Fiji? The reply: '*If* there were an Association with branches . . .' Possibly a prudential *if*; I had glimpsed Ratu Emosi far up the Wainibuka valley, spreading the message to a stolid village group standing around in their work-stained clothes, all head and shoulders taller than he, bulky in proportion, and held—for the time at least—by his personality. Daku is an 'exempted koro', a village outside the sphere of Fijian Administration, and thinking that his ideal would be a loose, almost anarchist, federation of village communes (within themselves, however, highly autocratic) I asked whether we would need a Fijian Administration if all Fiji came into the New Life. 'If we four around this table were running Fiji, there would be no need of Government' was the reply. I hastily backed out of a Provisional Ministry.

This revolution, technical, social, in part political (only in part, for Ratu Emosi believes in the traditional rule of Ratus), will of course need a great deal of educational effort. This is the significance of New Antioch, for here will be the College with its array of courses: trades courses—bakery, carpentry, metal-work; political science—'Law and its purpose, being set free and its meaning', 'Chiefly system'; social —'Time and its use in work', 'Political life and individual life', 'Organic life of the village'; religious—'The Bible and hidden things in it', 'Fijians did not come from Africa [i.e., are not Children of Ham; this refers to a discredited ethnolinguistic hypothesis of a link with Tanganyika] but from Israel, for they too have a Messiah'. Most fascinating of all to a geographer, 'Continents and Islands: their differences and the differing systems of justice which should be applied to each'.

'Continents and Islands'

Here, and in the reference to the Messiah, is the key to this fantastic village-state. Naturally I fastened on 'Continents and Islands' and demanded explanation. The explanation was very revealing.

It is a wrong approach to say that this is the 'Age of Money'—then the Fijians will turn their minds to money, neglecting other values. [This is indeed the kernel of truth in the traditionalist attitude, and the element of danger in 'progress'.] This might be suitable for 'continents', where life can be regulated on a basis of money; but if we could isolate the Fijians from other races, the life they should lead is the Christian life, based on mutual love. This is the most suitable life for 'islands', where people are brought up to live in groups, to look after each other, where each man is his brother's keeper [. . . and Big Brother is the keeper of all?].

In contrast, the foundations of life are quite different in 'continents'. In a big country, each man fends for himself; there is nobody to look after him, to tell him what to do, to guide him aright; so men cheat each other, rob, murder. . . . [Although Ratu Emosi did not put it in these terms, his point—not to be shrugged aside—is that mass societies have no inner discipline, are fundamentally lawless, can only be managed by an *external* law.] There is only one end to this—war. Then people are killed off, their societies are reduced to manageable size, and they can relearn the true principles of living: until then, the place is too big, and nobody cares about what happens to his fellows.

Within the limits of its data—but they *are* limited—this is a coherent and acute sociology. It should be noted that while Ratu Emosi can follow, with some difficulty, a conversation in English, he is not at all at home in the language. For practical purposes, he is dependent on Fijian; and I hardly think it an exaggeration to say that there is but one real *book* (of more than local significance, anyhow) available in Fijian, and that is the Bible. So his sociology is in part acute first-hand observation of the very small sectors, splinters almost, of European and Indian culture available to him—offshoots of vast impersonal societies, without Tradition (that is left behind, in India or England), fundamentally lawless—that is our fault, we have shown the Fijians (and how many others?) the worst face of the West, Money and little else. At least this is so in small places like Fiji where the scale of things inhibits any effective display of the real spiritual and intellectual achievements of Western civilization. But another, and perhaps a larger, part of Emosi's system springs from an acute mind feeding on the crazily inadequate data of the Old Testament: for what is the contraposing of 'continents and islands' but a translation into Fijian terms of the struggle of Israel—small, traditional, theocratic, conservative, cohesive—against vast agglomerate Empires of lower moral values? Indeed, one might almost call the Israel of today a better-found and better-reasoned Daku.

The tragedy is that such an acute mind, such a powerful personality, is compelled, for lack of external standards, to turn in upon itself, to waste its talents in sterile brooding upon legend.

Congeners of Daku

This interpretation is confirmed by the fascinating iconography of Government House. Most Fijian homes have a 'picture-gallery', usually on the main cross-beam: family and group portraits; Pan-American Airways posters; perhaps some posters from the Department of Agriculture; often Ratu Sukuna, the outstanding (and truly so) modern Fijian leader, and Cakobau, the 'King' of Fiji before Cession to Britain; almost always Queen Elizabeth II.

The photographs in the great hall at Daku are mainly groups—though they include two portraits of Ratu Emosi in his study. The groups are mainly concerned with 'the Work': the Church, the Sunday school, the lieutenants, and so on. Among them is one real freak, a card with six small photographs of a European fancy-dress ball, the chief personage being a woman got up as a she-Mephistopheles. In this Puritanical environment, this seems so crazy that one fancies it a hangover from Ratu Emosi's enforced Suva days. More significantly, the great hall has a glass cupboard containing three white uniform jackets with red cuffs and red crosses on the left arm. . . .

The little parlour behind the hall has an even more revealing selection of photographs. Three are groups of 'the workers'; then there are three minor portraits of Emosi; finally—in marked juxtaposition—a full-length portrait of Cakobau, a Coronation portrait of the Queen and the Duke of Edinburgh—and a very fine study of Ratu Emosi, with Isaiah 11.10 (in Fijian) typed beneath it: 'And in those days there shall be a root of Jesse in the land, and he shall be as an ensign for the people. . . .' Big Brother is always in evidence at Daku.

Surely Daku now falls into place: a place in the distinguished line of ideal commonwealths. The principles of New Fiji, of the New World, were formed, says Ratu Emosi, 'as though out of a dream'; but the dream, not an ignoble one, has been shared by others. Daku has its congeners, many of them. Not all collectivist, as Daku is, but all theocratic and authoritarian: the Cities of the Sun of the revolted Graeco-Syrian slaves in Roman Sicily; Münster of the Anabaptists; Canudos under O Conselheiro in Brazil, as displayed in Euclides da Cunha's tempestuous panorama *Revolt in the Backlands*; in their ways, Salt Lake City before Mormons became respectable, and Qadian, seat of the heretical Ahmaddiya Muslims, like Daku one of the most vivid memories of my life.

The future?

It is too easy, and too sad, to forecast the future of Daku. Practical as he is in the everyday affairs of life, one feels that at any moment Ratu Emosi might be revealed The Messiah, and Government would take notice. Even, on a lower plane, he might run into money troubles. As he says, 'the goldmine of the place is in mangroves'; but the bakeries of Suva are rapidly changing over to Diesel-fired ovens: on such mundane considerations may depend the fate of a Prophet! And even if there is no catastrophe, when Ratu Emosi goes he will leave behind him a sect, and it is the normal fate of such a sect to dwindle into a ghostly parody of the heroic days.

In its way Daku *is* heroic; but it is not the way forward. Its implied criticism of mundane progress is not without point and relevance; but it is vitiated, as a guide to action, by the extreme narrowness of its base, its complete lack of any wide experience to use as a standard of reference for its value-judgements. It is with no disrespect for the human effort of Daku that we leave it for a fresher and a saner air.

There are other millenarian zealots in Fiji; Ratu Emosi is not alone, only first among his peers. But there are also —and here, in my view, lies the hope for a new life for the Fijian people—several hundred obscure men and women who have had the resolution and the stamina to break through the multiplied folds of Custom and 'live of their own'. In a society like that of Fiji, with its load of Tradition and hierarchy, to do this also requires courage—the unspectacular peasant courage which, in the last resort, has underlain even the greatest civilizations.

These Independent farmers or *galala*—and indeed all Fijians who live outside the village system, except a few specified categories such as ministers of religion—must pay a special Commutation Tax to obtain exemption from the communal labour-services of the village. The *galala* are also subject to other restrictions—they must for example make £100 gross a year, a provision which seems inequitable—and on the whole they have not been regarded with favour by the Fijian Administration, except in some individual cases. Clearly, they are 'un-Fijian'; to run your own farm is 'to live like the Indians'. But then, in the countryside it is often enough seen and stated that 'the Indians are our best schoolmasters'.

Despite all prejudice and the difficulties raised both by traditional Custom and by the disfavour of local officials, there is no doubt at all that the Independent farmers contribute a much greater proportion of Fijian economic productivity than their numbers warrant; and the man who, for whatever motives, runs his own farm and ploughs back his profits, builds up in fact a little business, is in reality doing more for the viability of his people, who are now numerically a minority and economically outstripped, than the man who simply lives in the village, does all the village headman tells him, and keeps all the rules—if indeed there are any such! Nor does it seem to me that the transformation of Fijian rural society to a community of small independent farmers threatens the integrity of the Fijians as a people: the bonds of language, religion, and inherited culture are too strong for that. Rather, this seems to me the only evolutionary way in which the Fijian people can become a really going concern—can in fact be a live people and not merely the servants of a fossil Way of Life.

The *galala* have their failings; anxious to display their success in the new ways, they are apt to diffuse their energies, to rush off to Suva unnecessarily to show what big businessmen they are, and so on. But many of them are very good farmers indeed, better than most Indians, and solid men who—after the essential initial phase of living hard 'like the Indians'—play a full and respected

64

part in the social life of their locality. It is a fallacy to think, as some of the literature would suggest, that the *galala* are despised pariahs living in the bush. In fact, their views, often forcibly expressed, are listened to with respect and find an increasing response.

For—and this is the most important point—apart from the zealots, they alone among the Fijians seem not divided in their minds. They feel that they know what they would do and should do; they have ceased 'Wandering between two worlds, one dead, The other powerless to be born.' They feel that they have at least set their feet firmly on the path into the new world—and that this is the path for the Fijians. After eight months of very intensive study, I think they are right.

One last vignette. It had been a very good and prolonged night session at Saweni; next day I was at Draiba, sunk in the misery of frustration I have already described. To my surprise Onesimo, the *galala* from Saweni, came over: something of a yeoman type (and how badly the Fijians need the yeoman spirit!), he reminded me of Cromwell's 'russet-coated captain, who knows what he fights for and loves what he knows'. The discussion dragged on through the usual dreary winding channels, the helpless 'we'd like to get on, but the Customs, the burdens, the obligations, the laws, all hold us back . . .' It was the same in forty-odd out of fifty villages; but then old Onesimo came out of his doze, sat up, and became very eloquent, repeating with variation and embellishment and much force the substance of his final speech at Saweni. That had been the shortest Fijian speech I had ever heard: 'What should we do? Why, stand on our own feet, be our own masters—*Tu Vagalala!*'

Note: The field experience on which this essay is based was acquired while carrying out a survey of the economic life of the Fijian people for the Colonial Welfare and Development Fund and the Government of Fiji. My thanks are due to many officials, Fijian and European; my gratitude to the Fijian villagers who welcomed me will, I hope, be apparent from the text. The views expressed are of course entirely my own, and must not be taken as representing those of the Government of Fiji or any agency thereof. The essay was written long before the riots of December 1959.

Progress at Mbananakoro

*A Case-Study in Culture Contacts and their Adjustment**

THE Island of Kerekere is one of the brightest remaining jewels of the British Crown. During those romantic days between the abandonment, under Missionary suasion, of direct action to maintain the Kerekerian Way of Life† unchanged (but for the total assimilation of some European elements into the local diet), and the statesmanlike Concession of 1889, when the Ruling Chiefs put their trust in God and Queen Victoria, the advance-guard of civilization providentially reserved for European enterprise the more extensive and fertile plains. Here, rustling groves of pawpaws, rich fields of pineapples, supply those fractions of the Australian and New Zealand markets which local growers, owing to their ridiculously low tariffs, find it inconvenient to serve.

These crops, the staples of the Island's economy, are grown by an industrious and happy immigrant Nesian tenantry, whose propensity to work hard and make money has raised them from indentured coolies to substantial farmers and small businessmen. This propensity, it is admitted in all European clubs, has indeed assumed the proportions of a vice. At the same time, the clubs are agreed

* The author's thanks are due to the liberality of MISMAMCUD (the UNESCO Fund for the More Intensive Study of Monetary Acceptance in Micro-Communities of Undeveloped Dependencies), which made possible the fieldwork on which this study is based.

Needless to say, it follows that this narrative makes no reference to any actual people or happenings in any actually existing British Colony. UNESCO is not responsible for any statements or opinions expressed.

† Hereafter referred to as KWL.

that the indigenous Kerekerians, simple children of nature
with every known virtue except that they will not work
hard and make money, being less industrious and hence
poorer than the Nesians, are even happier than they. Owing
to their lower level of education and abstract thought,
Kerekerians and Nesians find some difficulty in grasping
this ratio;* but its validity is shown by the further fact that
the Europeans, who exist to maximize the happiness of the
other communities (we are of course speaking of the commercial rather than the administrative section), are much
the most industrious, least poor, and unhappiest of the
three.

This brief outline of the Island's polity perhaps does the
indigenous people less than justice, since in its modest way
the Colony is also a dollar-earner, and in this important
sector the native Kerekerians play, or at least in its initia-
tion played, a significant role.

For, in a secluded cove not too distant from the airport,
at the modern and luxurious Blue Lagoon Hotel—a subsidiary of Pacific Beaches, Inc.—the tourist with a day or
two and a lot of dollars to spare is privileged to observe one
of the most notable examples of successful acculturation in
the whole Pacific area. For moderate charges, visitors to
the Blue Lagoon are entertained in the most traditional
manner, though not without all modern conveniences, by
the adjacent Chiefly Village of Mbananakoro. The kava
bowl is never empty, night or day, the *lali* gong rarely silent,
while during those hours when colour photography is easy
the most barbaric and photogenic dances are constantly on
view.

But it must not be thought that the village folk have
been degraded to mere entertainers. Individual gratuities
are strictly forbidden by the High Chief, and curios can
be bought only at the Co-operative Store: individuals are
thus shielded from the demoralization and consequent
loss of happiness which too often arises, alas, from over-

---

* *Spate's Law*: $X = fY = g\dfrac{1}{Z}$, where X = happiness, Y = hard
work, and Z = wealth, f and g being constants.

indulgence in a monetary economy. Far from degenerate, the villagers raise their simple crops with the most modern appliances, and while their fishing parties are perhaps more spectacular than effective, an ample supply of tinned pilchards preserves the protein balance. When not engaged in their major economic activities of the kava and the dance, the people continue to till the soil and so maintain that most essential feature of the KWL, the living link with the land.

This happy result has not been attained without strains and stresses. That these have been overcome is (of course) due to wise and moderate native leadership, to the benevolent paternalism of Government, to sympathetic encouragement from local European businessmen (all of whom, it goes without saying, Understand the Native), to enlightened investment from overseas, to the influence of the Mission or the South Pacific Commission, or to any one of these according to taste or prejudice.

It is true that a really acute observer might note some differences, physical and cultural, between the Mbananakoro folk and the generality of Kerekerians; but such visitors are rare and are rightly discouraged from enquiries which, however well-meaning, might have a disturbing effect on the Island's contribution to the sterling bloc's dollar assets. Discouragement, naturally, does not take the crude and un-British form of direct interdiction or official harassment; but there are no villages along the five miles of well-paved road between the airport and the Blue Lagoon, while beyond that point few tourists are hardy enough to travel, despite the proffered services of the ever-cheerful and (for due consideration) ever-obliging Nesian taximen. The state of the roads provides a simple but effective check on indiscreet explorations.

*   *   *

The potentialities of economic growth in Mbananakoro were first perceived by Mr Theodore J. Diddenheim III, one of the Los Angeles directors of Pacific Beaches. Owing to a missed connection, Mr Diddenheim had to spend not only a night but a day in his own hotel. Drinking gloomily on the verandah, he enquired of the Nesian barman why that damned shack was allowed to detract from the meticulous beauty of the Blue Lagoon grounds. Told that it belonged to the adjacent Kerekerian village, he strolled across to negotiate with the owners for the removal of the village, lock, stock, and barrel, to a less obtrusive site. This resolve weakened a little when he reached the village green and was confronted by a whole array of traditional Kerekerian houses, which (as is well known) in the old days reached a pitch of craftsmanship unparalleled elsewhere in the Pacific.

By great good fortune the first person Mr Diddenheim met was the village school-teacher, a well-spoken and for a native an intelligent man, who at once conducted him to the High Chief's house and stayed on to act as interpreter. In the gloom, the chorus of deep bass vocables from the dozen or so figures sitting cross-legged on the floor, still more the throbbing rhythm of resonant hand-claps, were a little un-nerving; however, when the High Chief motioned one of his servitors to hand the visitor a coconut bowl brimming with some brown liquid, Mr Diddenheim rightly surmised that this was one of those Quaint Native Customs and that its intention was friendly. He gulped the drink down—to his surprise it had a mildly meliorative effect on his hangover—and then (perhaps it was the kava) a first-class Public Relations idea struck him. He turned to the teacher:

'You askim—he like dancey-dancey this village? Him savvy, dancey-dancey, like this, hey?'

The question seemed rather long in Kerekerian, and the reply took an eternity: it was as if the whole history of the village from remotest generations was being chronicled, as in fact it was. At last the flow of strange sound ceased, and after some rather gruff expressions of assent from the company, the teacher translated:

'The High Chief requests me to inform his distinguished guest that in the old days Mbananakoro was indeed re-

69

F

nowned throughout Kerekere, and as far as Tonga, for pre-
eminence in the dance as in all other arts. Under the influence of the Church, however, we have for long put away
these superstitious practices.'

Deadlock. Still, that brown stuff wasn't so bad. Something might yet be done with that. The Mission now—
they must need money, they always did. Some good men at
the top now, so he'd heard. Who was Pacific Beaches' local
agent? Mr Diddenheim decided to cancel his onward book-
ing forthwith, and (after a harrowing taxi-ride) that same
day saw him in the Island's capital, Mboloni, closeted with
the agent, Mr Percy Lanter of the old-established house
Atoll Traders Pty Ltd. He was brief and to the point.

'Look at the Korolevu in Fiji—wonderful show, damned
good local chief they've got to run it, it's the real thing.
With our LA resources, we could go better.' Mr Lanter
looked. He saw the point. Much respected by all communities as head of one of the Old Island Families, he was (to
give him his just due) sincerely attached to Kerekere; his
affection for the Kerekerians was not, as with less firmly-
based Europeans, entirely due to the perception that the
Nesians in the not distant future might compete decidedly
too strongly, and in the present were decidedly too sharp:
it was in fact a genuine liking. He really desired, also, that
Kerekere should be better known to the outside world;
this precious stone set in the silver sea, as in a moment of
reminiscent emotion he once styled the Island (to the
acclamation of the Old Mboloni Club), was worthy of wider
repute. He had to perfection the Old Island Family touch
when speaking to the Kerekerians: 'We are all one family
and I just happen to be Elder Brother.' But he believed
this himself, and (unlike some more far-flung houses) Atoll
Traders did now and then pass something back to the atolls:
a clinic here, a scholarship there, unusual credit or even a
small loan somewhere else. In short, by his very virtues,
old-fashioned as some might think them, Mr Lanter was an
admirable local front for the designs of Pacific Beaches, Inc.

*   *   *

There was much activity all round. The Mission had to be squared: fortunately it had at its head far-sighted and broad-minded men, men who were prepared to admit that, in the first ardour of the Gospel, the heroic pioneers had unwittingly destroyed, amidst so much that was bad and depraved, some things that were innocent or even good in the old Custom; had taken much of the colour and vitality out of the KWL. It would do no harm to put some of it back—under safeguards, of course; nothing more alcoholic than kava.

The Secretary for Kerekerian Affairs, appointed guardian of the KWL, was more difficult to convince; but when it was pointed out to him that those grand old traditional houses, so splendid to look at but so confoundedly difficult to keep habitable, would be preserved for all time, he came round. The Department of Agriculture, as always avid for experiment, was splendidly co-operative. The Treasury, scenting dollars, had less than no objections. The Chamber of Commerce was enthusiastic. And finally His Excellency, reflecting that nothing much seemed to have happened yet under his reign, gave the Project the weightiest backing.

Agreement was soon reached. Direct subsidy for traditional houses—no small item, for owing to the decline in building standards their effective life was six years, and it took the whole village six weeks (not counting the kava time, of course) to build one of them; moreover, reeds and bamboos had long been in short supply and would have to be trucked thirty miles or so. Royalties on all traditional ceremonies and dances, but film and TV rights strictly reserved to Pacific Beaches. Necessary kava—and a liberal allowance for off-duty drinking—to be supplied free by Pacific Beaches. Traditional dress compulsory so far (the Mission was firm on this) as compatible with decency.

The controlling Liaison Committee consisted from the native side of the High Chief, his Master of Ceremonies, and the teacher: the accidental raising of a commoner beyond his traditional status caused local comment, but his bilingualism made him indispensable. From the promoters, there were Mr Lanter, the manager of the Blue Lagoon, and a nominee of Pacific Beaches. A representative of the Secretary for Kerekerian Affairs was neutral chairman, and finally the Curator of the Kerekerian Museum was co-opted, in a strictly advisory capacity.

There was only one minor difficulty at this point. The Curator, the most respected authority on Island antiquities, was able to reconstruct some truly striking dances; it was pointed out, however, that some censorship was essential. Back in the 1840s the most virtuous mission lady, while indeed stricken with becoming horror at the benighted heathenism of the dances, would not have noticed anything else wrong with them; her great-granddaughter might not bother overmuch about heathenism but (thanks to the advance of psycho-analytical studies in the United States) would be immediately and perhaps painfully cognizant of the esoteric symbolism of some gestures, a symbolism which would have passed over the head of her ancestress. In this aspect, then, the KWL must be subject to some modification. The more overt expressions of the procreative instinct were quietly toned down; not indeed suppressed out of existence, but reduced to an agreeable titillation of the senses, the recollection of which would go down well at parties in Shaker Heights, Ohio, or Virginville, Pa.

It was rather more difficult to sell the idea to Mbanana-koro itself. For one thing, the gravest doubts were expressed as to the propriety of offering kava to females. By great patience the people were at last brought to realize, if they could not understand, that America was a matriarchy. Incomprehensible as such a concept was to all rational men, and utterly repulsive to all Right Custom, it was at length conceded that a nation so rich and powerful was entitled to its own Custom, however childish and unworthy of human dignity it might be.

The High Chief and his sub-Chiefs were at heart deeply suspicious of the whole idea; but the prospect of unlimited kava on the house was a draw, and the younger men, some of whom had worked in Mboloni, were all for the Project. The High Chief was used to dealing with the younger men, but when the Mission supported them he weakened. The final blow was the defection from tradition—for so, of course, the resurrection of older tradition seemed—of the Secretary for Kerekerian Affairs, known to the people as The One Who Sits Up On High.* Bethinking him of the realism shown by the Ruling Chiefs of 1889, the High Chief of Mbananakoro at last yielded gracefully.

*   *   *

The first year's working of the Project exceeded all expectations. Suffice it to say that Kerekere Airport became a stop-over on four more airlines, that the Blue Lagoon rated a double-spread colour display in six consecutive issues of *The New Yorker*, that the entire capacity of the Japanese pearl-shell industry was diverted to producing souvenirs from Kerekere, and that all-time highs were recorded for the sales of Kodacolor and Agfachrome. Even in Britain, where the whole affair was regarded with some natural distaste, the Secretary of State for the Colonies was at least forced to appoint a working party to study the Project with a view to adapting Mbananakoro principles for the rehabilitation of the tourist industry of the Bahamas and Bermuda, which had entered on their worst depression since the liberation of the slaves had all but ruined West Indian sugar. But in Mbananakoro itself, source and fountain-head of all this prosperity and depression, the disposal of the royalties raised the gravest problems.

The total was impressive. The High Chief, his sub-Chiefs, and the teacher went into a sub-committee on their own, calling in from time to time (in a strictly advisory capacity) a Nesian building contractor. They could hardly believe the dazzling future that he displayed before them. In three years' time, if the current rate of monetary inflow was maintained, the entire village could be rebuilt in wood with corrugated iron roofs!

---

* It must be admitted that this honorific has reference less to his exalted rank in the official hierarchy than to the location of his office on the top floor of the Secretariat, which by virtue of its four storeys, unparalleled elsewhere in the Colony, has produced a very powerful impression on the Kerekerian mind.

This proposal, duly and respectfully submitted to the Liaison Committee but showing such lamentable disregard of the basic principles of acculturation, naturally created utmost alarm and despondency. The Chair rather high-handedly forced through an adjournment, and the cables between Mboloni and Los Angeles became red-hot. A meeting was arranged at which not only The One Who Sits Up On High himself would be present, but even Mr Didden-heim. In desperation before this dastardly blow of the double-crossing natives at the very foundation of the Project, Pacific Beaches even rang up the University Department of Anthropology. As it happened, most of the staff were attending an International Conference on Social Liquefaction at Rio de Janeiro, but the Acting Chairman (who was very sore at being left out) readily granted himself leave to be at Mr Diddenheim's disposal in this situation which obviously called for the services of a trained anthropologist. Besides, having spent the best years of his life as Resident Anthropologist with a Navajo Indian family in Arizona, he felt the need to widen his field. So it was that (in a strictly advisory capacity) Dr Endorn Weltsz enters the story.

The full meeting was difficult. In vain was it pointed out that the traditional houses were not only far more beautiful but also decidedly more comfortable and hygienic than wood-and-iron; that their expensive upkeep, the only point against them, would be met by the largesse of Pacific Beaches; that wood-and-iron houses were too small, and their floors too hard on the haunches, for the constant hospitality so integral a part of the KWL, so that the people would have to buy furniture and learn the uneasy and undignified art of sitting on chairs.

All these rational arguments were assented to, but all foundered on one inevitable rock: the near-by village of Korovuaka had wood-and-iron. And while Korovuaka was inhabited solely by hewers of wood and drawers of water, Mbananakoro had always been Chiefly, had always been Top Village.

Kerekerian is a highly roundabout language, enumerating all things, entirely innocent of that useful little contraction '&c.' and all this took some hours and much kava. Poor Mr Lanter broke first. Quite forgetting the Elder Brother touch, he burst out (very naturally), 'What the hell has that got to do with it?'

Dr Weltsz shuddered: never, never, never should one put to one's informants a direct suggestion, however simple and relevant. But the Chiefs of Mbananakoro shuddered yet more: could it be that the revered Mr Lanter, their Elder Brother, whose grandfather had been the Elder Brother of their grandfathers, was thoughtlessly equating Mbananakoro with Korovuaka? Perhaps the heat was affecting the old man; at all events, courteously but firmly, let him be recalled to a sense of what was right. Another round of kava, to put him at his ease (it is notoriously diuretic, and Custom forbids . . .) and to give them time to marshal their arguments, and they would give him the works.

They did. It appeared that in the introduction of cannibalism, in the suppression of cannibalism, in the acceptance of the Gospel; in gardening, canoe-building, fishing, and dancing; in the making and drinking of kava; in the wars of heathen days, in the wars of the Church, in the Great Wars; in education, in sanitation, in procreation; in the formation of co-operative societies and in the playing of rugby—from the time of the First Ancestors right down to the Coronation of Her Majesty Queen Elizabeth II— always, always, had Mbananakoro been Top Village, her Chiefs Top Chiefs.

From this merely general statement of the case they moved on to their ancestral claims to most of Kerekere, and the proceedings threatened to resemble a session of the Lands Commission, before which the most toughened administrators blench.

At this point Dr Weltsz had his great idea. Reckless of customary propriety, of the fallacy of direct suggestion, and of his strictly advisory capacity, he broke into the flow.

'What you want', he said, 'is a tractor.'

The Mbananakoro spokesman checked. This was a new one on them. The Europeans balked also. Really, a tractor in this traditional village would be rather vulgar.

Dr Weltsz rose superior to them all. In his mind's eye he saw as in a flash the frontispiece of his next book—and thousands of colour-slides: a tractor driver in traditional costume, apt symbol of the marriage of ancestral order and enlightened progress in a model Project, with which the name of Endorn Weltsz would ever be associated.

And so he spoke with simple eloquence. It would be, he said, in this noble old-time village, holding fast to all which was good in the KWL, a symbol of a New Age—of the blessing and plenty which science and technology could bring. It would preserve that living link with the land which was the basis of Mbananakoro's proud sense of individuality and pre-eminence. It would enable the people to produce more food in less time, and so to devote themselves yet more ardently to the meticulous rehearsal of the dances, not to mention more time for káva. Thus it would not weaken the traditional pride of craftsmanship, it would rather enhance it. They might even sell their yams and taro in the Mboloni market, and in due course, with the aid of skilled cooks, some of the less repulsive roots might figure on the menu of the Blue Lagoon itself, with notes explaining their significance in ceremony and folk-lore. So the fame of Mbananakoro would spread wider yet and wider. All that was best in the old, all that was best in the new, might meet in this machine, devoted to the immemorial arts of the soil, yet enshrining the latest devices of technology. Besides, Korovuaka hadn't got a tractor.

The tractor was carried by acclamation.

*　　　*　　　*

The next developments are perhaps best presented by some extracts from those journals, household words in the South Seas, *PIF* and *PAM*:

Pacific Anthropological Monthly, 14/6/19—

> *Notes and News*: Dr Endorn Weltsz, Acting Chairman of the Department, has recently returned from a brief visit to Kere-

kere as Adviser to Pacific Beaches, Inc. While there, Dr Weltsz was privileged to materially assist in the problem of acculturation to touristic impacts on the part of the inhabitants of Mbananakoro; his draft plan for mechanization of traditional agriculture was enthusiastically accepted by the people, and has been taken up by the local official and business community. Phase II of the Mbananakoro Project bids fair to blaze a beacon for the rapid adjustment of such fractionally ethno-centered communities to extragenous pressures, and this University feels privileged to have been associated with it. Pacific Beaches, Inc., has announced its intention of endowing a new Chair of Vacational Studies, and is to be congratulated on its far-sighted realism in calling in trained anthropological help to the understanding of a complex problem of sociological progressification.

Pacific Islands Fortnightly, 22/7/19—

Kerekere Comments: Pacific Beaches, Inc., well-known LA hotel chain, is to be congratulated on its far-sighted realism in calling in the well-tried local experience of Mr P. Lanter, of Mboloni ('Perce' to his innumerable atoller friends), to 'sell' to the natives the idea of putting their traditional customs to some real use. Once again it has been shown that the best friends of the native are those who really understand him, practical men who know the islands and have no need of the Mboloni bureaucrats or long-haired anthropologists to teach them how to manage Johnny Kerekere for his own good.

PIF, 5/8/19—

Kerekere Comments: As was to be expected, the bureaucrats of Mboloni are moving in on the Mbananakoro opening. Rumour has it that various high officials will descend from their air-conditioned offices and brave the perils of the road in order to get rather more than their share of the kudos. The official photographer will know his job, of course, but everybody really informed about what goes on in Kerekere will tell you that the real behind-the-scenes work has been done by the practical men who know the islands and have no need . . .

PIF, 5/9/19—

Kerekere Comments: It is officially announced in Mboloni that His Excellency the Governor, accompanied by the Secretary for Kerekerian Affairs and the Director of Agriculture, will attend the formal opening of the Mbananakoro Project next week. H.E.'s practical interest in native progress is of course well-known to readers of *PIF*, but it is none the less gratifying to Atoll Traders and their trans-ocean backers, Pacific Beaches, Inc., that this practical contribution to solid native advance will be inaugurated under the highest auspices. It is less usual, though on that very account quite as gratifying, to find that some of the high officials from Mboloni are following H.E.'s lead by taking some belated interest in real development instead of sitting in their air-conditioned offices dreaming over fancy schemes of education and the like. Who knows, they may even—perhaps—be willing to learn a little from the best friends of the native, practical men who know the islands . . .

*　　　*　　　*

The official opening of Phase II of the Mbananakoro Project was expected to rank as a notable event in the annals of the Colony. This expectation was more than fulfilled.

The tractor—supplied by Atoll Traders—had arrived some time before. There had been difficulty about a driver. It was, of course, unthinkable that the star role should go to anyone not of Chiefly rank. But even had they been able to conquer their inner reluctance to come to terms with the actual machine of progress, none of the Chiefs was willing to undergo instruction in tractor-driving. It was not for them, Kerekerian gentlemen, to learn such base mechanic arts; besides, something might go wrong, and their standing in Mbananakoro be imperilled. If one cannot control things with gentlemanly ease and mastery, it is better to stand aside, adding to the dignity of the proceedings and at all events preserving one's own. Yet it *was* the star role. . . .

A solution was found by the unearthing from a Mboloni motor repair-shop, where he was happily employed as an admirable foreman, of the black sheep of the Mbananakoro Chiefly families. This un-Kerekerian young man, David Ravutagana (Wielder of the Club, a name inherited from one of his more ferocious forebears), had left the village at an early age—the girls were one Chiefly and one un-Chiefly, a problem incapable of local solution since the Mission had suppressed polygamy.

In the course of a roving career, David had driven a bulldozer with great aplomb as a Sergeant in the 1st Kerekerian Pioneers, a unit with a fine record in the Solomons. When first approached with the proposal that he should return to the village, he replied briefly 'Damn the village! what happens to my beer permit?' An eloquent appeal from the Secretary for Kerekerian Affairs, coupled with assurances that his permit would remain valid and that his emoluments would include a generous allowance—by the case—from the bar of the Blue Lagoon, won him over, and he returned to Mbananakoro fully determined to play his part in leading his people forward to the New Age.

At last the dawning of the New Age broke. All that was anything in Kerekere was there—H.E. and his Departmental Heads, Foreign Consuls, Mr Theodore J. Diddenheim III and Mrs Diddenheim, Mr Lanter and directors of all the Island firms, the Mission, the Armed Forces, Chiefs and commoners from all quarters of the Island, the Press, radio, film and TV men by the score, the Deputy Mayor of Mboloni (a Nesian), and the Official Photographer.

The reader may have noticed the virtual absence from our list of the Nesian community; but then, we did say 'all that was anything', and the community was by no means under-represented off the official platform. Distinguished as always by an ardent desire to widen the horizons alike of Kerekerian village folk and of overseas visitors, every Nesian bus and taxi driver (which means every bus and taxi driver) in the Colony had converged on those five golden miles.

There was a slight hitch as to venue. To entertain its distinguished guests, the Blue Lagoon had erected a fine pavilion—of course in traditional materials—commanding an excellent general view of the village. Unluckily, a few days earlier the villagers had planted yams immediately in front of the pavilion—and this without consulting the

Liaison Committee, an omission which in the light of later events might seem ominous. Making a virtue of necessity, the Blue Lagoon side proposed that this unsightly patch of earth should be used for the formal driving of the first furrows which should open the New Age in Mbananakoro. The village demurred: they would need the yams, and only half a mile away (true some three hundred feet up, by bush track) was an admirable patch which really needed a tractor to plough it; David, too, was anxious to show his virtuosity on a 30-degree slope.

H.E. was game for the walk, and his Departmental Heads —*noblesse oblige*—were willing to follow, though the Director of Agriculture muttered darkly about soil erosion. But then the Americans, the ladies, and particularly the American ladies . . . Moreover the lines for the broadcast would have to be relaid . . . The objection of the villagers to the loss of their yams was overcome by the immediate issue of store vouchers for a more than equivalent amount of bully beef and tinned pilchards, and David sullenly acquiesced.

After drinks in the Blue Lagoon bar, the official party moved out to the pavilion, to the accompaniment of the British and American national anthems, played by the band from a U.S. cruiser which just happened to be in the offing that day. A full-throated roar burst from thousands of sturdy Kerekerian lungs, and shriller but not less animated cheers rose from the Nesian taximen.

Customary Kerekerian presentations are not things to be cut short with impunity, and there were so many presentees . . . not forgetting, the reader will be glad to learn, Dr Endorn Weltsz, only begetter, almost, of the New Age. It was too damned hot out here and the bar was inviting, so —following H.E.'s excellent example—speeches at least were short. At last, at a nod from H.E., the High Chief gave David the signal.

David and the tractor had long been waiting. In honour of the occasion, the bonnet of the tractor had been decorated with a traditional design by Dr Weltsz—vaguely Melanesian in general feeling but showing distinct signs of

Navajo influence, thus setting a delightful problem for some future Heyerdahl. As for David, he looked every inch the Noble Savage: his fine torso gleaming with coconut oil, his chest adorned with a superb gorget of pearl shell, and all the brawny rest of him that was not swathed in tapa rustling with croton leaves. At his side he wore, in what had been his Sergeant's belt, the actual war-club of his famous ancestor Ravutagana, on loan from the Kerekere Museum, whose Curator was keeping anxious eyes on his treasure. That renowned weapon—*Na Uti ni Ravutagana*, the Phallus of Ravutagana—was to be David's undoing. Or perhaps his making.

For as he shifted into a good position on the tractor seat, he pulled the club round a bit—it was a confounded nuisance, butting into his ribs—and cut his thumb on one of the shark's teeth, no less useful than ornamental, which in their time had let much more blood. Yet perhaps no blood-letting had been so historic in its results as that little spurt, for with it, unleashed, gushed out all his ancestral passions in one dark atavistic tide.

As he put the tractor into gear, the enormity of the thing he was about to do at once dazzled and darkened David's mind. To waste the good yams—nothing, surely, could be so displeasing to the Ancestors, those Spirits of the Land and of Fertility. Spending half the annual output of the village on one tremendous belly-distending feast was one thing—*that* was not waste, it was use, for it established clearly that the givers of the feast were noblest of clans, their village richest of villages, and the Ancestors would approve. But this wanton destruction of food yet in the womb of Mother Earth, this wickedly uneconomic waste of wealth—in a flash David realized that he could never lift up his head if he bore art or part in it. And then all the fighting blood of the Chiefly Ravutaganas rushed to his heart, bore him away in a wild ecstatic charge . . .

Events, as someone has said somewhere, now moved rapidly to a climax. With a tremendous yell of the old war-cry—*Na Uti! Na Uti!*—which had once been the terror of Korovuaka and indeed of all villages within fifteen miles,

David pushed the throttle right out and the tractor lunged forward, through the thatched walling of the pavilion. The official party split up with alacrity, and the tractor came to rest against the bar counter of the Blue Lagoon . . .

*   *   *

The teacher, a quick-witted man, was the first to take action. A few words and a few shillings to one of the Nesian taximen, and, unnoticed in the hubbub centring round H.E., some artistic disrepair work was put in on the steering. The resultant correspondence between the Secretariat, the Blue Lagoon, Atoll Traders, Farm Mechanix, Inc., Pacific Assurances, and the Police Department (and their respective solicitors) behold, is it not written in three vast files in the Secretariat of Kerekerian Affairs? However, nothing was proved. . . .

Dr Weltsz also moved quickly. He too, in crisis, had the good sense to rely on the adroit Nesian community. The airport, he knew, would be watched, the hotels and the beaches combed, but a swift taxi to Mboloni enabled him to shake off pursuit long enough to go to earth with a friendly Nesian lawyer who, feeling that *habeas corpus* might be a thin reed, eventually smuggled him off on a leaky Chinese copra boat.

As for David, he pleaded a temporary loss of control. That was his story, and he stuck to it. Nobody noticed the ambiguity in the phrase.

*   *   *

At this point we may let the Press take up the tale again:

PIF, 29/9/19—

Kerekere Comment: Not for the first time, colonial bureaucracy and the irresponsible agitation of 'enlightened idealists' from outside, ignorant of the basic realities of islands life, have led to the frustration of the productive energies of Pacific people. Were this journal ever disposed to say 'I told you so', the fiasco at Mbananakoro would give ample justification. Practical men who know the islands could have told the long-haired anthropologists and their bureaucratic backers in Mboloni what was likely to come of rushing the native along too fast. It is clear that had the advice of local businessmen been acted upon from the beginning, the frustration which faces the Mbananakoro people could have been avoided. As it is, the demand for a sudden change in their fixed ideas has been too much for them. Most likely, as usual, the damage done by this reckless 'social experiment' will have to be undone by the real best friends of the native, those who understand Johnny Kerekere and how to manage him for his own good.

Mr P. Lanter is giving up the local agency for Pacific Beaches, Inc.

PAM, 20/10/19—

Notes and News: Not for the first time, bureaucratic colonialism and the irresponsible pressures of unenlightened local interests, ignorant of the basic realities of island life, have led to the frustration of the productive energies of the Pacific peoples. Although this University was not officially associated with the Mbananakoro Project in any way, it has contacts which amply justify comment on the fiasco. Competent social investigators could have told local 'big' business and its official backers in Mboloni what was likely to come of inadequately conceptualized interference with indigenous developmental processes. It is clear that had the advice of trained anthropologists been acted upon from the beginning, the frustration which faces the Mbananakoro people could have been avoided. As it is, the demand for a sudden transference of motivation in a highly integrated traditional continuum has undermined the basic channels of social action and produced excessively ambivalent tensions. As so often, the damage done by this reckless commercial exploitation will have to be undone by the patient work of those who really understand the archetypal socio-economic behavioural patterns of the island peoples, and how to guide them onto the path of integrated adjustment to new procedures of entrepreneurial responsibility.

The resignation from the Faculty of Dr Endorn Weltsz has been accepted.

*　　　*　　　*

But Mbananakoro did not die. The dawn of a New Age was not a false dawn.

It is true that an impasse seemed to have been reached. The High Chief was unable to withstand the surge of popular feeling in favour of David Ravutagana, who seemed destined to become a cult leader; but despite this inexcusable attitude of the people, it was not possible, for easily understood political reasons, for Pacific Beaches to press its demand for the immediate dispossession, without compensation, of the village. For many years Kerekerian land has been inalienable without the full consent of the whole clan, and to tamper with this would be to strike at the very roots of the KWL.

The dilemma was obvious. The disloyal attitude of the villagers made it quite impossible to work with them; but without an inflow of money income the traditional houses would soon decay into shacks and hovels, and the existence of such an eyesore on the very doorstep of the Blue Lagoon could not fail to affect its turnover adversely, and this would be an embarrassment to Government, a loss both of prestige and of dollars. The continued prosperity of the Blue Lagoon (on which Pacific Beaches was now more dependent than it cared to admit) necessitated the maintenance in good order and close proximity of the traditional village. Or at least of *a* traditional village.

There was the key: any old village would do, provided only it were traditional. Once more, as when Dr Weltsz had his happy inspiration (for I would not be ungenerous to my unfortunate predecessor, since despite its proximate mischance his idea remains an essential factor in later Mbananakorian development), an academic *deus ex machina* did the trick. It is with some diffidence that this writer reveals that (as just hinted) he it was who was privileged to find the just solution, maintaining essentially unimpaired the rights of Mbananakoro, ensuring the continued commercial prosperity of Pacific Beaches (with all that implies for the sterling bloc), and moreover affording some relief to a serious social problem in a neighbouring British dependency. Always rather more geographical than anthropological in his thinking, it occurred to him that a simple transfer of populations might provide the answer.

On the one hand, the wilder and rockier hills of Kerekere contain much undeveloped tribal land: the failure to
use it gives occasion for just reproach of the Kerekerians,
more especially from the Nesian community. On the other,
many Micronesian atolls suffer from an increasing pressure
of population on their minute patches of dry land. Seen in
this light, the solution seemed as obvious as the dilemma.

There were no real difficulties. Up in the Kerekerian
Reserves there was a considerable tract of land suitable for
subsistence agriculture, which by some quite inexplicable
oversight was not specifically claimed by any Kerekerian
tribe. The Department of Agriculture, as always avid for
experiment, gladly agreed to assist in bringing it to a fit
state for cultivation. The Mbananakoro folk, heartily tired
of their experiment in progress, were ready to go, demanding only that they be rehoused in wood-and-iron. Pacific
Beaches was reluctant to meet this demand, but the Secretary for Kerekerian Affairs was firm in pointing out the
unescapable alternative: the permanent existence just outside the Blue Lagoon of this unco-operative, unhygienic,
unprogressive, untraditional, and above all unphotogenic
group. A compromise was reached: in return for a once-
for-all payment for wood-and-iron houses of specified standard, Pacific Beaches was relieved of any further claims and
retained the goodwill of the name 'Mbananakoro', in which
a good deal of advertising capital was locked up.

To repopulate the old site, a group of Egbert Islanders,
an intelligent and reliable people, were overjoyed to exchange their scrap of coral sand for the good volcanic soils
of Kerekere. They gladly agreed to the stipulations of
Pacific Beaches, and have loyally honoured their contract.

So it is that the speech, the dances, the costumes, the
curios, of Mbananakoro are no longer Kerekerian but
Egbertese; but no matter, they are all very traditional, and
kava is common to both.

*   *   *

As for the original people, they too are happy, tilling the
soil in the traditional way and so maintaining that most

G

essential feature of the KWL, the living link with the land (*v. supra*). Indeed, as they are much poorer than the Egbertese, it is a fair presumption that they are also much happier (*v. supra* again).

There are changes. There is no real road to their new village of Ravutaganakoro—they regret a little the Nesian taxis—so it is difficult to get in materials for the maintenance of their wood-and-iron houses, even were there any money now that they have cut adrift from Pacific Beaches. But bamboos and reeds are far more plentiful than on the coast, and already, on my last visit, I observed that one or two of the more progressive younger men were beginning to build traditional style houses. . . .

There is one exception to the general disrepair. On the highest site in the village, lovingly tended, bright with white walls and red roof frequently repainted (at Lord knows what cost—non-monetary—in labour, humping the drums up the jungle track) rises the home of the new High Chief, David Ravutagana. At all feasts, and they are many, the story is retold with advantages: the tractor by this time has taken on the size of a not so small locomotive. Every visitor to the village must hear it again, and Kerekerian visitors are numerous, bringing rich gifts of shell and mats, so that David's house is glorious within as without; indeed, inconveniently over-furnished even by non-Kerekerian standards. For David is now a man of great wealth: in his house the kava bowl is never empty, night or day, and before it the *lali* gong is rarely silent.

He is indeed the Grand Old Man of the KWL: to speak with him, The Man Who Drove The Tractor, young men who desire to impress their girls (and what young man does not?) resort from great distances, and his word, his rulings on Custom, are law throughout the hill country. He retains his beer permit; it would be politically dangerous to withdraw it.

Rumours of this influence, of these pilgrimages, filter through to Mboloni and cause Security some alarm. They need not worry: the High Chief David Ravutagana has no desire to be a prophet or the vulgar leader of a cargo cult.

As his fingers curl lovingly around *Na Uti ni Ravutagana* (it is always missing when emissaries of the Curator arrive), he knows that he has already achieved a far higher destiny. By one glorious act his fame is famed through the land, and when he passes on he will be more than an item in a genealogy, more than another eponymous shade amongst those shadowy collective ancestors. He has earned, not merely inherited, the proud style of Ravutagana II, Wielder of the Club; in his own lifetime, he is well assured, he has become an Ancestor.

*   *   *

The teacher, when I last heard from him, was doing quite well in UNESCO.

The Compass of Geography

The Compass of Geography

The past

Exponents of the social sciences are wont to introduce themselves with apologies for the youth of their subjects. Whatever the shortcomings of geography, as theory or practice, that excuse cannot be made. It is true that, one obscure and short-lived American appointment apart, the first University Chair of Geography was that founded in Berlin in 1820, and when the first holder, Karl Ritter, died in 1869 even this lapsed. At the end of last century there were probably no more than a dozen Chairs in all the Universities of the world. The rise of modern geography is generally and rightly associated with the name of Alexander von Humboldt, probably the greatest scientific traveller who has ever lived, and he began serious geographical work about 1799. But Humboldt and Ritter built on solid eighteenth-century foundations, notably those laid by the Forsters, father and son, the companions of Cook on his second voyage, and by Immanuel Kant himself. Kant's discussion of the placing of geography among the sciences is still relevant; in fact his equation 'history : time :: geography : space' forms a main thesis in Richard Hartshorne's *The Nature of Geography* (1939), by far the most searching discussion in English of the philosophy of our discipline.

Academic geography is thus younger than the major physical sciences, and roughly of an age with geology, though a fair case could be made out for that science being an offshoot of geography. We must admit the existence of the Woodwardian Chair of Geology at Cambridge as early

An Inaugural Lecture delivered at the Australian National University, 8 September 1953.

as 1731, but its claim to academic standards may be judged by the fact that an early incumbent took it simply as a more agreeable option than the Chair of Arabic. Those were the days before undue specialization!

But as an ordered study, based firmly on the comparison of numerous observations, and with something of coherent system about it, geography is far older. Passing over the remarkable systematization of Varenius in the seventeenth century, and the mass of truly scientific research by the great Renaissance discoverers—especially, perhaps, the Portuguese—we come, as so often, to a long interregnum (not without its own interest) and beyond that to the classical foundation. Here at least two names stand out as of permanent significance: those of Ptolemy and Hippocrates.

The work of Ptolemy (*c.* A.D. 90-168) included a treatise on projections for a world map, with a list of latitudes and longitudes of some eight thousand places as its basis. Such maps were undoubtedly made in classical and Byzantine times, and Renaissance reconstructions from Ptolemy's coordinates show remarkably good outlines between Spain and Arabia. The rediscovery of Ptolemy's *Geographia* and its Latin translation in 1405 form a great event in the general history of the world, for its firm framework of reference exercised a strong influence on the forward planning of the discoveries; though, ironically enough, this was most effective by virtue of Ptolemy's double error in accepting for the circumference of the globe an estimate about one-third too small, and then stretching Eurasia over half this reduced circumference instead of not much more than a third of it. There have been few errors more fruitful, for without them Columbus might never have conceived the idea of reaching Cathay by the Atlantic, or if he had might never have secured any practical support.

In the fifth century B.C. the physician Hippocrates wrote *Of Airs, Waters, and Places*—a text which in this century has still been taken as a sufficient exemplar of the view that physical environment is largely or even mainly the determinant of human societies and their history. In this, as in

geographical matters generally, Toynbee is much misguided; but the fact itself speaks to the early maturity of
our study as a subject fit for generalization, even if errone-
ous.

This, so far, is respectable antiquity; though other social
sciences also could trace to Plato or beyond. But we can
without special pleading go further back still. Most appro-
priately, the documents on which we base ourselves are
maps: the maps of ancient Egypt and Chaldea, witnessing
to a developed land survey and to wider regional interests;
indeed angular measurement by multiples of 60, which we
use for latitude and longitude, comes to us, through the
Greeks, from Babylonia. Perhaps even more remarkable are
the maps and charts of non-literate peoples such as the
Eskimos and the Marshall Islanders. With such evidence,
I do not think it an exaggeration to claim that the twin
sisters Astronomy and Geography are in fact the oldest
branches of human knowledge dependent on exact observations and record, as distinct from empirical crafts such
as metallurgy or the magical rationalizations of, say, primitive physiology. In other words, they are the oldest sciences.

Geography in Australia

Let me now come nearer in both space and time: to Australia and to this century. The Australians are a geographic-
ally-minded people: in few countries, for example, is an
elementary knowledge of rainfall distributions so widespread. It has to be. On a more academic level than the
saloon-bar discussion of inches and points, little historical
writing of a general kind (as distinct from the detail of
political history) can disregard environmental considerations: witness the pages of Coghlan, of Shann, of Hancock,
of Crawford. In politics itself New State movements, in
administration regional planning, have clear and important links with geography. Early land policy, selection,
closer settlement, decentralization, all these are to no small
extent geographical themes. And yet the academic development of the subject has lagged, and no other great country

of the Western world is unrepresented in the International Geographical Union.*

This lag, and the youth of the Australian National University, offer a minor compensation on the personal plane: one is at least spared the ordeal of the neat tribute to one's predecessors. If one says with obvious sincerity that they were better men, this is the passage which carries most conviction to the audience; if they were notorious failures, that audience is sadistically alert for one's crash through the veil of thin irony. But I cannot with any comfort to my conscience omit the names of two precursors. J. W. Gregory's stay in Australia was only from 1900 to 1904, but some of his work here was of considerable significance, and it is an indication of his quality that he met his death by drowning in an Amazon headwater while engaged on field-work at the age of 68. And so far as honest and forthright work by one man could be responsible for the realism which marks much current evaluation of this continent, in contrast to the boosting of the twenties, that work was done by Griffith Taylor, who has a particular association with Canberra: for the first full account of the Australian Capital Territory was given by him to the Royal Geographical Society in 1914. To these two I would like to add the name of one less outstanding as a geographer in the strict sense, but a teacher and leader of the first order: Frank Debenham, a pupil of Edgeworth David and the builder of my own Cambridge school, which may fairly claim to be one of the half-dozen leading centres of geographical training in the English-speaking world.

And yet, despite this early leadership and an obviously favourable geographical environment, the promise of the start has not yet been fulfilled. Only three years ago there was but one full and autonomous University Department, under Professor Macdonald Holmes at Sydney; elsewhere geography was under the wing of geology or commerce. The last three years have seen a most gratifying change in some of the State Universities; and our friends in these new

* [Australia was admitted into the Union in 1960.]

departments will not, I know, need to be assured of the lively and most cordial interest which all of us at Canberra feel for their work.* By its geographical position, if by nothing else, the Australian National University is well placed to be a clearing-house for the flourishing multilateral traffic in men and ideas which has already sprung up between us. But we have all of us very much work to do before academic geography in Australia has the scope and status which it should have by right of its intellectual and social values.

One result of the lack of autonomy has been a serious lack of balance in the development of the subject. There is a marked bias on the physical side towards climatology, on the human towards agricultural geography, with an obvious linkage. To a point this is natural and legitimate in Australian circumstances; agro-geography is most certainly not to be neglected, nor will it be in our Department: indeed the first and the latest of our recruits are working in this field. But looking through the twenty-five years of *The Australian Geographer*, one notes a swelling volume of papers on the branches named, and a fading out of geomorphology—the study of landforms—and political geography, for both of which Australia gives ample and rewarding scope; though it should be added that of course this survey omits such wide-ranging studies as Professor Macdonald Holmes's *The Geographical Basis of Government*.

The topics named—climatology, agrarian studies, geomorphology, political geography—are all most important branches of the subject, and perhaps of special importance in Australia. But even together they cover only a fraction of our legitimate territory. The bias in Australia is not to be denied, and I think it has gone too far for healthy all-round growth. I do not wish to suggest that the departments in State Universities are at fault in their conception of geography; indeed within the limits of their resources I think their work is all that can be desired. But in some

* [There are now (1964) a dozen fully autonomous Departments of Geography in State Universities, and a second (undergraduate) department in the Australian National University.]

geography must still follow the bent of its local parent, and where new departments exist they are, like ourselves, too young to have made much significant change in the emphasis, and they are of course affected by their geographical and academic environment and heritage. The complete lack of prior attachments, as well as the freedom from undergraduate teaching, imposes a special responsibility on the staff of the Australian National University; and I hope I shall not be thought presumptuous if I say that for its Department of Geography this responsibility includes an effort to redress this lack of balance by emphasizing what we may call pure geography—certainly not instead of application, but as essential to a whole and balanced view of the subject.

The problem of geomorphology

To begin, then, with geomorphology, the study of landforms from continents down to the miniature river-terraces of Sullivan's Creek, or even to crab-holes. Historically and logically this is the foundation of the modern geographic structure, and yet it is a marchland debatable with geology. In some sense its relation to geology is like that of politics to history: its processes are the geological processes of the present, and just as politics and history illuminate each other if discreetly handled, so do geology and geomorphology. But though observation of contemporary physiographic processes by Hutton and Playfair, at the end of the eighteenth century, provided an essential key for unlocking the sealed record of the rocks, geomorphology has now but a marginal interest for most geologists. Concerned as they are with the complex details of the mineral composition of the rocks, with the intricacies of the fossil record, with mighty changes in the distribution of land and ocean, with the major problems of geophysics, and above all involved in a time-perspective of scores and hundreds of millions of years, geologists can hardly be expected to divert much attention to the recent and relatively minor riddles of the structure and growth of sand-dunes and shingle-spits, the recession of valley-slopes, or the mechanism of glacial erosion.

Not, of course, that there are not geomorphological problems of first importance for the development of geological concepts: questions of the erosional levelling of the land to form an almost flat surface or peneplain, for example, or as to whether changes in the relative level of land and sea are isostatic, that is due to comparatively local adjustments in the absolute level of the land, or eustatic, due to changes in the general level of the oceans or in the volume of ocean water, which latter is obviously greatly diminished when much of it is locked up in the vast ice-sheets of glacial periods. On a minor, or even minute, scale also, observations of the rate of silting in a salt-marsh, or of the disposition and movement of sand in a dune, may aid in the interpretation of ancient strata. Conversely any type of geological survey may make an important contribution to the data of geomorphology.

It must be added, parenthetically, that the close relation of geomorphology to geology is more apparent in a country like Australia than it is in Europe with its finer geological texture and its far denser settlement-pattern, which implies a wealth of rock-sections in shafts and cuttings of all sorts. In Australia the general lack of good topographical maps and the difficulty of adequately covering huge tracts of often forbidding country make geomorphology a valuable reconnaissance tool; the major terrain types are often indicators of geological materials and structure. It is perhaps geographically significant, then, that while in Europe geomorphology is generally left within the province of geography, in less closely developed lands it is much more a concern of geology. The fact that this basic component of geography is in Australia so largely a necessary tool for the geologists, who have naturally developed it for their own ends, may well be in part responsible for the lag in academic geography. Indeed, so obviously and directly do geographical factors enter into all the field sciences of Australia, and into such studies as economic history, that their students have perforce to acquire a necessary quantum of geographical facts and concepts (often rather crudely), and geography as a whole tends to be lost in a swarm of part-geographies.

Be this as it may, there are (especially in the United States) other and more academic reasons for the relative abandonment by geographers of a field largely pioneered by them. For plausible objections can be raised to the comprehensive inclusion of geomorphology within geography. Essentially, I think these stem from a rather dubious empiricism. Geomorphology is nothing if not genetic, and it is in many cases far from clear that the genesis of a land-form is of any real relevance to its significance as a part of the geographical picture. Narrow gorges between two wider and more open vales may have diverse origins. An escarpment may be the direct expression of a geological fault, an actual break in the strata; or of a great bend or monoclinal fold between two stretches of gently inclined rocks; or again it may be simply the forward edge of a sloping bed of resistant rock standing out above a lowland developed by the erosion of softer materials—to mention but three of the commoner cases. These distinctions may matter in geology, in unravelling the geography of the past; but what does it matter to the geography of today whether the Blue Mountain scarp overlooking the Sydney lowland was formed by faulting or by monoclinal folding? What matters is not the process but the physical expression of the process, the brute fact of scarpiness. So runs the empirical argument, and it is empirically very often valid.

It is intellectually unsatisfying, of course, just to leave it at that, but then those empiricists who merely drift into that philosophy (or never drift out of it) are often easily satisfied people. However, besides the appeal to intellectual curiosity, there is the fact that there are cases, perhaps relatively few but of crucial importance when they do occur, in which origin does matter to the geographer, even on the narrowest view of his task. On a straightforward material plane, untold thousands of pounds have been thrown into the sea by mere failure to consider the mechanics of wave-erosion and the behaviour of beaches—and this behaviour is part of the province of coastal geomorphology. Here the genesis is directly relevant to the geography of today: whether waves or currents, dominant or prevalent winds, are the major agents in shore-processes, are questions of real significance even in terms of cash. For the remedy must be adjusted to the cause of the disease, and it is empirical tinkering in bits and pieces which has littered the coasts of England—and of New South Wales—with wrecked sea-walls.

Let us take, however, an example rather more academic, though by no means hypothetical. A demographer or a historian, a student of agrarian sociology or economics, will no doubt recognize the general significance, within a continent or sub-continent, of its alluvial plains. They are after all usually the areas of greatest population density, of long-established agricultural and urban traditions. But naturally these specialists are interested merely in the end-product of geographical study, as the converse is notoriously true of geographers. To our colleagues, then, an alluvial plain is simply an alluvial plain, no more and no less; at least initially, for if the geographer does his job properly the others may wish to revise their findings, to reckon with unsuspected differentiations.

The plain may occupy a great geosynclinal trough—that is to say, the solid rock-floor under the alluvium may be a long fore-deep, produced by the buckling of lower layers of the earth's crust before the tremendous drive of advancing mountain-building. On the other hand it may be merely the down-warped edge of an old plateau or peneplain covered with the detritus brought down by rivers. With reasonably uniform climatic conditions, these two types of alluvial plain might look just the same—except to geographical analysis. But while appearances may be thus similar, the differences are in a double sense profound: the difference between an alluvial filling a mile and a half deep and a veneer a hundred feet thick. And on this genetic origin may depend phenomena not superficially apparent but highly significant to human life and so to social scientists: water-tables, the behaviour of rivers, the risks of erosion. On it might well depend whether it is possible to raise a poor catch-crop three years out of five by dry-farming, or whether the tapping of underground water at depth enables a stable all-year agriculture to be developed.

The difference described is in fact the difference between the main mass of the Ganges plains and their southwestern margins, where they overlap onto the foreland of the ancient block of the Indian peninsula. A thorough regional survey would disclose significant differences in human occupation even now—in size and spacing of villages, in farming systems, and so on. And the physical difference may be vital in terms of future irrigation development, as the vast underground water resources of the deeper alluvium are tapped.

At this point doubtless the social scientist—economist or planning engineer—may well take over; but it is the geomorphologist (hailing from any of four or five earth-sciences) who establishes the primary fact, and it is decidedly the geographer who, by virtue of comparative studies as well as local research, establishes the human significance and, initially at least, evaluates the potentialities of that fact. Quite apart from the intellectual challenge it presents, and the concrete human concern it sometimes possesses, I think that the genetic study of landforms has thus clear relevance to geographical analysis, and hence that any view of geography which does not include geomorphology as an integral part of the subject is seriously incomplete.

It must be added that geomorphology is not a closed system. It is a part of what might usefully be styled—as it was by T. H. Huxley—physiography: the study of the whole complex of physical materials and processes which has produced the bony framework on which the existing surface of the earth is moulded, and also much of the detail of that surface. These processes are also the object of other studies—oceanography, climatology, hydrology, pedology, and so on. To the geographer, such studies have a double existence: in their own right, and as involved in the physiographic complex, which is his own territory. It follows that it is incumbent on geographers to master at least the rationale of such parts of such studies as impinge on their own sphere. Not all parts will do so.

In case it should be thought that geographers must be Jacks-of-all-trades (it must be admitted that this is a very entertaining thing to be), I would add that individual geographers have individual tastes, capacities, and limitations; there can be no such thing as *the* training of *the* geographer, with select doses of X and Y in standard proportions. There are some things which are essential geography, even though not wholly and solely belonging to the study: among them are geomorphology, climatology, cartographical technique.* But beyond this core each should follow the bent indicated by the accidents of personal inclination; or sometimes, whether by acceptance or revulsion, by the inclination of the founding fathers of his particular school. There is also the element of opportunism, or adjustment to a geographical environment accidentally given: thus it was in war-time India that I found myself, rather to my surprise, a political geographer, and ceased, rather to my regret, to be a geomorphologist.

To sum up: in addition to the physical details of the earth's surface, the objective of the study of physical geography includes the structural framework on which that surface is modelled; as in anatomy for artists, to understand the surface it is essential also to understand the skeleton. That understanding in turn can only be justly apprehended, in the last resort, by a genetical approach. That is to me the essential definition of geomorphology, and at the same time the vindication of its inclusion *en bloc* within the ambit of geography. Nor can we neglect the dynamic and organic processes which play their part in the shaping of landforms and the furnishing of the earth's surface: hence we must include also such studies as climatology and ecology in large part. In short, physiography is indivisible.

There remains that other large sector of our field which is given the odd and omnibus title of 'human' or 'social' geography.

* [To these I would now add some statistical expertise.]

H

The problem of human geography

This too, whatever its limits—and they may probably never be defined to the point of logical satisfaction—is essential to an understanding of the existing surface of the earth; and on any definition of geography now current, such understanding is either the whole task of the geographer, or at the very least a major part, an essential tool; this latter for those who would consider the earth simply as the setting for man's activities. Yet, as we shall see shortly, although in practice human geography is unquestionably central in the development of the subject, in theory its position is rather less assured than that of physiography. No one doubts that physiography, in whatever departments of knowledge it be included, is a coherent system, its data amenable to generalization and the rule of scientific law. But from this point of view human geography is undeniably shakier, and at the same time, like physical geography, it always runs some risk of disintegration, since it is even more composite. One can study geomorphology with little reference to human activity; not with none at all, since man himself is no insignificant geological agent. But human geography must take into its reckoning the vast corpus of physiography, and large elements from most of the social sciences as well. A Leviathan indeed; and some think Leviathan a monster in the fullest sense of the word.

It is important to realize just how large and significant is the scope of this human or social sector. I do not refer here to the wide variety of its methods, ranging all the way from statistics to aesthetic impressionism; nor yet to the long list of topics with which it deals. Rather I refer to the fact that while physical processes monopolize the moulding of the structure on which the earth's surface is in turn modelled, we cannot say that all even of the major lineaments of that surface are exclusively patterned by such forces.

Over vast areas indeed physical factors hold absolute sway: in the great deserts, in Polar regions, even in Amazonia and High Asia, the patterns of human activity are little more than faint detail scratches on the edges of a blank plate, or flecks on its surface. But elsewhere, over realms not so vast but extensive enough, it is hardly an exaggeration to say that the surface aspect of the land is essentially a human work, and that the physical founda- tions crop up in patches of detail isolated, though highly significant. For the aspect of the land is in large part a vegetational aspect, and in such areas as the North China and the Ganges plains, much of the American Middle West, the Nile valley and delta, the greater part of Europe, the vegetation itself is man-made. Elsewhere, in dust-bowls and in the greater conurbations, the vegetation has been not so much re-fashioned as annihilated. The sum total of the built-up areas of the world is not small: in England, for example, it is between five and ten per cent of the land surface.

Of course nothing can detract from the fundamental im- portance of the underlying structure of plain and valley and mountain; and although the man-made changes are often called revolutionary, for revolutions they are singu- larly law-abiding. The North China plain is the domain of an overwhelmingly artificial vegetation; but that vegeta- tion is wheat and kao-liang millet, and not the rice domi- nant in the Yangtse plains adjacent to the south. Despite advances in agricultural technique, the changes remain on any reasonable view changes within defined limits.

They remain also of the utmost importance, and recog- nition of this has led to a not unnatural reaction against the often crude and overstated positions of the earlier geo- graphical determinists, who in fact were as often as not historians. In this century there has been a wide accept- ance of the opposite doctrine of Possibilism, perhaps best summed up in the words of Lucien Febvre: 'There are nowhere necessities, but everywhere possibilities; and man as the master of these possibilities is the judge of their use.' The unreasonable view just implied is that exaggera- tion of Possibilism, not so rare as it should be, which is dazzled by the undoubted fact that you could grow potatoes at the North Pole; as the Siberian peasant remarked, all that this needs is enough hot-houses and a professor to every plant.

The conflict of Determinism and Possibilism is one of the central issues of modern geographical thought, though Possibilists affect to assume that the question is closed in their favour.* An adequate discussion would be too pole-mically involved for an occasion such as this; but since I hold with the minority, I think it only fair to state my own view: that while negatively Possibilism has cleared the ground of a mass of pseudo-scientific junk, and also has positive elements of value, its proponents in turn have overshot their mark, and often end in a woolly empiricism. Possibilism is still by long odds the majority view, but there are signs at least of a neo-determinism more subtle than the old, less inclined to think of environment as exercising an almost dictatorial control over human societies, but con-vinced that it is far more influential than the current view admits; and with this trend I would identify myself.

It is time to return to the main theme, and to attempt to vindicate the autonomy of human geography while de-fining, or at least suggesting, its scope. So far, but for one hint, I have assumed that the standing of geography as an independent discipline needs no defence. On the physical side this is clear enough: we deal with a material object, the earth, and we deal with it in a manner which marks off our study from the other earth-sciences. Oceanography, meteorology, the study of soils, these and other components are sciences in their own right, and geographers can claim but a share, and not the lion's share, in their development. But with all this, with our frontiers vague and shifting, by common consent those who attempt to comprehend at one and the same time both the material elements and the dynamic processes of physiography are physical geographers.

I believe, and shall attempt to show, that a similar argu-ment holds good for human or social geography. But the issues are less clear. It is easy enough to see that physical geography has its definite principles and laws—the hydro-logical cycle of evaporation and precipitation, the cycle of

* [It seems now to be closed in their disfavour.]

erosion, and so on. It is much less easy to see any principles, any definite recurrences of much significance, in the all but infinite complexities of man's relations with his environment. It is true that the austere definition of geography now current, that it is the study of areal differentiations on the earth's surface, avoids reference to this time-honoured concept; but though it thus seeks to escape the problems of environmentalism it perforce comes back to them soon enough, since such relations inevitably bulk large in the actual data of differentiation. Yet, except on the crudest and most discredited determinist view, it is very difficult indeed to distribute these data into categories, except with an intolerable burden of cross-classifications, or on scales either too broad or too minute to be of much use.

So, although good geographers from both the Determinist and the Possibilist camps have written books called *Principles of Human Geography*, I am not at all sure that they have really found any. I think their books would be better entitled *Some Leading Features of Human Geography*. For given areas, even large areas, the thing can be done; I would be quite prepared to set forth principles of human geography for India, perhaps even for Monsoon Asia; but generalizations valid here would not be easily extensible to a world survey.*

In other words, it seems to me that in human geography we are as yet forced back onto the empirical plane. But this only after the survey of alternatives, and empiricism is only a bad thing when it is a synonym for a lazy or timid refusal to contemplate any other approach.

Perhaps the nearest things to significant recurrences are the perennial motifs with a strong geographical backing which run through the course of human history, and it may be of interest to outline two or three of them: the perpetual conflicts between sower and herder, city and countryside, seapower and landpower.

Most striking, perhaps, is the secular struggle of peasant

* Hence, perhaps, the recent tendency for branches of our much-adjectivized subject to set up house for themselves under such names as 'tropical geography', 'colonial geography', and so on.

and nomad on the frontiers of the desert and the sown, which have shifted back and forth with climatic changes, with the rise and decay of strongly organized states, with changes in the technology of war and peace; until at last aircraft and wireless have outstripped the nomad's mobility, and the conflict has been finally decided in favour of the sedentary societies. Yet even within these it has had, as it were, its outlying eddies: the antagonism between cultivators and the *mesta*, the great droving guild of Spain; or that given dramatic physical expression by the *travessão* of Brazil, on the coastal side of which all grazing land must be enclosed, while inland the onus of fencing is on the cultivator. And indeed it is not fanciful to see an echo of this secular cleavage in our own country in the feud of selector and squatter. So spectacular have been the changing fortunes of this struggle that some have seen in it a main key to the course of history; this idea lies at the base of the cyclical scheme put forward by the great Arab philosopher of history, Ibn Khaldun, in the fourteenth century, and it contributes to the elaboration of Toynbee's more complex but not unrelated thesis today.

Less spectacular but no less deep-seated is the immemorial tension between townsmen and farmers, foodconsumers and food-producers, obviously a source of conflict, though the links of interdependence between the two groups are normally strong enough to confine the field of action to the market. But we find it in the parasitic growth of Rome, sucking the life out of Italy first and then the provinces of the empire; in the struggle, often open and armed, between the Italian city-states and their surrounding countrysides. It played a major part in the Populist revolt of the 1890s which arrayed the mining and agrarian West of the United States, mortgage-ridden and still with a strong frontier colouring, against the urban and plutocratic East. And nearer home, again, New States movements and the rise of the Country Party express the same resentments of inland Australia against the economic stranglehold of the five great ports.

As for the littoral-continental tension, that has been in

effect the *raison d'être* of British continental policy in the five hundred years since that was first clearly enunciated (on a local scale) in *The Libelle of Englyshe Policye* of 1436. It has thus been largely responsible for the fact that in every century we have formed and equipped a Grand Alliance to protect western Europe from the domination of any single power—or, as it appears from the continental angle, of any *other* power, whether the Spain of Charles V and Philip II, the France of Louis XIV and Napoleon, the Germany of Wilhelm II and Hitler. It is of most immediate relevance to us today, the theme of one of the most influential books ever written by a geographer. This is Mackinder's *Democratic Ideals and Reality*, with its antithesis of seamen and heartlanders, an antithesis in my opinion somewhat overdrawn, but taken much to heart in the America of to-day, over against the formidable continental mass of Russia. And I daresay that in Moscow also they revamp Mackinder's maps, but with the arrows in reverse, pointing into the heartland rather than out of it.

Finally there is another recurrent theme, this time not in itself one of conflict: the widening of the sphere of civilization. This was perhaps expressed most neatly by the Russian geographer Menschikoff—a heartlander!—at the end of the last century, in his concept of riverine, thalassic, and oceanic phases of historic development. The early civilizations based on the irrigable floodplains of the Nile, Tigris-Euphrates, Indus, and Wei-ho, were largely succeeded by cultural realms centred around such seas as the Mediterranean, the British seas and the Baltic, the Arabian Sea and the Bay of Bengal, Indonesia, the Sea of Japan. Finally, with the Renaissance discoveries, the oceans became the great avenues of trade and the links between societies—until in our own time we have seen the first truly oceanic war, from the Coral Sea to Midway and the Philippine landings. To this day, indeed, the *oecumene*—the economically effective area—of the continents, with partial qualification in the United States and the Soviet Union, is dominantly peripheral; and in our own continent most of all. Following this line, Salvador de Madariaga has suggested that the ocean-basin and not the continent is the true macro-unit of geographical study. But here, as in other things, politics overrides logic.

These are all significant themes. In addition we can make a few valid generalizations in political geography, largely concerned with the siting and shifting of frontiers and capitals. We can also usefully distinguish on a geographical basis a dozen or so broad cultural or economic categories— nomad pastoralism, plantation colonies, island realms, monsoon agriculture, irrigation patterns, and the like. And there, I think, we have nearly all the general categories of human geography which hold much significance.

Attempts at the enunciation of laws there have been: a 'Law of Increasing Territorial Aggregates', for example. But on analysis they dissolve into a heaping together of more or less apposite and rather less than more authentic facts, some of which are ambivalent according to context. 'Two voices are there—one is of the sea . . . And one is of the mountains: both are free'; but the reader of Semple's *Influences of Geographical Environment* finds that the voice of liberty also hails from the desert, the fen, the forest, and what have you. And so indeed it does, in different seasons; for the voice of freedom is the voice of free societies, and these are not to be explained simply in terms of external conditioning. They have an autonomy, an inner life.

But it is only too obvious that even the examples we have cited are far from being exclusively geographical. The economist and the historian must have their say, and an attempt to understand them in strictly geographical terms alone would be ludicrous and disastrous, though the converse is also true. What then is the distinctive note of the geographer's contribution to the study of society?

In simplest terms, it is his concern with space-relations, and not with those of one or two phenomena, but with the totality of terrestrial distributions; with the ecology of man and its correlation with other world-patterns such as those of the great climatic, botanic, or soil zones, or on the regional scale with the more detailed texture of a given area.

The Compass of Geography

Most human activities have some spatial reference; many are incompletely apprehended if geographical factors are neglected; some can be best understood by a primarily geographical approach. But not all geographical distributions are geographically meaningful, as it were: we must beware of maps for the sake of maps. Others have significance on a restricted and elementary plane only. Thus one could write a geography of astronomy, since in some important respects the practice of this science is absolutely conditioned by environmental factors: observatories are not built in foggy valley-bottoms, Greenwich time no longer comes from traffic-shaken Greenwich, and the Pole Star cannot be observed from Mount Stromlo. But once these elementary dictates are complied with geography has little or nothing more to say; it is only on an absurdly *a priori* theory that a study of astronomical technique would have to take a geographical view. The links are in fact the other way round, since our fundamental framework of locational reference—latitude and longitude—depends on astronomical observation. For all that, there are some intriguing convergences in the careers of the twin sisters: was astronomy or geography the greater gainer from the observation of the transit of Venus at Tahiti in 1769?

There is one sector of geographical enquiry on which the popular interest of mankind has always been fixed, but which must embarrass the discreet geographer: the question of the direct psycho-physiological influence of environment (especially climate) on the human individual, and through him on the group. Hippocrates and Aristotle led the way: under their hot climes the inhabitants of Asia are clever but effete and cowardly, apt subjects of despotism; the peoples of the cold North are valiant freemen, stout types but dumb. Between, enjoying the happy mean, lies Hellas, and the consequences for the Hellenes are obvious. This approach was given new life by Montesquieu, who thought, *inter alia*, that the English were not only a revolutionary lot, but 'a nation so distempered by climate as to have a disrelish of everything, nay, even of life itself', and so 'apt to commit suicide most unaccountably'. Nor is it dead yet, witness Ellsworth Huntington's amazing table of the great religions in order of latitude and ethical value: naturally Christianity is highest in both rankings, and perhaps only a decent prudence forbade a further latitudinal division between Latin Papistry and Nordic Reformation.[1]

The plain fact is that this is a matter of both medical and geographical science, and practically everybody who has written on it has been a layman on one side or on both, while many writers have had a racial axe to grind. Most work has therefore been pseudo-scientific, and while geographers as a body have striven to avoid subjectivity, they have not succeeded in avoiding impressionism. Among the workers who have maintained good standards are two Australians, Grenfell Price and Douglas Lee; they would probably be the first to admit that only recently has the essential team-work between medical and geographical specialists been taken in hand. Good progress is being made, for example in Carlos Monge's studies of acclimatization in the Peruvian Andes, or the *Atlas of Diseases* sponsored by the American Geographical Society. But on the whole, though this is a legitimate item of the geographical agenda, and perhaps excites more lay interest than any other, I would wish its consideration to be referred to a small sub-committee to report a lot later.

Leaving aside this dangerous aspect, the main fields of human activity in which geographical factors are highly significant are these:

> the production and distribution of food, shelter, clothes and comforts;
> the location, development, function, structure, and appearance of habitations, and other constructions;
> political organization in its territorial aspects;
> war.

It will be seen that they cover a wide enough tract of country.

All of these four major fields are also treated by other disciplines, and of their sub-divisions many fall largely or even wholly outside the field of geography. Obviously the theoretical treatment of production and distribution is the task of economists; it is not geographers but architects who build houses, and political scientists who study political parties. Given this great overlap from all quarters, it is not surprising that social scientists—especially perhaps the successors of Durkheim in France—have sometimes queried whether human geography as an independent discipline has any standing at all. The question is perhaps most clearly and precisely posed in relation to anthropology and sociology. Here I will be bold to say that the encroachments have come from these sciences rather than from geography. I would add, rather hastily, that as regards anthropology I am quite sure that the cessions of territory have been gracefully made, and that their loss is a clear gain to geography. As to sociology, I am not so sure: I feel that many social surveys would be the better for a more conscientious geographical stiffening, and there is a tendency, fortunately not widespread, to take over such terms as *region* and *frontier* and disembowel them of spatial significance. As sociologists must also use these terms in their true locational sense, the semantic confusion can be quite serious.*

The shift of emphasis from physical ethnography to social anthropology by and large tended to the production of specific case-histories of the life of small groups, or even of a part only of their life—though when that part is sex it must be conceded to be no small part. The heroic days of *The Golden Bough* are over. A wider approach, by syntheses in topical terms, is indeed gaining ground: it is sufficient to mention two names associated with the Australian National University, Professors Firth and Nadel. But on the whole the trend towards the application of highly refined technique to the elucidation of particular cases is still strong. Such studies will often, perhaps usually, include the organization of economic activity—the exploitation of environmental resources. Now this has obviously a large geographical element; and sixty or seventy years ago, in the

* This objection does not apply to social psychology, where *frontier* is well established in a special technical sense and in a context not likely to lead to ambiguity.

days of Ratzel and Elisée Reclus, studies of this sort were regarded as being within the scope of geography, certainly as regards their synthesis. He would be a bold geographer who risked his hand now.

It is assuredly no bad thing that these studies of peoples are now the preserve of anthropology, and that not only because they call for an elaborate specialized technique. For they are studies of people rather than of land; and while every tract on the earth's surface is theoretically unique, it is on the whole likely that there will be more repetition of practically standard variations on the land than in social organizations; and many social institutions have not even a remote link with geography. It is thus more economical to tackle even the man-land relation from the angle of the men rather than of the land, since the social organization has to be worked out afresh each time, whereas the essential features of a regional assemblage may often be broken down into a number of types, the individuals within each not differing very significantly. Thus in Japan or Malaya the small coastal lowlands are built up of say three to six terrain-types—beachhead dunes, deltaic flats, high and low detrital terraces, and so on—and it is pointless to go through each lowland unit in a remorseless manner, one by one. We must indeed have an initial reconnaissance to establish that they are in fact so built up; but having done this we can select some type-specimens and need not, for practical purposes, repeat our analysis in detail for each and every unit. But it is not pointless to analyse the social organizations of African or New Guinea tribes one by one, since their diversities are so great; though one may indeed suspect that diminishing returns will set in sooner or later, and that the thousand and first tribe, though differing from all the rest, may not present any very significant novelty.

This looks like selling the pass: all the contributions are to come from the anthropologist, except perhaps a mere descriptive framework of geographical reference. It is the anthropologist who, if he does his job well (and he usually does), will put the people he is studying into their setting —and so must analyse their environment. The regional

112

geographer, if he so wishes, can then come along and abstract the bits to make his geography, tacking them onto similar scraps from the field sciences. How can we say that there is any geographical independence or contribution?

There are answers, and I think sufficient ones, to this question. To begin with, it is all very well to say that if the anthropologist has done his case-history properly he will have analysed the environment. He will not have done this as an end in itself, but only as a means to analysing the society: quite properly. This, however, means that he is not interested in the environment as a totality; he will pick out of it the factors which seem to him relevant to the matter in hand. This is almost sure to fall far short of a full analysis; and, unless he is exceptionally gifted or exceptionally lucky in having a very simple case, he is likely to overlook even elements which are relevant and essential to his own task: our former example of the two types of alluvial plain is to the point here. On his own terms the anthropologist (or any other social scientist) runs a risk of serious error unless he has a fair grasp of the scope and general method of geography; only so can he be sure that the environmental aspects he seizes upon are really all the relevant ones that exist. He need not of course have a full training in the subject, but he must be able to assess its full relevance. This can come only from consideration of its scope and method; and the establishment of these, for any study, has been arrived at only by the practice of the study in and for itself.

It goes without saying that the converse is strictly true for the geographer, whether working in this field or in historical, political, or economic geography; hence in fact the existence of such specialisms within the subject. Really of course the student should have rather more than a general grasp of the rationale of other disciplines bearing on his own special concern; but even in the Australian National University that is a counsel of perfection.

There is a broader and more self-sufficing answer to this question of independence. Other workers, whether in social or natural sciences, are interested only in the end-products

of geography, in those facts and factors which have immediate and obvious significance for their individual themes.
They need not have, if social scientists, any interest in the
genetics of the non-human phenomena; nor, if natural
scientists, much concern with the human aspects of geography; doubtless with some small exceptions in each case.
But since these human and non-human elements are linked,
someone must be interested in both if our understanding
of the world is to be complete and coherent within the
limits of our mental capacity. Hence the geographer, concerned with the analysis and synthesis of areal differentiations both human and non-human, can certainly claim that
this clearly distinguishes his studies from those of others,
say geologists on the one hand or sociologists on the other.
To a large extent the objects of study form a common
field; but no other discipline has the same range or
approach.

This width of interests is obviously dangerous to the
cohesion of the subject, as well as being a constant temptation to the diffusion of energy: that must be admitted. But
on the other hand it has been valued as the last stronghold
against academic over-specialization: and from it we snatch
a fearful joy. This is of course especially true of regional
work: since it is impossible to know any fair-sized area with
the personal intimacy of the anthropologist in his village,
every clue must be followed up and all is grist to the mill:
a passing reference to a crop or a building-stone in a
medieval poem, a footnote explaining some anomaly in a
census table, an assemblage of heavy minerals in an old
river-gravel, the detail of a minor campaign in a forgotten
war, the name of a pub—any of them may be significant.
With more formal borrowings, and with his own field research, the geographer tries to work out genetic relations,
sets individual data against a background derived from
comparative studies of other areas, above all tries always to
apprehend the altogetherness of things.

With all this, I do not think that there is anything esoteric
in the practice of geography. Full mastery of it, as of anything worth while, demands of course time and devotion;

but considering that the founding fathers of academic geography were usually either geologists or historians, we can hardly say that a specialized training is a *sine qua non*; though it is true that the subject has increasingly elaborated its techniques. Nevertheless there is a large literature which is good geographical writing by laymen; and not only by historians and anthropologists, naturalists and geologists, though all these have given us much. I think rather of such things as the description of Attica in Zimmern's *The Greek Commonwealth*; of George Stewart's most exciting novel *Storm*; of passages in Aldous Huxley's *Jesting Pilate*, or Lawrence's *Sons and Lovers*, in C. E. W. Bean's *On the Wool Track* or Euclides da Cunha's *Revolt in the Backlands*; of the wonderful portrait of France prefixed to Michelet's history—it is twenty-five years since I read it, and its undertones are with me still; and finally I would add the glorious close of Arnold's *Sohrab and Rustum*. A feeling for the scene, accuracy and vividness in its delineation—these are the only essentials for this kind of geographical writing. There is but one qualification: this is art, not science, and geography has always claimed, rightly, to be scientific. But I wish that geographers had more of such art, which is not incompatible with scientific accuracy: some seem positively afraid of good writing.

But if geography is not esoteric, why are there people who style themselves specifically geographers? This is not the same question as whether there is an independent geography, but I think that at bottom the answer is the same; the scope of the subject. All the things which we study, I think without exception, are studied with more or less intensity by others; it will be apparent that some topics universally regarded as geographical are in fact studied more fully and deeply by other specialists than by most geographers. But no other discipline concerns itself primarily with spatial distributions, whether of the totality of phenomena within a restricted region, or of the combination of several major sets of phenomena (such as landforms with climate with vegetation) on a continental or world scale. And these are tasks which are well worth doing, whether from the point of view of practical application or of intellectual appeal.

Once more, this raises above all the difficulty of avoiding over-specialization without falling into superficiality. Doubts have been expressed as to whether the professionalization of the subject has been to the good: is it respectable to borrow or steal so much? since we do not claim to study soils so fully as the pedologist, or society so fully as the sociologist, why duplicate their work at a lower level? should not such studies be left to their technicians? what, in short, is there left for the professed geographer to do?

There is much point to these questions, and in particular cases the answer is not easy. It is true that no one geographer can possibly know all that he should know. But what is not possible individually is possible collectively. It is, I firmly believe, feasible for a geographer to penetrate into subjects which suit his individual bent far enough to be able to evaluate the results of more specialized workers without risk of serious error, and even on occasion to present original work of value, even if not on the full specialist plane. This is clearly not possible for more than a very limited number of topics in each case; but it is more than the specialized technician will in general attain. And its value in co-ordinating linked disciplines, and even some at first sight not closely related, can hardly be over-stressed. But, as I said earlier, it follows that there can be no such thing as *the* training of *the* geographer, certain basic skills (such as mapping technique) and bodies of data and concepts apart. Beyond this core every geographer should have at least one field in which he can claim to be not a specialist in the full sense, but at least a student serious enough to be treated with respect by its professionals, be they climatologists or historians, ecologists or economists. I do not think this unattainable, and I do think that it meets the case.

I sometimes think that we worry too much about the apparently amorphous nature of our study. The least claim for it is an honourable one: that it has contributed to the universe of knowledge an immense body of ordered data and not a few general concepts of significance; and if we have faith there is still an immense task ahead on these lines. And beyond all this there is the general vindication, that no one else will take either the world-view of systematic geography or the comprehensive view of regional geography, and that these views are necessary to the understanding of the world in which we live and move and have our being.

The values of geography

So much, and indeed quite enough, on our subject academically considered. In conclusion I should like to speak, briefly, on the humanistic and cosmic values which I believe to be fostered by its study, and which indeed seem to me its life and spirit; and here I must speak for the most part subjectively.

Some of these values have been suggested already, notably the stress which geographers lay on the altogetherness of things, the value of the discipline as a standing and practical protest against narrow technical views: it is not for nothing that in most Universities where geography is well-developed, it has a footing in the Faculties both of Arts and of Science. Others are often overlooked because they exist largely in the humbler but not less honourable world of school education: and here I would enter a strong plea for a wider recognition by educationists of the fact that local geography can offer an unrivalled training in forming habits of rapid but accurate observation, surely a thing of the greatest value on any view of educational functions and in any walk of life. Yet other values are universally recognized and in fact self-evident: the contribution which geography has to make to international understanding, its practical utility in the world of economic activity and public affairs. Of all these I shall say no more. The values with which I am now concerned go deeper.

To begin with, there is a delight which can only be called aesthetic. At its simplest this is little more than the pleasure of a matching game, the recognition that correspondences are working out, that the shifts of the various frontiers on our maps are marching together. But it becomes a far more active excitement as we go on to unfold the geneses and the inter-relations of our diverse phenomena; an excitement in part subjective as we feel the synthesis as it were shaping itself half-alive under our hands, in part objective as we contemplate the massive assemblage of the fact. But this, I imagine, is common to all creative scientific work. Tracing the correlation of physical lineaments with the cultural patterns superimposed on them, noting how a broad correspondence narrows down to a coincidence, unravelling the divergences from the pattern, tracking down the shift in the balance of factors which locally breaks the expected rhythm—these things bring a pleasure at least similar to that derived from great verse, when the formal pattern of couplet or stanza is varied, always within the limits of the form, to meet the demands of the theme.

And just as a knowledge, however slight, of the principles of metre enriches beyond measure the understanding and enjoyment of poetry, so I venture to think that no one, except by brief flashes of intuition, can be fully penetrated by the power and majesty of landscape* unless he can see beyond its surface lines and colours, and feel it in its organic structural harmony. Here we have a direct aesthetic value. It is a large claim, and I do not expect it to be accepted; it is subjective, and so not provable. But it is inherently so probable. Consider: most of us do not imagine that we can fully experience great art without attaining at least some idea of its history, its techniques, and its principles. But if a grasp, even of a general kind, of the principles of composition, of the opportunities and difficulties of the medium, assists us in the comprehension and enjoyment of a landscape painting, why should we suppose that we can fully appreciate the real landscape of which it is a representation without any effort to understand the elements and processes which have formed it in its turn?

* I have rigorously avoided using this word hitherto, since it is of great but much disputed significance in the technical vocabulary of geography. It is used here entirely in a lay sense.

Beyond this, and immeasurably greater, is the feeling of the vast unity of the physical world, the peculiar province of geography. Not the unity of man with nature; except in the obvious sense that men are natural organisms I find it difficult to attach much meaning to this concept. And yet we are men and must reduce things to our own scale and our own values before we can be at ease. I think we often delude ourselves into being too much at ease; and this is the root of a danger to which our study is particularly liable, or perhaps I should say a vice to which it is addicted: that of glibly personifying Nature, talking of her plan, of which no one has seen the blue-print. Often this is fatal to scientific detachment: the Possibilist talks airily of subduing Nature, the Determinist counsels submission to her laws, and both alike seem unaware of the teleological implications, utterly unwarranted by anything we know, of this anthropomorphizing. I can understand and respect this, as part of a theistic or pantheistic order of the universe; but not when it springs merely from a looseness in the use of emotive terms. In the hands of extreme Possibilists this tendency topples over into the Pathetic Fallacy on a grand scale, and ends in a mystical marriage of Man and Nature, and a left-handed marriage at that. Let me quote from a book not without merits and repute: man 'appears less a subject of Nature's decrees than a partner who enables her to reveal new amplitudes of power . . . and not without grace and beauty to share with man the great experience of life'.[2] It is a kindly thought to allow nature some grace and beauty, even by the patronizing gesture of a double negative; but to this high-flown teleology I vastly prefer Carlyle's retort to the lady who 'accepted the Universe': 'Gad, Madam, you'd better.'

And yet the great vision of the Cosmos remains, defaced but not devalued by these petty flourishes of a human vanity which sees in nature merely a fickle mistress to be wooed or coaxed or forced. If we must personify the earth as nature, it seems to me to be more in accordance with our position on the scale of things to do so in the terms of de Vigny's noble lines:

119

Seeing nor hearing them, unmoved I bear
Alike of ants and men the populations,
Nor tell apart estate from grave, nor care,
Though wearing them, to know the names of nations;
You call me Mother, and I am your tomb;
My winter sweeps your myriads to their doom,
My spring feels nothing of your adorations . . . .
When you are gone, still silent I shall roll
Alone, serene, towards an unknown goal,
With lofty breasts and brow cleaving the heavens.[3]

Before this majestic vision we can have no feelings but those of awe. It is this which informs the vast bulk of Humboldt's *Cosmos,* inspiring its dry and involved prose with a craggy harmony akin to that of Lucretius, who also wrote *Of the Nature of Things.*

This is an austere, even a bleak, view of man and nature; what is left to us in such a world, face to face with 'the eternal silences of infinite space'? For my part, the answer is given once more by the lineage of the great pessimist poets: to make what we can of this our earth, and if the cosmic order holds nothing for us either of despair or hope, to find our happiness in social duty and private love. And here there is no human pursuit less disillusioning than the pursuit of knowledge. To the attainment of knowledge and understanding of our terrestrial sphere many great minds have given a passionate devotion, and many men their lives, from the Greek navigators passing the Pillars of Hercules into the unknown and fatal Ocean to those who have died in the solitudes of the Polar ice-caps or of Everest. For them all there is but one epitaph, and but one epigraph for the great work which remains to us their successors: the Lucretian rule, *naturam primum cognoscere rerum.*

'Region' as a Term of Art

To the confusion of tongues, the curse of mankind since Babel, has now been added that species of confusion within the same tongue which has arisen from the specialized jargon of various academic disciplines. 'Jargon' in its origin and in itself is not necessarily a word with a pejorative connotation; no branch of human activity can be carried on without its own 'terms of art', to use a delightful and neglected phrase. The trouble arises from the excessive cultivation of jargon, if not for its own sake then for the sake of an assumed prestige which, in turn, is fostered by the sense of esoteric privilege inseparable from a quasi-private language. And matters are made far worse when the jargon of one discipline borrows terms which have a clear meaning, or at least a useful symbolic value, in that of another, with a reckless disregard of their nuances or even their real connotations. It is a main purpose of this essay to suggest some of the semantic difficulties connected with the word 'region'. If the villains of the piece are sociologists and political scientists, the virtuous victims geographers, that is inherent in the fact that 'region' in modern English is in origin and essence a geographical word.

'Region' as a geographical term

The concept of the 'region' is by no means clear in geography itself; it is indeed surrounded by a cloud of metaphysical dubiety. The criteria by which we may delimit regions are extraordinarily varied: relief, geological structure, soil, climate (itself much sub-divided), vegetation, drainage patterns, and many other factors on the physical side alone; add to these the complex variety of human

Reprinted from *Orbis*, Vol. 1 No. 3, 1957.

factors which can also be used to divide any fair-sized area into smaller units, and it will be seen that mapping all the 'regional boundaries' would produce a mosaic in which a few relatively blank core areas would be surrounded by ravelled bands of boundaries: the frame would dwarf the picture, and much, if not most, of any one comprehensive region would be in a transition zone to the next—just as all ages are after all ages of transition. The geographer's region, unless more narrowly defined by an adjective ('climatic region', 'market region', and so on) is really an approximation for the sake of working convenience: an essential tool to handle the multiplex data, the arrangement which represents the highest common measure of agreement among the various criteria selected as significant, and the least violent distortion of any of the more significant alternative organizations on physiographic, climatic, economic (and so on) bases. From a strictly objective point of view, there may be nothing in the actual phenomena which is a true referent for any given fully comprehensive region; but if such regions do not exist, we have to invent them to manage our data. They are in fact isolates for study.

Although then this 'geographical region' is not, as a rule, a very close fit to more than one or two of the variables involved in its delineation, it does correspond after a fashion to the distribution of the phenomena. Empirically it works: geographers disagree a great deal in their definitions of a region in the abstract, but, given the task of dividing up a given area into specific regions, their divergences are not as a rule so great that one cannot readily see a family likeness. Of course a great deal depends on scale: if one is writing, say, a county monograph, one will use a finesse impossible if the subject is a continent: on the one scale whole states would be included in one major region, on the other a small tract of land may be divided into yet smaller units. The British geographer J. F. Unstead in fact put forward a whole hierarchy of units, from 'stows' of a few square miles—for example, the floor and flanks of a watergap through an escarpment—to 'major regions' of subcontinental size. In practice the scale of the work makes clear which order of regions is being used; and although different geographers might differ in the detailed delimitation of such generalized regions as 'the Paris basin', 'the North Italian plain', 'the Appalachian Piedmont', there is sufficient agreement for any geographer to recognize at once what is meant; a picture is formed sufficiently clear for all normal comparative purposes. On this scale of work, which is the norm between studies on a world or inter-continental scale and the detailed local monograph, the only serious difficulty arises from the fact that, when we have delimited our regions by what seems the most generally significant set of criteria, we are sometimes left with an anomalous nondescript area on our hands, the remnant or residue when the more definite regions are marked out; but this is an internal problem of specialist concern only.

So much for 'regions' as most commonly understood and used by geographers. When sociologists studying an urban or an urban-rural milieu lightheartedly scatter about words like 'region', 'boundary', and 'frontier' with such promiscuity that it is difficult to be quite sure whether they are speaking in terms of place, people, or group functions, the geographers from whom these words were lifted may perhaps be allowed to apply for an interim injunction until they are sorted out.

The irruption of American Academic

This loose borrowing is a facet of one of the least lovable features in the modern world (though admittedly only a minor plague): the rise, or rather the spread, of American Academic as a style of writing. One must distinguish: the objection to American Academic is not that it is American or academic, but that it is not clear writing by any standard. The present writer, an Englishman, does not like, for example, what seems a good standard American usage in the placing of adverbs: the trick of habitually invertedly positioning them before their verbs, a practice to which he hostilely reacts, to concretely illustrate the point. (In really well developed American Academic the last clause would probably run 'to illustratively concretize the specific terminological procedure exposited in this technique of writer-reader communication'.) But this adverbial mannerism is at least clear. By and large historians seem to write good American English as a rule, anthropologists often, sociologists rarely. Does this reflect an increasing preoccupation with looking scientific, and a decreasing assurance of scientific authenticity?

In its essence American Academic expresses a resolute determination to appear scientific on the part of writers many of whom one may suspect, not uncharitably, of not being too sure of their scientific status. This determination leads to desperate but often floundering attempts to secure systematic precision, to find a fixed terminology of distinction between sets of data which may in fact overlap to such an extent that real accuracy can be found only by searching for shifting nuances of expression—in other words, by an artistic rather than a rigorously scientific approach to the problem of formulation. Tactically a common solution is the use of what may be called the 'transferred substantive': the borrowing from another field of study of a term which looks good and so comes to have prestige value irrespective of whether it is or is not really fit to bear the meaning which it is desired to attach to it in its new context. When we find a culture described as an 'informational economy' it is perhaps time to cry halt.

There is often a coarseness about this approach which defeats its own object of precision: often the borrowed terms are mere crude approximations, and in bad cases they may give rise to semantic confusion.

It may be seen, from our general discussion of 'geographical regions', that, even when working on a large scale in which great masses of data can be analysed with considerable refinements of detail and technique, it is difficult indeed to draw regional boundaries with meaningful precision. For this reason, incidentally, geographers make a clear distinction between 'frontier' and 'boundary'—a distinction which workers in other fields appear to neglect completely, using the words as interchangeable. It might be, however, that this distinction would be of much more use than the widespread loose employment of 'region' already discussed, and for that reason a short digression on frontiers and boundaries may be helpful.

Put shortly, a frontier is always a zone and a boundary always a line within it. The frontier zone is one of transition—between region and region, or even between state and state. It is easy to see, for example, that between a region in which one particular geographical (or economic or political or social) factor or aspect or set of data is dominant, and an adjacent region in which it is conspicuously absent, there will usually be a transitional zone of mixed character: between the region dominated by corn and pork and that of winter wheat, between the hinterland exclusive to the port of Bombay and that exclusive to Madras, between the area owing allegiance to the Crown of France and to the Holy Roman Empire, between the area of French and German speech; between the indubitable land and the indubitable ocean is always the zone, a few inches or many miles wide, under the alternate sway of tidal flood and ebb. In nature there are very few, if any, definite linear boundaries: perhaps the nearest approach is when an abrupt change in geology—say, granite to limestone—is reflected in an abrupt change of vegetation or land use; but even here there are salients, embayments, outliers which spill over the lithological break, and so form a zone: it may be so narrow that in practice we are justified in disregarding it and speaking of a boundary. In economic and social geography, again, it is usually difficult or impossible to draw sharp boundaries between, say, port hinterlands, urban fields, types of settlement or farming or houses. But in political geography the artificial linear boundary is of great significance, demarcated often with the nicest precision and maximum rigidity.

A caveat may also be entered against the inadmissible use of the term 'natural boundary' as between states: there is no such thing. All state boundaries are in their nature artificial, though they may conform to natural features—indeed the natural and social history of boundaries would make an instructive and entertaining essay by itself. Even state boundaries, sharp as they are on the ground, lie within frontier zones, wide or narrow: in areas where the boundary runs through wild uninhabited country customs posts may lie well back from the actual boundary; in other cases there may well be a zone marked by special police regulations, restricting or facilitating intercourse across the boundary; where a boundary (such as that between France and Belgium) runs through urban areas with at least some economic integration, passport formalities must be modified to meet the needs of inter-state commuters. The most usual outward and visible sign of the frontier zone is the appearance of bilingual notices.

'Region' as a political term

Returning to our discussion of the word 'region', we have to face a new difficulty, this time one which in a sense affects the relations of geography with other disciplines. This is the use of 'regional' to denote a political grouping of states, or in the endeavour to identify certain major parts of the world as having some common geographical character, but not necessarily for geographical study: such concepts as 'the Middle East', 'Southeast Asia', 'the Far East', 'the Pacific Basin' (actually a convexity!).

Not much need be said about the former category, since nothing can be done about it. 'Regional' in this context has lost all meaning: the North Atlantic Treaty Organization has a regional name and is regarded as a regional political grouping; but it does not include Eire and Spain and does include Greece and Turkey; and on no possible interpretation of the word 'region' could the former pair be left out and the latter pair kept in any region with 'Atlantic' in its name. We simply have to accept it as an anomalous term in political geometry, like the Trotskyist 'parallel centre' and the Rome-Berlin-Tokyo 'Axis', and to continue to call these groupings 'regional' on the clear understanding that the adjective is meaningless except as an arbitrary identifier, or at best refers to a bloc with a faint suggestion of a local habitation for its name.

Concepts such as 'the Middle East' and so on are much

more important. They may fairly be regarded as macro-regions of the world, culturally or geopolitically considered. The trouble comes when geographers are asked, as they often are, to provide some geographical rationale for a division of the world which is not really geographically rational. It may be a mere *ad hoc* division to provide an isolate for non-geographical study, or a confused popular concept not far removed from vulgar error, or a valid but essentially historical grouping with a mainly locational basis. Now, location is very important in geography, but it is very far from being the whole story. When we seek to delimit such 'regions', we meet the same difficulties of overlap as when we are working on the really geographical regions already discussed; and yet our colleagues naturally want definite and precise entities, a demand which is very difficult to satisfy with a good geographical conscience.

Consider, for example, 'the Middle East'. Originally there was a Near East, a concept linked with the 'Eastern Question' and so referring, roughly, to the lands of the Turkish Empire around the middle of the nineteenth century. Beyond it was the Middle East, which in some views included Turkish-ruled lands (Iraq, parts of Arabia), and in all views Iran and Afghanistan. There was then a vast gap, beyond which the Far East began at Singapore, or even at Hong Kong, and in any event did not include Indonesia. This anomaly worried some writers, who logically pushed the Near East rather further eastwards to the borders of India and regarded the Indian Empire (which included Burma, often grouped with Siam and Indo-China as Further India) as true Middle East. Two wars compounded the chaos. The liquidation of the Turkish Empire and hence of the Eastern Question demolished the Near East; and in the last war military expediency created a 'Middle East Command' which at its height extended from Iran to Italy, inclusive.

Most of the minor complications are left out in this rough summary, but an attempt to settle the question by a detailed analysis of usage and authority would be intolerably tedious. The term may now be taken as meaning Asia

127

from Iran (inclusive) to the Mediterranean, plus Egypt. We may accept the anomaly of a Middle which has no Near and is separated by thousands of miles from the Far East, and try to see what is the basis for the retention of the term. The basis is simply that throughout history there have been the closest links between the components of this area, the secular bridge or barrier between Europe and Asia, and (despite diversity of race, creed and language) a considerable common character in its economic and social life; while today (as indeed for long periods in the past) it is indubitably one of the main foci of geopolitical forces. The only other term which seems appropriate is 'Southwest Asia'; and here we wish very frequently to include Egypt in the analysis—its culture and history are more closely linked with Asia than with the continent of which it is a nominal part. Even so, there are still difficulties, since we often wish to consider the area *excluding* Turkey and Iran, the former of which especially has today a pronounced difference in polity from the rest. I forbear to mention Israel. . . .

We meet similar difficulties at the other end of Asia. 'Southeast Asia' is sometimes taken to include India and China, a practice completely indefensible and fortunately rare: if we do wish to consider all this area together, we may fall back on its truly geographical common characteristic and call it 'Monsoon Asia'. We may note in passing—merely as a curiosity—that on a geometrical definition Southeast Asia is exiguous: the median latitude of Asia is 34°N (three degrees north of Shanghai), but the median longitude is 108°E, close to Dalat in the east of Vietnam; this is due to the usually unnoticed protrusion of Siberia into the Western Hemisphere. All that is left to 'Southeast Asia' is a corner of China, a sliver of Vietnam, Shikoku and Kyushu in Japan, Formosa, the Philippines, and Indonesia less Sumatra and a third of Java. Fortunately geographers are not geometers; 90°E is a suitable middle longitude roughly dividing Asia into halves areally, and this would leave us with Burma, Siam, Indo-China, Malaya, Indonesia and the Philippines. But this unit, convenient enough in some ways, is not too homogeneous. We could make a division between mainland and insular Southeast Asia; but this involves leaving Malaya, so closely linked culturally and economically with Indonesia, with the geographically very different Indo-Chinese lands (in a broad cultural sense) from Burma to Tonkin, the lands whose cultures derive from India and China in varying proportions.

The inadequacy of general definitions

At every turn, then, we find that it is impossible to lay down really comprehensive general definitions for such 'regions'. Many more examples could be given—for example, how to separate Danubian from Balkan from Mediterranean countries? It is no use asking geographers to provide a ready-made suit which will fit everybody; political scientists, publicists, sociologists must do their own tailoring in accordance with the particular purpose in hand. Geographers can provide good cloth.

On the other hand, the use of such terms as 'Far East' has been attacked as irrational but is rationally defensible. It is true that the Far East is West to Americans; it provides a salutary shift of emphasis when Australians call it the 'Near North'; but the words 'Far East' are not 'devoid of meaning' to Americans who employ them, as has been asserted. Longitudes are not geographical absolutes as latitudes are; there are no East and West Poles. But we must start our reckoning of co-ordinates from some datum line, and although what was once a historically valid convention is now a rather arbitrary one, it is not silly or meaningless so long as Greenwich remains longitude 0°. East is East and West is West and never the twain shall meet, except along 0° and the International Date Line.

Finally we may note another fertile source of confusion: the search for a fictitious unity based on a fallacious misreading of physical geography—the unity of river basins, for example, or even 'the essential unity of the Pacific area'. This is a fine phrase, but what does it mean? The significance of this unity, or even perhaps its existence, is hardly manifest enough for us to adopt it as a guiding concept without further enquiry. What factors of unity are there between Australia and Andean America, for example? between the Soviet Far East and Hawaii? between New Guinea and Alaska? Translate the phrase into concrete geographical terms (and it is surely geographical or nothing) and a certain obscurity becomes apparent. Or look at it historically: this 'unity' is thought of as a product of our 'global century' (more political geometry, of a space-time order!), but the superficiality of the concept is shown by the ironic fact that there was far more contact between Australia and South America a hundred years ago (when ships still rounded the Horn) than there is now; or, even further back and further away, more between Kamchatka and Hawaii in the days of the Russia America Company at the beginning of the last century.

I may seem to have come a long way from American Academic. But these misunderstandings of reality come from the same source as the terminological excess of the jargoneers: from that pseudo-scientific habit of mind which seeks precision where precision is not, a new scholastic nominalism. Most certainly the most rigorous definition of terms is necessary—it is, after all, looseness in the fitting of borrowed clothes which produces these odd appearances. But we must beware of fitting the phenomena to the terminology instead of the converse. In the last resort 'understanding is more important than classification'.

Geography and Racism

THIS discussion is under the title 'Geography and Racism',
not 'Geography and Race'. 'Race' itself is a scientific concept of some difficulty, and it can scarcely be said that there
is as yet any complete and generally satisfactory definition
of the word; nevertheless it does stand for an undoubted
objective fact: the fact that groups of men show inherited
physical differences. [I could wish indeed that I had thought
of Mr Rafiullah's excellent formulation: 'It is the man of
flesh and bones, not of deeds, moralities and intellect who
has held sway over the minds of those scientists who par-
celled humanity into racial groups and invented labels
which, most unfortunately, became more important than
the peoples they were coined to represent.'] This indeed is
'Racism': not in the least a scientific concept, it is rather
a subjective attitude to racial differences, so subjective and
so loaded with prejudice that serious students of Race are
often tempted to abandon the term in favour of some such
neutral euphemism as 'ethnic groups'. But behind Racism
does lie the concept of Race, valid if only we can pin it
down and define its limits. And behind Race—or rather
on the face of it—lies the most obvious, though far from
the most reliable genetically, of physical criteria: Colour.
However erratic as a guide to ethnic origins, and totally
worthless as a measure of human worth, for Racist doctrine

Delivered as the Chairman's closing address in the section on 'Geography and Racism' of the International Geography Seminar held at
the Muslim University, Aligarh, India, in 1956. Passages in brackets
do not appear in the preliminary version of the paper printed in the
Proceedings of the Seminar (Aligarh, 1959, 124-33) but are taken from
the notes of the oral delivery of the paper. These passages owe much
to the Seminar contributions of Mr S. M. Rafiullah of Aligarh and
Mr M. B. Naidu of Durban, to whom I am grateful.

Colour is what counts. Anti-Semitism is in part an exception to this, but only in part, for nothing is more standard in Racist writing than the bracketing of Jews and Negroes.

We must therefore come to terms with these words Race and Colour: that is to say, as geographers, we must try to find out whether the fact of the existence of human groups varying in colour and other physical characters, and unequally distributed on the earth's surface, affects significantly the relations between man and earth, and whether it is intrinsically meaningful in the analysis of spatial variations. I think the answer may well be that this fact has such significance and meaning, but objectively to a minor degree: that differences of Race and Colour are, by and large, less important to the geographer than differences in language, historic tradition, occupation, ideology, material culture, and even in some cases mere numbers on the ground. Beyond Race, however, there is Racism, which in a scientific sense is illusion and prejudice, but is none the less a human fact of very great import and an urgent object of scientific study. We may well find that geography has little that is objectively material to contribute to the scientific study of Racism (that is more properly the province of sociology) but that Racism has a great deal to contribute to the problems of social and political geography.

The geographical relevance of Race

To begin with Race: on the usual test of a species, all mankind is one: so far as experiment has gone—and one feels that few of the possible experiments have not been tried—all branches of the human family can interbreed to produce offspring in turn fertile. But within this human unity there do exist variant strains, distinguished by various heritable characteristics: stature, the proportions of the skull, the cross-section of the hair, the shape of the nose, the colour of the skin. To these criteria has recently been added the division into blood-groups.

Some of these variations correlate to some extent; for example, most of the inhabitants of Africa south of the Sahara are so dark as to be legitimately called black, and while not

132

all Negroes have extremely broad flat noses, such are practically confined to Negro and Mongoloid peoples, while extreme aquiline ones are found only among certain white groups. Familiar also are the 'slant eyes' formed by the epicanthic fold which (in the adult) is characteristic of yellow-skinned peoples; and again the great central belt of broad-headed peoples occupying the highland zone of Eurasia.

But these correlations are so shot through with exceptions and anomalies as to make it clear no one physical character is completely linked with another. Thus Dravidians and Australian aborigines have skins quite as dark as that of the average Negro, but wavy hair like that of Europeans. Not only does the range of individual variation in height and colour overlap—we are taught that the Japanese are a short people, but the only Japanese prisoner of war I saw in the Burma campaign was taller than I am— but so also does that of whole groups within races; nor does the cephalic index—the ratio of breadth to length of skull —show any fixed correlation with other traits. Thus the shortest and the tallest groups are both Negro, the narrowest and the broadest heads both Amerindian. Blood type again is definitely genetic, and there is some concentration: group A in Europe, group B in eastern Asia. Unfortunately the Australian aborigines are also A, and there is plenty of B in Europe.*

From a geographical point of view, what all this amounts to is that true racial or ethnic divisions are either too broad and simple or too minute and complicated to be of primary significance for our task. On the one hand we have the grand divisions generally agreed on: Caucasian, Mongoloid, Negroid. Even disregarding a current tendency to regard the Caucasian type as really a specialization of the Mongoloid, clearly the varieties of physique and mental attitude, of historical experience and of daily life, within these great groups are so numerous that in themselves they say virtually nothing to the point for the geographer. The

---

* In making such generalizations, the effects of modern migration are ignored.

categories are too broad and simple, and moreover they are cross-cut by categories which are of greater geographical significance: nomads, peasants, Communists, professors, may be white, black, or yellow.

At the other extreme, if we try to analyse the genetic composition of a selected population—of Great Britain say, or of the Deccan—we are faced with overwhelming evidence for long and intricate racial mixing. It is of course true that patient and devoted work by physical anthropologists has isolated definite ethnic strains, some of them with a history which can be traced back to prehistoric times, such as the Aurignacian (Upper Palaeolithic) types surviving in the Welsh hills and those of Auvergne. But these are as it were fossil splinter groups, and such elements as we can finally distinguish are scarcely of significance when we consider all the other variables arising from environment, tradition, occupation, and so on. Virtually there are no pure strains, though there are *relatively* homogeneous types concerning which we may if we please generalize, contrasting Celtic imagination with Saxon stolidity and so on.

In short, the situation was well summed up by Daniel Defoe's *The true-born Englishman* in 1700:

> All these their Barb'rous offspring left behind,
> The dregs of armies, they of all mankind;
> Blended with Britons who before were here,
> Of whom the Welsh have blest the character,
> Norwegian pirates, buccaneering Danes,
> Whose red-haired offspring everywhere remains;
> Who joined with Norman-French compound the breed
> From whence your true-born Englishmen proceed;
> By which with easy search you may distinguish
> Your Roman-Saxon-Danish-Norman English.

And B. S. Guha in prose has performed a similar service for India.

To put it in another way: scarcely one man in a hundred thousand can say with any accuracy what his racial origins really are. But everyone knows what his mother tongue is.

Ethnic distribution then has a geographical aspect: it

can be mapped and thus treated as a geographical problem in that it involves the analysis of spatial variation. But one cannot read much truly geographical significance into the fantastic jigsaws which arise from mapping the distribution of specific physical criteria—if we superimposed transparencies of such distributions, most of the composite map would be a maze of boundaries.

We may perhaps understand the problem better by an analogy with botany. There are important broad correlations in plant geography: the distribution of conifers and eucalypts, the climatic associations of grassland and forest. But, while precise plant geography throws much light on the geography of the past, for the geography of the present the point is less in whether a certain genus is represented both in Mexico and Malaya, but in the relations of the Mexican and Malayan floras to their environment. The same family may include plants utterly different in their climatic and edaphic adaptations, and to us it is not so much the genetic link that is relevant as whether the plants are xerophytic or hydrophytic.

Similar considerations apply to human races; though here correlations are even less clear-cut since man is the most mobile of animals. There is of course great intellectual interest in tracking down human origins and dispersals whether on a global or a regional scale; and whatever may be thought of Griffith Taylor's specific theories, he has shown, with his accustomed vigour, how useful geographical techniques can be in this pursuit. But the pursuit itself belongs essentially to physical anthropology or ethnology, as plant geography (distinguished from ecology) belongs essentially to botany. To us, on the whole, the social differentiations, so much more definitely linked with environment, are more important: language, religion, occupation, density, demographic trends. Ecology, whether of plants or men, rather than genetic classification, is the heart of the matter for the geographer.

I do not of course mean to suggest that there is not much of great value—one may even say of ultimate value to our philosophies of life—yet to be discovered in the vast and sketchily-known borderland between the biological sciences, including those which study man, and geography. Some aspects indeed are of very direct concern for us: the study of acclimatization, for example, which is obviously highly relevant to the political geography of the tropics—and not least in Australia. But speaking in the broad it seems to me that the objective scientific *fact* of Race is of less immediate concern to us, as geographers and as men (that is, political animals) than the highly subjective but immensely potent *factor* of Racism.

The nature of Racism

We must distinguish Racism from mere national preju-dice, although the latter has at times found expression in a loose usage of racial terms—the Anglo-Saxon or the Latin races, and so on. (These are practically driven out even from popular journalism.) But national prejudice is rarely so intense as racial feeling: its proponents will as a rule admit that at least individuals in the despised nation are equal to themselves, and there is not the fundamental sanction against intermarriage: social disapproval perhaps, but no absolute bar.

National prejudice then does not strike its roots nearly so deep, it is indeed often at the mercy of political ex-pediency: the Portuguese are comic dagoes or Our Oldest Allies according to context. But indeed few things are so liable to change as immutable national characters: con-sider for example the stereotype of the German before Bismarck, an amiable but ineffectual musician or pedant, and that of the Hun or Nazi. To continental publicists, the eighteenth century English were a turbulent crowd always ready to chop their King's head off: as Montesquieu said in 1748, 'a nation so distempered by climate as to have a disrelish of everything, nay, even of life itself' and so 'apt to commit suicide most unaccountably'. It follows that 'they cannot change the government without subverting the laws themselves'. After 1789 the French took over the role of revolutionary regicide, and both we and they then discovered the immemorial English genius for compromise. In fact 'innate national character' is usually the last refuge of the historian absolutely baffled for an explanation.

National prejudice sometimes, Racism on analysis always, is rooted in fear, often indeed open and avowed. This results in an aggressive projection of the dominant group, often culminating in the assertion of absolute and automatic superiority. Physical differences are translated into intellectual and spiritual values; not the real differences which must exist between groups of vastly different cultural traditions, but the assertion that all *individuals* of the one group are intellectually and morally superior to all those of the other: the *Herrenvolk* theory, older than Aristotle, that mankind is divided on a racial basis into natural masters and natural slaves. Of course there are human weaknesses in the practice of all but the completely unbalanced: 'Some of my best friends are Jews', 'When he's not spoilt the black is really quite decent', and so on. But as the motivation is fear of losing a dominant position, such admissions are dangerous to group solidarity and, once the initial premiss of racial inequality is granted, tactically the extremist position is logically correct and the extremists make the running: a process seen with utmost clarity in South Africa.

Apart from anti-Semitism, which grew up within the European society and has far more complex origins, Racism is associated with the intrusion of a technologically advanced society into the area of less advanced societies with different cultures and racial origins. Although colour is often a very unsafe token of actual genetic history, it is the most obvious of physical differences, and it does to a large extent correlate with great human groups which have an objective existence in their own right, not just a subjective existence as a popular illusion. The illusion lies in not recognizing the overlaps and blurred edges between the groups, and in equating difference in the one specific feature of colour with a general inequality.

It is of course easy enough to demolish Racist theory. Temperamental generalizations on a group basis may be to some extent valid, as say that between Celts and Saxons, but the range of individuals within the groups cuts across such categories: if the tallest Negro is taller than the shortest Nordic by a few inches in six feet, the most intelligent Negro is more intelligent than the stupidest Nordic by a much bigger proportion. Then there are groups which the most resolute Racist can scarcely fit into his preconceived pattern: Arabs, Parsees, Polynesians. There was the awkward fact that the true German Aryan had to be blond like Hitler, tall like Goebbels, slender like Goering: this had to be carried off by such double-talk as discovering that Nordic souls could inhabit non-Nordic bodies, and in the end the Japanese became honorary Aryans.

This is between ourselves, between people of like mind, and it is preaching to the converted. So also Sir Alan Burns' book *Colour Prejudice,* well-intentioned as it is, is beside the point: it amounts to recommending courtesy when speaking to Negroes, and those who need the lesson will never read the book. Indeed on a cynical view one might say that the most likely anti-Racist effect of such courtesy might be to keep Negroes from becoming Racists on their own account. . . .

The geographical relevance of Racism

How is the study of geography connected with such questions?

In one sense the connection is obvious enough: without some study of Racist policies, or even much milder inter-racial tensions, much of the social geography of such regions as Andean America, the West Indies, and of course South Africa, cannot be well understood: indeed Racism often finds an actual physical expression in the cultural landscape of segregation. Conversely geography has much to say on the understanding of Racism, mainly because the expansion of Europe is in large part a geographical theme underlying the historical development of Racism. Again, economic geography can offer a devastating analysis of the fallacies of South African *apartheid*, the more telling as the case can be made on strictly material grounds, with no reference to the abstractions of humanity and justice.

In this field indeed there is an immense agenda for geography, in careful alliance with social psychology. There is, for example, a marked difference in the attitude to miscegenation of people of Dutch descent in Indonesia and in South Africa: at least a tolerance of intermarriage in the former, the most complete repudiation in the latter. Environmental factors certainly count for something in this: in one case a land already fairly densely populated by a civilized society, and climatically more suitable to European sojourning than settlement; in the other a relatively scanty and purely tribal population, yet one perhaps more difficult to subjugate, in a country climatically quite favourable to permanent residence by Europeans.

Yet we should also have to consider the possibility that the main body of the intruders in each case may have come from a different *home* environment—from the polished mercantile cities of Holland or the much ruder peasant society of Groningen. Religious factors also might come into play. The Dutch bourgeoisie in the East was notably secular in its approach—as is exemplified by the tale that they purchased their trading monopoly at Nagasaki by annually trampling on the crucifix: this of course was spread and doubtless invented by trade rivals, but nobody would have thought it up about the Portuguese! But in the semi-nomadic patriarchal society appropriate to the grasslands of South Africa the toughness of Calvinism was less liable to erosion. And here too a difference in sophistication in the home environment might be significant.

At the opposite pole, the case of Brazil would likewise repay study; and here again a simple geographical explanation obviously will not suffice. Not all of Brazil is equatorial, or even tropical, and the social history of Portugal itself is clearly important. Again, although it is to the honour of the Roman Catholic Church that in general it has proclaimed the brotherhood of all in the Faith, irrespective of colour, this alone is an inadequate explanation of the Brazilian development, since pride of race is acute enough in Andean America while Brazil alone has adopted a policy of avowed racial and cultural fusion. This is not to say of course that colour prejudice does not exist in Brazil, for example in the army and in diplomatic circles; yet even under the Empire, when Negro slavery was still an established institution, people of colour could reach some of the highest positions in the state. Much therefore may be related, in the last analysis, to the historical geography of the Iberian peninsula and the environmental contrast between the arid and aloof Meseta and the Atlantic coastland. Perhaps more important is the historical tradition in Brazil itself: in the mid-seventeenth century the northeast was held, and ably held, by the Dutch, and it is not for nothing that the struggle to expel them was traditionally led by a Portuguese of Portugal, an Indian, and a mulatto.

'White Australia'

You will, I feel sure, agree that in opening a discussion on Geography and Racism, it would be disingenuous in me to evade the issue posed by the policy of the country which I now feel to be my own, Australia. [I did not intend this paper to lead up to and hinge upon a defence of that policy; but at about two o'clock one morning I realized that it would be indiscreet not to mention the subject. Mr Rafiullah has covered so much of my general ground that this particular section may bulk larger in the delivery of my paper than in its conception.]

'White Australia': on the face of it the term is both geographical and Racist, and it is irrelevant that it has never been the official title of a restrictive immigration policy. With perhaps more courage than sense, I will be frank and defend the thing and not the name, since that name is strictly a misnomer.

It is of course easy to rationalize: one Australian textbook remarks that in the United States the Red Indians were 'driven out or exterminated'; in Australia the aborigines 'withdrew' before the white man. There are now probably less than 50,000 full-blood aborigines in Australia, and the average white Australian certainly feels more tenderly towards them than his forebears did when the numbers were more nearly equal—although from the beginnings some efforts were always made to hold the scales of justice true.

[Here I think that I may make one valid point in criticism of Mr Rafiullah: it is not fair to blame men for not being enlightened enough to see in 1650 or even 1850 what we think we can see in 1950. To take one of his examples, how was it possible for the earlier American pioneers to foresee that their use of land for the plough, unlike the Indians' use of it for hunting, would lead to soil erosion on the Great Plains? What possible bases were there for co-operation between peoples who knew nothing of each other's societies and potentialities? As a matter of fact the early English in North America were not 'animated by an intense race superiority'; they were simply very fierce competitors for very scarce resources. They may have detested, but they also respected, as always happens when virile peoples come into conflict.

In Australia well-meant attempts were made, from the very first week of white settlement, to 'civilize the aborigines'. They collapsed on the ground of complete mutual incomprehension, and this was natural between men in the Stone Age—practically Palaeolithic at that—and more modern men in a pre-anthropological and pre-psychological age. Thus the aborigines, living by hunting, naturally saw in cows and sheep simply a new source of food, with much more meat than kangaroos and wallabies and, because they were tame, immeasurably easier to spear. To the whites this was simply 'theft', to be suppressed. And, hard as it was, would anyone seriously wish that the continent of Australia should not make the contribution it now does to the food and clothing of the world?

As for the scales of justice: very much violence, and disgraceful violence, was done. But when in 1838 there was a shocking massacre of aborigines at Myall Creek, seven white men were hanged; and there has never been a second Myall Creek, though isolated murders on both sides continued.]

141

It is true that much of the sparse pastoral development of the North is largely based on cheap aboriginal labour; true that in small outback towns where there are enough aborigines to be noticeable, colour prejudice becomes overt —though never without protest. Nor are aborigines, even when living a settled life, full citizens; most of them are subject to disqualifications such as liquor prohibition (with heavier penalties for white suppliers than for black recipients). Since they may have a compulsory vote, this has once or twice carried the paradoxical corollary that they might hold the balance in a referendum on the hours of closing of bars to which they had not legal access.*

Nevertheless aborigines can work on the same terms as whites, many obvious mixed bloods pass in ordinary society, and in some areas at least nobody bothers too much about liquor laws. Again, there is a striking difference between the general attitude to Melanesians in Papua, which was first British and then since 1906 Australian, and in the Trust Territory of New Guinea, where the pattern was set by the Germans. But while colour prejudice certainly exists, it is not an important strand in Australian psychology. The Australian does not mind difference so much as inequality. One may be cynical and say that there is not much colour contact: but 'White Australia' was aimed mainly against the Chinese, and yet the descendants of the Chinese who came to the gold rushes remain Chinese in appearance, in name, in family custom, but they are assimilated to Australian society with no reservations whatever. [In small towns the Chew Sings, the Nom Chongs, may be pillars of the local church and the local football club; and one cannot say more than that!]

'White Australia' is indeed fundamentally not so much Racist as social and economic. The Australian ethos in the formative years was biased to an egalitarian and homogeneous culture. The objection to Asians was on the one hand economic—the fear, not ungrounded, that large-scale Asian (or indeed *any*) immigration would mean a pool of cheap

* [Many of these restrictions are now (1965) being abrogated.]

labour bringing down cherished standards of living—and on the other a fear, again not irrational, that a small society still struggling to make its way in the world might be overwhelmed by the problems inseparable from the introduction of large bodies of men of completely alien tradition. Of course there was much sheer prejudice, often base, sometimes of sublimest stupidity: when the Commonwealth of Australia was seven years old, a Senator spoke of the Chinese as 'a nation of yesterday'. Yet in the same debate the greatest statesman whom Australia has produced, Alfred Deakin, spoke in terms not of inferiority but of incompatibility, going so far as to call the Chinese a *superior* race. By this he meant that they worked harder and had as it were more economic single-mindedness, and he was right; but if this be Racism, it is rather in reverse.

I think that the argument of incompatibility still holds; and surely Burma and Thailand would recognize Deakin's picture of the superior Chinese. Looking at the suffering caused by minority problems almost throughout the world, I think that any society lucky enough to be reasonably homogeneous is justified in trying to stay so. Australian society is limited in many ways, but on the whole it works reasonably well, and it could not fail to be subverted by *large-scale* immigration of men of completely different culture. Be it noted that from the Australian point of view the argument of incompatibility applies not to Asians alone but to many Europeans as well; there are few more burning questions in Australia today than that of the 'New Australians', a term which applies to all non-British migrants but more especially to those from eastern Europe. The numbers so far admitted form a very welcome cultural leaven, but it may be as well that political circumstances have imposed some check to this particular influx [since the carry-over of ancient feuds into a land where they are irrelevant has caused some political strife]. And, by the repatriation of 'kanaka' labour and the consequent heavy subsidization of their one large tropical agricultural industry, sugar, Australians have shown that they are willing to pay for their ideas.

I think then that it must be admitted that a really large-scale immigration of peoples of utterly alien culture would mean a severe strain on the integration of the small but functioning Australian society. [I think it almost axiomatic that no nation having the power to do so would fail to prevent the entry within its borders of men of alien *mores* in numbers sufficient to threaten the stability and cohesion of its own culture.] Nor would such social loss be accompanied by an equivalent gain to Asia: to be of material value the immigration would have to be on a scale larger than the physical capacity of the continent would warrant. The 'empty spaces' are not empty without good reason. [Here we may be victims of our own over-optimistic propaganda in the past.]

Tropical Australia is a very hard land indeed, hard to get at, harder to scratch a living from. It has a monsoon climate but none of the geomorphological features which have enabled great populations to develop high civilizations in Asia. There is not a single river perennial for more than about two hundred miles from its mangrove-choked mouth; no snow mountains to feed massive irrigation work; no great alluvial deltas. The few pockets of good land are liable alternately to savage drought and to disastrous flood. [Were the features of monsoon Asia found in monsoon Australia—say a 12,000-foot mountain range running down diagonally from Cape York—there might be many times the present number of Australians. Or, to be more accurate and realistic, they would probably be Malays. The Malays certainly knew northern Australia long before the first white settlers, the Chinese very probably; had it been of any use to their economy, would they not have settled it with something more than an occasional ephemeral fishing camp?]

Agriculture in the tropical North, on any significant scale, would require an almost fantastic degree of capitalization; and even assuming that unlimited shipping were available, it seems to me highly unlikely that in two decades one could settle more than five or ten million people on something like average Asian peasant standards; in other words, a mere increase in the area of agrarian poverty. But what are five, ten, twenty millions to Asian population increases? One cannot empty an ocean into a pint-pot.

All this does not mean that we in Australia should be complacently content with things as they are. The popular name for Australia's immigration policy is of course very prejudicial to good feeling, and it is obvious that very many Australians are ashamed of it—and hence, unfortunately, they tend to deal with it in the embarrassed manner of a Victorian parent evading questions of sex. The policy is often administered with ludicrous rigidity; there is a growing body of opinion desirous of changing this by the introduction of a quota system. Even more there is a realization that whatever justification there may be for a policy of exclusion, it carries with it a correlative duty to develop the land to the fullest extent. But here there is sound geographical reason to hold that, while the North should not be neglected, Australia can make a better contribution to the welfare of the world by a more intensive development of the already settled areas as a base for further advance. Given the capital and technique available, it may be doubted whether any people would have done more with our pleasant (where habitable) but intractable continent. And if there is as yet only a handful of people in the North, it is not for want of a century of pioneering effort.

To sum up: Australia in effect has no fundamental race problem: seeing the misery which race problems cause, should we really risk another South Africa? At the same time, those of us in Australia who think thus have strongly opposed the opening of New Guinea to large-scale white immigration to produce 'a second Kenya'. We see no virtue in dreams of a White Melanesia; and this in no spirit of *apartheid*, but in a spirit of co-operation and intercourse so channelled as to help the people of New Guinea to reach an integration they never had before. Government educational policy in Papua and New Guinea aims at fostering a solidarity which could never exist in a tribal society.

[Before we in Australia are condemned for our selfishness, I would appeal to my Asian friends to look into their own hearts. Are there no such conflicts here? Mr Naidu has spoken, with magnificent frankness, of the aloofness between Bantu and Indian in South Africa; and in Asia itself, are there not restrictive policies on essentially the same basis as that of Australia? Let us look at one example only. From the point of view of cultural self-preservation, the Arab states may be perfectly justified in seeking to contain Israel—I omit the matter of destroying it. This is not Racism—Arabs and Jews are both Semites. Religion enters into the conflict, but Judaism is not proselytizing and Islam is avowedly tolerant, and both are religions 'of the Book'. Economically the Israelis have added to productivity and pointed a way to wider prosperity by the application of capital and technology—and it is difficult to see this in a converse case as between Asia and Australia. Is not the basic factor underlying both the Arab and the Australian stands a similar one, and hence if legitimate in the one case legitimate in the other? That factor is simply the defence of a culture: and if that be a sin, let the nation that is without sin among you first cast a stone. . . . Ethically as well as ethnically, are we not all children of Adam?]

The human problem

In conclusion, it seems to me that the essential division of mankind, geographically speaking, is that of the great cultural realms. On any division there are innumerable cross-classifications: subsistence peasants, industrial workers, railwaymen, intellectuals, may be of any colour and any creed. But we can separate out areas wherein diverse peoples have broadly a common environmental background, common cultural traditions and contacts, common interests: Anglo-America, Latin America, the Soviet World, the Far East, and so on. Of course they are interconnected in a thousand ways, and they have to adjust themselves to co-existence, in which large task the deepening and diffusion of geographical knowledge have an arduous and honourable role, both on the material plane of economics and in fostering respectful understanding between peoples of various cultures. I am sure that I need not stress this further in this country and this University.

All this comes back to the point that ecology and not genetic classification is the heart of the matter for geographers. While the relations of geography, as of any honest science, to Racism must be negative, positive insistence in the schools on this non-racial categorization of mankind can indirectly contribute to the erosion of Racist feeling more than refutations which appeal only to abstract intelligence. Racists are never abstract and rarely intelligent; they thrive on the empirical clichés of the cheap novel and the cinema. In direct argument I think the only effective means of penetration is on the practical plane of direct human experience. Had I ever held by the omnibus categories of the Racists, I do not think they would have survived the human experience of serving under two white and two black sergeants, one of each pair being a good and intelligent soldier and a good man (I may add that of the black pair the inferior type had the good Saxon name of Brown while the better was a mere dago called de Sousa).

We must also I think see that our own houses are in order. Racial and national prejudices are far from being the only enemies of the one world or even of the peaceful co-existence which India has done so much to uphold. I have been frank about Australia: I will be frank about India and say that it seems to me, despite the authority of Radhakrishnan, that caste theory to the average man cannot fail to be a demoralizing assertion of group inequality; and while I rejoice at what has been done to subvert caste feeling, much remains to be done. And while the Bandung conference was in many ways most valuable, it would be tragic if, while 'We Europeans' are fighting hard against Racism in our own society, it took a new lease of life from the ashes of colonialism.

But here I myself am preaching to the converted. I would like to conclude on a more positive and universal note, and I cannot do better than quote the inspiring words of the great founder of modern geography, Alexander von Humboldt, in *Cosmos*:

Whilst we maintain the unity of the human species, we at the same time repel the depressing assumption of superior and inferior races of men. There are nations more susceptible of cultivation, more highly civilized, more ennobled by mental cultivation, than others—but none in themselves nobler than others. ALL ARE IN LIKE DEGREE DESIGNED FOR FREEDOM.

Quantity and Quality in Geography

I. REASSESSMENTS

To judge from recent open attacks and internal reassessments, the study of geography is once more facing a crisis, or at least a difficult phase of adjustments and transitions. All life is adjustment and transition, and only people and institutions already dead have no further crises to face. The object of this paper is to present a critique of some recent programmatic statements and tendencies. Any serious discussion of the state of the subject in 1960-1 must at least consider, if it cannot answer, such questions as: Where is the current trend towards increasing quantification taking us? The second part of the paper will be specifically concerned with such questions.

In the upshot—and without descending to the question-begging definition 'geography is what geographers do'—the scope and method of any study are what its practitioners make of them, and, provided they avoid the opposing perils of dogmatic *a priori* schematism and the shallower type of empiricism, they will produce data and generalizations which will be accepted as of solid worth by other specialists. Indeed, since in large part our study is not very esoteric, we may have to take time off now and then to discount generalizations fathered upon us by amateurs who have picked up, but not digested, a quantum of glittering and attractive geographical bits and pieces—for an excellent example, Toynbee, Vol. II, *passim*. Or we must explain that we really cannot provide a suit of ready-made clothes which will fit everybody; cannot, that is, provide a set of 'geographical laws' for the historian applicable in detail to any

Reprinted from *Annals of the Association of American Geographers*, Vol. 50 No. 4, 1960.

L

time or place, or divide the world into a neat set of formal regions, without gaps or overlaps, which will be useful to political scientists, economists, culture historians, businessmen, botanists, or whomever. What we can do is provide good, honestly woven cloth, and helpful advice on cutting. The status of geography in the world of learning and affairs, on the whole a rising status, testifies that we are doing it.

Ackerman and 'fundamental research'

As a starting point to our discussion of geographical re-assessments, we may take the brief but solid contributions of E. A. Ackerman (*Geography as a Fundamental Research Discipline*) and Richard Hartshorne (*Perspective on the Nature of Geography*).[1] Both of these, I think, are 'musts' for serious geographers. In the new and important sense of 'regional' as concerned with a distinct spatial theory, there is also a lively, though as yet perhaps somewhat inchoate, activity in numerous papers by quantifiers and regional scientists. Their approach is more abstracted than that to which geographers have been accustomed, and revives in a more refined form the idea of 'regions' as concrete realities. This idea has been generally abandoned by geographers, who see in regions either convenient isolates for study (at times little more than boxes for data), rather dubious metaphysical concepts, or at best—and I think it is often a very good best—subjective images, mental constructs which can be very illuminating and which have indeed some correspondence with real referends, provided we realize that these referends are not fixed things-in-themselves but incompletely precise apprehensions of reality, shifting though not evanescent. There is much valuable insight to be gained from this last idea of the region, but the irritant counter-stimulus of a more abstract model is perhaps essential as a stiffening: a warning against falling completely for either side of a dichotomy ('real' versus 'construct') which may turn out to be largely notional after all.

At all events, whether we like it or not, regionalism of a new sort has broken loose from strictly geographical parental control, though in my opinion this breaking away need not spell catastrophe for the family welfare. As things have turned out, it is perhaps the chief defect of the contributions from Hartshorne and Ackerman that the former makes no reference and the latter little reference to Isard and this new school. The trend—if that is not too weak a word—has produced plenty of reforming zeal, but not as yet much in the way of programmatic synthesis, though hints towards a manifesto are not lacking. I will discuss the hopes and fears which it evokes in more detail later in this paper.

There is a great deal worthy of discussion in Ackerman's short but tight-packed pamphlet, though some comment may be subsumed in dealing with Hartshorne. Perhaps Ackerman's most important independent contribution is the stress on distributional *change* as a 'near-universal' object of study. Allied to this stress is his recognition of erosional and depositional processes as the major nonconstants of the physical milieu. These concepts, it seems to me, if fully refined and followed up, could provide an important integrative factor between the 'human' and the 'physical' sides*—more subtle than Jean Tricart's interesting Marxist manifesto,[2] but probably leading to conclusions more favourable to genetic geomorphology than those in Hartshorne's *Perspective* (Ch. VIII), which I feel to be the weakest links in his argument. Very important also are Ackerman's remarks on 'space-adjusting' and 'resource-converting' techniques, remarks which link onto the new functional concepts of regionalism discussed below.

The need and the opportunities for fundamental geographical research increase with the intensification of human activity, itself a resultant, amongst other things, both of new technologies and of the mere multiplication of human beings. This Ackerman clearly shows. But Ackerman adds the salutary warning that such research can as yet hardly lend itself to large-scale synthesis—the dream of

* I use ' "human" and "physical" sides' without prejudice to the question of their really separate identities, but as 'isolates for study'; in this sense we all know that they have an existence nonetheless important for being largely subjective.

all who think of themselves in some sense, however humbly, as scientists. In Ackerman's phrase, such research must be as yet disaggregative because at this stage there are simply too many things to learn about the new tools lying to our hands or indeed thrust upon us. This warning certainly has much point for old-style geographers like myself, who now and then are tempted to see ourselves as 'near-universal' geniuses.

But the warning may also have some point for adepts in the newer methods, carried away as innovators always are, and on the whole properly, by the sheer thrill of their innovations—and so sometimes inclined to think that they have found the universal key. It is not only proper but necessary that from time to time ardent spirits should attempt the heroic task of *the* synthesis; without this temperament, we should never get anywhere. But many of us, whether we know it or not, stem from the great tradition of English empiricism—Bacon, Hobbes, Locke, Hume— and, while applauding the spirit of the Universalists, are very rightly suspicious of their findings. The systematizing urge does sometimes carry the risk of supersonic flight out of all rational orbits.

Hartshorne and 'relationships'

I think that undue importance may be attached by some to the revision, at an early stage of Hartshorne's *Perspective*, of the formula that 'geography is the science of areal differentiation'. It is not in any sense a recantation or a jettisoning of the old concept; simply a recasting, a spelling out of it into *'geography is concerned to provide accurate, orderly, and rational description and interpretation of the variable character of the earth surface'* (p. 21; italics in original). With this, who can reasonably quarrel? Yet there is room for diversity in unravelling the implications of even so cautiously qualified a formula as this. Hartshorne, for example, does me the honour (and these words are meant sincerely and not in the least ironically) of meeting an old point of my own by pointing out (p. 18) that on such a view relationships are indeed included; but on the further question of *what* relationships are significant, and *how*, we may still diverge. Ironically enough, indeed, it would apparently be the extremists of Determinism and Possibilism who would meet on the priority—not admitted by Hartshorne, if I read him aright—of Man:Nature relationships to our study.

I make no apology for introducing once more these time-hallowed terms. We do not need to consider 'relationships' as *synonymous* with Man:Nature relationships (pp. 55-6) to recognize that these are very important ones; nor is it enough to declare that environmentalism arises as it were from environmentalism simply because if you think there are causalities you will find them. Certainly argument may be biased by an *a priori* determination, albeit subconscious, to find conditioning 'laws' in the Semple manner, though even Semple deserves mitigating qualifications, as Hartshorne very fairly points out (p. 56). Yet pure induction—it is a truism—is just not possible, is not a feasible method of coping with the multiplicity of data; one cannot even start without some ideas of relevance and significance, as a rule if not indeed invariably inherited. (And who are we to repudiate the inheritance of three millennia of better brains?) As Preston James puts it, 'in spite of the ever-present and essentially human temptation to find what one is looking for, one cannot well go to the extreme of refusing to look for anything'[3]—which latter is pure induction. At the same time, we do well to remember Hartshorne's warning (p. 52) that an undue presumption that 'human features' are effects and 'natural features' causes may lead to an unwarranted discounting of the reciprocal causative effects of human activity—a belief in which, however, is quite consistent with a modest geographical neo-determinism. I feel no inconsistency at all in maintaining the direct conditioning action, in certain contexts, of 'physical factors' together with an insistence on the importance of cultural factors to an extent not recognized by the purists of 'this-is-not-geography'.[4]

There are some Man:Nature relationships so simple and universal that they may be counted among the 'naïvely given

phenomena' recognized from the very beginning of coherent human thinking: the elemental relationships, one
might say, of men with air, earth, and water. Not for
nothing is Hippocrates' *On Airs Waters and Places* given
a place of honour (temporally the premier place) in the
history of our subject, however naïve its method and detail.*
With all the refinements of technologies and argument,
these basic relations are not without power even today. And
it is surely presumptuous simply to set aside the long tradition of common human experience, a tradition more in-
ductive than deductive, empiric rather than *a priori*. (I
speak not of the aberrations of, say, geomancy and astrology,
but of the solid common-sense observation and reflection
of mankind, which by and large goes wrong in the measure
in which it is deductive.) That tradition is that man's
fashioning of his home is far from a free choice; he may
have revolutionized the aspect of large tracts of the earth's
surface, but his revolutions are—or perhaps today I should
say have been—rather law-abiding. And, as we pitch more
and more radiation into air, sea, and earth, we may find
that we have revolutionized our environment to a degree
all too determinative of our destiny.

Some of the confusion is semantic. 'Influences', for example, have been banned, and yet *influence*—both etymol-
ogy and normal usage show it—denotes not a total and automatic control, but only one strand in a complex of conditioning, one element in a resultant of forces. I do not
think that the question can be entirely begged by James's
distinction between a changing and a relatively stable environment; in the former case, whether due to physical or
biotic processes, 'a positive determinism can exist'. But
allowing for the fact (an odd one to be overlooked by anti-
environmentalists) that environment is inseparable from
the environed, can the existence of any relatively stable
environment be 'demonstrated by acceptable method'?
Those environments which seem least changeable—ice-

---

* And hence, naturally, the Aunt Sally for Toynbee's discussion of
environmentalism. One does not demolish atomic physics by refuting
Lucretius.

caps, deserts, great ranges—seem also most conditioning. James is quite correct in saying that correspondence of patterns is far more common than coincidence; but this negates only the extremest and crudest environmentalism, that which expects a strict and rigorous application in detail. Application is limited by qualifications such as those suggested in discussion of the word *influence,* by considerations of probability rather than either strict necessity or mere possibility, and by concepts analogous to a margin of error.[5]

I do not think, then, that the problem is outmoded—else why must Hartshorne still discuss it after so many closures? Nor is it merely verbal; we need not be afraid of the semantic fireworks of logical positivism, themselves, if one may so put it, now under fire. In strict philosophical language, 'determinism' is the wrong word to employ, unless, like Victor Cousin, we wish to assert a total, completely necessitarian control by physical geography; but of course environmentalism can legitimately be recognized as one component of a general determinism. In not a few ways and places, and to a significant degree, human activity is affected by external environment—that is all that neo-environmentalism claims, and it does not rule out causative effects of human effort. But the attempt to rule out environmentalism leads to difficulties.

It is not really a demonstration of the invalidity of studies which 'seek to determine the relation between human and natural factors' to say with Hartshorne (pp. 53-4) that 'no sound conclusion can be drawn until the study is complete, which will generally be impossible', since further investigation may remove some errors but introduce others. Of how many complex bodies of knowledge or theoretical approaches could this not be said? How, if this dictum were acted upon, would there ever have been scientific thinking, except in mathematics? It seems to me that here Hartshorne does not quite measure up to his usually rigorous standards: environmentalist studies *did not* produce increasing certainty, though some 'appeared more convincing'—'but *one knew* that later still more thorough research *might* appear to demonstrate entirely different conclusions'. The italics are mine; they point up a shift of emphasis which seems revealing rather than convincing.

'*Physical*' and '*human*'

At other points also Hartshorne's discussion (pp. 65-6) of the important question of physical:human dualism seems to me not quite successful. For the dualism to be valid, there are two criteria: 'within each division the categories of facts studied would be more nearly similar', and the line between the divisions 'would rest on readily observable distinctions in the naïvely given facts'. The lack of homogeneity on each side must be readily admitted, and while I do not feel that it carries quite the weight which Hartshorne places on it, it is very true that the dualism is often overdone, and that this leads to the fallacy of failing to ask 'Environment for what?' Nevertheless the problem is far from simple, and it seems to me that when Hartshorne claims that 'even after laborious research by many able scholars it may not be possible to separate features of the earth resulting from nature exclusive of man from those that result primarily from man', he may be liable to misinterpretation.

At first sight, one is tempted to retort in terms of naïvely stated facts. We might suggest, without laborious research, that there are such features on the natural side at least: the oceans, the ice-caps, the Himalayas. The rejoinder would have to be, one would think, 'Ah, but *in their totality* some aspects of these features—shipping routes, weather stations, mountain villages—do result from man.' However, with characteristic subtlety and caution Hartshorne has parried the surrejoinder that if one uses the qualifier *primarily* one is not entitled to use *in their totality*—and yet, contemplating the scale of man's works with Antarctica or the Himalayas, this might seem an inescapable phrase. But then there is the significant difference: *exclusively* from nature, *primarily* from man. Unless indeed the variation is merely stylistic, our naïvely given response is estopped—but then there is a looseness of expression unlike Hartshorne's norm.

Yet—assuming that it is semantically deliberate—why the distinction, unless to reflect a definite difference between two sets of phenomena, of which one could conceivably be exclusive of the other while the other could not? In simpler words, the earth could and did exist with no men on it, but living men so far can exist only on the earth. Of course in the former case there would be geography only in the sense that Martian astronomers could produce a geographical handbook to earth; but there could still be at least that sort of geography, and it would be a geography of features 'resulting from nature exclusive of man'.

All this may seem over-subtle, but it is not merely trivial verbalistic debate. For it seems to me that the sentence we have been discussing leads back to the old question that Hartshorne sets aside, that geography is primarily a science of man:earth relationships. Totally speaking, of course, the reaction of man to the Himalayas does not result exclusively from nature but is a function of both parties, and a total geography of the Himalayas must count man in. But differences of degree may be virtually equivalent to differences of kind, and we must look to the scale of the contributions of each factor. From this angle, the Himalayas were there first, existed in their own right, and Himalayan man exists not so much in his own right as by his acceptance of and adjustment to a complex of pre-existing features originally 'resulting from nature exclusive of man' and still very dominantly 'natural'.

Whether or not this discussion is labouring the obvious, there is here a dilemma of much significance to the scope and unity of geography. From a 'common-sense' point of view, most people would say that Antarctica and the Himalayas are 'naïvely given' feature-complexes which 'result from nature exclusive of man', except that he has named them; although of course there may be, as time goes on, more and more interpenetration with features of human origin. The attempt to unravel this argument, however, seems to me to involve study specifically, perhaps even primarily, of man:earth relationships. But such study, we are told (p. 64), is an error introduced by environmentalism

—in spite of the fact that it perhaps reaches its fullest expression in such anti-environmentalist utterances as Kimble's definition of modern geography as 'the study of the localization of ways of living . . . [primarily] viewing the earth as the home of human communities and cultures'.[6] There would always be geological study of the Himalayas, but only geological study, unless on this 'relationships' line. In an effort to avoid this dilemma, are we not likely to fall into the error likewise repudiated by Hartshorne (p. 18) that 'geography is *limited* to the distinguishing of areas'? Perhaps a lurking consciousness of such implications is in part responsible for his distinctly cautious and qualified acceptance of genetic geomorphology later on (pp. 86-96); although there is such acceptance (e.g., on pp. 89-90), it is in my opinion unduly hesitant, so much so that a virtual dismissal might easily be read into these pages by a careless student. Kimble's is of course an unintended *reductio ad absurdum*: we have come a full circle, and one cannot see how one can have a geography of Antarctica, except very deviously through its effects on New Zealand weather and hence on dairying—which of course would be acceptable enough to most New Zealanders!

Hartshorne's formulation here seems to me to carry at least some risk of leading into this circle. His objective, to maintain and emphasize the unity of the subject, is very proper; but his argument, at any rate when filtered through minds less dialectically skilled, might tend to exclude very important factors of areal differentiation, and to darken counsel by confounding groups of phenomena which, as isolates for study, are properly distinguishable.

The Dodo that won't die: Determinism

In all this, I do not wish to suggest that necessarily and indubitably I am right and Hartshorne is wrong. I have far too much respect for his general thesis and powers of argument, and even were my respect much less than it is, the question is not a simple one. I do suggest that there is still much hard thinking to be done on this knotty and intractable and very central problem. Meanwhile, we have been assured that determinism is as dead as the dodo. But it seems singularly tough for an extinct animal: an Immortal Bird, not born for death. How often has its Positively Final Appearance on Any Stage been billed, how many self-appointed exorcists have laid the ghost to their own satisfaction! And yet it still walks abroad, a lively spirit—because it images a real and ever-recurrent problem of our life on this planet on which we live and move and have our being. And if we do move on, shall we escape the influences of selenography, or the Martian environment?

Doubtless there is inconsistency in the polemical passion with which some determinists defend determinism. If it is true, in a way it need not and cannot be defended. But this is a psychological rather than a methodological problem, and far from unprecedented: witness the ethos of Muslims, Calvinists, Communists, all in their theory fatalists, all in their practice so often ardent exponents of the Will. As Hartshorne points out, subatomic indeterminancy has little relevance to the problems with which social scientists have to deal. Whether or not a 'question of philosophic faith' has relevance for geography, for any one but a logical positivist it has much relevance for the attitude of individual geographers to their work. In this sense, if not in Hartshorne's, it does have its place in scientific discussion.[7]

But I am probably delaying too long on these epistemological disputes, and probably also giving an exaggerated impression of differences of opinion. Even when one disagrees with a formulation or the emphasis placed upon it, these pages of Hartshorne's are in many ways invaluable. For example, I feel that it is only on a very narrow view of our world that Hettner's generalization 'time steps into the background' is true and useful, and that there are inconsistencies in Hartshorne's discussion of it (Ch. VIII); yet it leads to a warning, much needed by young historical geographers (and *mutatis mutandis* applicable in other contexts), which might be summed up by saying that one rarely has to begin in the Pre-Cambrian. And for the later chapters of *Perspective* there can be little but high praise; those philosophic doubts which so often and so needlessly disturb geographers intimidated by the claims of scientism here meet a quiet, a modest, but in my opinion a triumphant solution. The discussion of the place of prediction in science and the role of 'scientific laws' (pp. 166-9), leading to the conclusion that the right question is not, 'Is geography a science?' but, 'What kind of science is geography?'; the demonstration, based on Hettner (pp. 173-8), that each of the systematic, chronological, and chorological approaches 'extends theoretically over the whole of empirical knowledge', and that each includes some elements of the others—these concepts are especially elegant and valuable.

Down with dichotomies!

Here Hartshorne is reducing to their proper proportions those seductive dichotomies which bedevil so much methodological discussion: physical versus human (my particular reservations above do not preclude general agreement), arts versus sciences, nomothetic versus idiographic, intuition versus ratiocination, in our own jargon regional versus systematic, and so on. All of these do in a way correspond to something, but not to absolutes. They are real enough if regarded as approaches, conveniences for the handling of data, functional emphases, mental constructs. It is essential to make use of them. But if they are regarded as things in themselves they lead only to a blinkered view of the Cosmos. As Hartshorne puts it in a rather more general context (p. 179, my italics):

> The organization of knowledge does not require a neat division into compartments, which would in fact be in violation of the essential unity of reality, but rather the recognition of coherent and manageable but *preferably* overlapping divisions.

The Altogetherness of Things—we will never really comprehend it, but if we fail to see that all these dualisms have a dialectic interplay, we shall never even apprehend that there *is* a cosmic unity. It is true that the magnificent archetype so deeply rooted in the thought and feeling of all peoples—*yin* and *yang*, male and female, light and dark, inner and outer (the list of couplings is endless)—is perhaps the most universal way by which we do apprehend Cosmos. Even if we think of Cosmos as a whole, as an emanation of some unitary Absolute or Godhead, we apprehend its manifestation in such dualities. But always it is neither the one nor the other alone which gives coherence to our vision, but the two together, without which there is no consummation—and this word is used in no restricted sense but in its full etymological connotation. Or even, perhaps, it is not merely fanciful playing with numbers in the Pythagorean manner if we now and then think, like Hegel and some Hindus, in Triadic terms: thesis, antithesis, synthesis. But never in terms of a single approach, a single factor, a single key: that way (sometimes literally) madness lies.

The foregoing may appear to be a romantic digression: that it has some relevance may, I hope, appear in my concluding paragraphs. Meanwhile, to come down to earth— a most proper thing for a geographer to do—I would repeat that Hartshorne's concluding chapters, and especially Ch. X ('Scientific Laws or Individual Cases?'), seem to me required reading. One need not agree but one must compare; one must weigh one's own evaluations on the precise scales provided by Hartshorne's meticulous argumentation. Here is the acid test by which one may assay one's own formulations and decide whether they express what one really thinks, or only what one thinks one thinks, a salutary exercise! The danger, of course, is that while Hartshorne is an invaluable irritant for those who are willing to endure the pain of thinking, he is too easily taken as gospel by those who are not so willing. One cannot justly blame a man for doing his work too well; but his assurance, his erudition, his anticipation of objections, his thoroughness —these provide very comfortable shelters for the timid and the lazy.

New concepts of regionalism

This thoroughness of Hartshorne's shows to advantage in his discussion of the newer concept of the region, dependent not so much on the integration of various elements in 'areas of a certain type' as on 'interconnections of places'. Not all his points on the older concept seem to me well taken, but on the whole the argument pays off, while his discussion of the newer type appears a considerable improvement on Whittlesey's.[8] Here too we have a realistic and effective use of dichotomy: both concepts can be effective tools of research, but they should be clearly distinguished. Of course, as Hartshorne duly points out, the integration-type region may be marked by functional interconnection within itself: and, one might add, in some cases this may be among the more significant criteria in establishing it.

For the two types Hartshorne, following Carol, proposes the terms 'formal' and 'functional', and these seem to me entirely acceptable, as Whittlesey's 'nodal' for the latter does not. In the case of functional regions 'the unity of area involved is a reality based upon dynamic connections among phenomena at different places . . . therefore . . . the expression of a theory of process-relationships' (p. 136). Since such relationships are often readily susceptible to abstract statistical treatment—in which theoretical models may play a valuable part, as they rarely (not quite never) could in 'formal' regions—this leads me to the ostensible subject suggested by the original title of this paper: geography and quantification. It may be reasonably suggested that I have been a long time getting there; but I think we must blame Hartshorne for that. . . .

II. REGIONAL SCIENCE AND QUANTIFICATION

The rise of 'regional science'

Perhaps any discussion of these problems of abstraction and quantification, which, though related, are not quite the same thing, should range around the work of the 'regional scientists'. Whether we like it or not, regional science is set for an independent existence. If, as Preston James says, geography has mothered it without much joy in the conception, perhaps that is because there seem quite a few claimants to paternity: economics, statistics, sociology.

To me, regional science already meets at least one of James's two criteria for existence as a discipline. Admitting that I have no statistical competence whatever, I do not think that this is a case of *omne ignotum pro magnifico*; perhaps for most of us, *pro ridiculo* is a more natural reaction, and we greet the Unknown with a sneer. I am sure that such a reaction would be disastrous for geography. (As George Stevenson remarked when asked whether a collision between his new-fangled locomotive and a cow would not be awkward, 'Very awkward—for the coo.') Quite as disastrous would be simple capitulation to the claims of some more extreme missionaries of quantification.

The first of James's criteria is that a discipline must be 'in its own right, a contemporary reflection of a process of growth'. Whatever else it may be, regional science is also just that. And I think that it is at least in process of meeting the other criterion of possessing 'a body of tested and accepted procedures and a set of concepts'[9]—even if both procedures and concepts must in varying measures be shared with other disciplines. Geographers, of all people, are hardly entitled to object to this sharing!

If anyone doubts the lustiness of this infant, let him go through the five annual volumes so far available of *Papers and Proceedings of the Regional Science Association*.[10] It is not indeed necessary to plough through the lot—I have certainly not done so. But I would draw particular attention to Walter Isard's 'Regional Science, the Concept of Region, and Regional Structure' and Morris Garnsey's 'The Dimensions of Regional Science'.[11] Both of these are extremely important, and it is important also not to be put off by the provocative air of some of Isard's sentences; allowance must be made for the fact that his paper is in some sort a manifesto, and of their nature manifestoes must be forcibly expressed.

Isard, for example, remarks (p. 13) that if we do not vigorously experiment with the new methods,

. . . we shall thereby be forced to rely on inferior additive processes . . . e.g. the addition of elements of regional economics, regional sociology, and regional geography. As a consequence, we shall fail to capture the essence of the region. . . .

This does not, as a hasty reading might suggest, *in itself* mean that regional geography is something *per se* inferior: only that the borrowing would alloy the purity of the type of abstract regional constructs which Isard sees, perhaps rightly, as the most promising line of advance. One may of course disagree, and it is essential here to hold firmly to Hartshorne's distinction of formal and functional regions. For the first, I think that (as of today at any rate) in the last resort we can only grasp the essence of regions, or a region, by a geographical empathy akin to the historical empathy demanded in Croce's famous passage about the Ligurian peasant,* and indeed some element of 'identification' seems to me to mark the best regional writing. But for the pure Platonic Idea of the Functional Region, Isard may well be right, although it must be said that in places (e.g., p. 17) he does seem to extend this 'essence' as if it were more than the Idea, and here at least he seems to adopt an over-zealous attitude, moderately expressed but capable of degenerating into exclusivism, if not arrogance.

More than one of Isard's ideas—perhaps designedly, to provoke discussion—seem to play a little incautiously with a grand general schematism, that desire for an all-embracing system which has seduced so many fine minds. He appears to believe in the region as, in certain contexts, 'a concrete reality' (which for functional regions might be corroborated by Hartshorne's 'the unity of area involved is a reality . . .', quoted above†), and envisages the logical possibility of a 'true' set of the best regions—and this definition few geographers would now be bold enough to accept. It has been effectively criticized by Arthur Maass[12] and by Preston

---

* Croce's *locus classicus* is probably most readily accessible in R. G. Collingwood, *The Idea of History* (Oxford: at the Clarendon Press, ed. 1946), p. 199. There are of course qualifications to be made, but the central idea has wide acceptance and seems to me profoundly stimulating.

† I understand from a personal communication that Hartshorne is now not entirely satisfied with this position.

James; the latter, beginning with the point that geographers must deal with concrete field phenomena ('concrete' of course does not mean only material objects) and regional scientists with 'symbols for things they have never seen', goes on:

> ... we must reject the idea that the description of any kind of process can be made so complete and all-embracing that 'the last *ceteris paribus* will have been removed'. 'Other things being equal' is an essential symbol for all those sciences which aim at isolating specific phenomena, and which define their fields in terms of the subject-processes investigated. When processes are examined in particular places, other things can never be equal. This is a field which has long been defined as geography.[13]

To the point of this passage, and of a similar protest of Collingwood's, I shall return. The excessive discounting or dismissal of variables has also been criticized—in my opinion, most effectively—by Lukermann, who points out the numerous difficulties, both theoretical and empirical, besetting those who, in a mechanistic manner, simply equate space with metrical distance.[14]

But in any case, Isard himself, when one reads him closely, makes *some* of the appropriate qualifications. Perhaps his point of view is best summed up in the following passage:

> Generally speaking, the region may be both a concept and a concrete reality. Yet in certain contexts the region, either as a concept or concrete reality, disappears into thin air and leaves as a residue a continuous set of points in space. Identified with this context is an extreme degree of abstraction, which, nonetheless, furnishes one fruitful approach to the development of the concept of region (p. 18).

This last sentence appears an unexceptionable claim, though it must be balanced against what seems to me an unwarranted territorial expansion on the preceding page— the procedures of regional science 'should involve the re-formulation and synthesis of existing concepts [in other social sciences] though to a decreasing extent as progress is achieved'. Does this mean anything except that other fields

165

M

will become superfluous? Again, one must protest vigorously against the very odd and indeed completely unfounded notion (p. 19) that the 'earthbound analysts' in these other sciences, for whom there is no ' "true" or "fixed" set of regions relevant for all problems [but] simply generalizations of the human mind', are *not* 'deeply concerned with the broad welfare objectives of society'. This assertion is nothing but a dogmatic value-judgement, and one may meet it with another, less dogmatic—that breadth of this kind, which apparently needs 'the ultimate in general theory' for its satisfaction, may very likely not be compatible with depth of understanding.

This statement of Isard's does not stand alone, and one may perhaps digress for a moment to consider the social implications of this approach. This true or fixed set of regions relevant for all problems—a very determinist, if not mechanist, concept—what is the point of it, if it is *not* simply a generalization of the human mind? As that, simply as an abstract model, it may well be valuable, despite all its omissions; but surely such statements as that just quoted imply more—that these models are blueprints for social planning. And here there is a revealing footnote in one of Isard's most substantive works: '. . . a "pure" theory *such as is relevant to social planning* [my italics] rather than a "realistic" theory wherein institutional forces are duly considered'.[15] (It is not meant to imply, one assumes, that pure theory considers such forces unduly.) But on what definition of 'social' can one legitimately leave out institutional forces, since society is just that—institutional forces? Presumably the pure theory, unlike earthbound analysis, will somehow help to maximize social welfare. Why and how? Only, so far as I can see, if the true and fixed set of regions is regarded not just as an abstraction to aid in understanding a general dynamic, but as a pure master plan for the region/country/world, to which everything else must be subordinated. Except in the sophistication of technique, this reminds one, irresistibly, of the doctrinaire constructs of the early Utopian socialists such as Fourier and Cabet: evenly spaced communities at such-and-such distances with so-and-so many citizens of each type, X acres per man and trust in Providence that each man has Y children (or, of course—we've improved—birth control and artificial insemination). Such are the pleasures of abstraction. Not that the intent of the regional scientist is in the least totalitarian, but to this earthbound analyst that seems the logical meaning of what is said.

Nevertheless, there are other things in Isard's regional views which very usefully supplement Hartshorne's discussion and are well worth study: for example, the relativistic nature of the concept of regional structure, the 'slicing' of the total field for the analysis of particular types of problems.

Despite what seems to me exaggerated hope for the eventual omni-competence of regional science, the continued relevance of geography is implicit in Isard's own words (p. 26): regional science must include, as well as abstraction, empiric field enquiry 'directly relate[d] to the unique characteristics of each place'; as James points out, this is geography. Neither the extreme view that regional science is 'an unwarranted invasion', nor its converse that regional geography in the older sense can be written off, is necessary or helpful. Though I think that regional science is at least approaching the status of a separate discipline, like ourselves it is interdisciplinary, with a narrower range, on the whole, but perhaps a more technical approach.[16] I do not think that geographers have anything to fear from the rise of a new discipline, at any rate after the first fine careless rapture is over. Regional science may well act as a pacemaker for geographers—even if the pace is initially hot! All the same, in the last resort probably most geographers will be content to be, as they must be, 'earthbound analysts' if the alternative is to be quite so space-happy as Isard is in extremer moments.

The rise of quantification

Regional science is perhaps only the most spectacular expression of a trend which must be reckoned with. It is clear that in many, quite likely in most, branches of our subject there must be added to the core of basic skills some statistical expertise beyond medians and averages. Not necessarily every geographer will need these skills, just as not every geographer need know how to construct complicated projections. But he must know the properties of projections; even if he can normally get a specialist to construct the sort of projection he needs for a special purpose, he must know enough to be aware of why he needs it. Much the same applies to statistics; and increasingly, young geographers will feel that they are not properly equipped without some statistical *nous*. (I am very relieved that I am not a young geographer.)

The rise of quantification has been startling in its suddenness. Of the papers abstracted in the *Annals of the Association of American Geographers,* those which employed statistical techniques of any sophistication in 1938 were at most seven per cent—more probably, *nil.* By 1958, the minimum which could be so regarded was about 15 per cent, the maximum 25 to 30 per cent. The Association now has special sessions devoted to measurement and statistical geography. This development is obviously here to stay. In 1954 *American Geography: Inventory and Prospect* included no chapter dealing specifically with geographical applications of statistical techniques. Such an omission would be very unlikely in 1960, and would probably occasion a legitimate outcry. Incidentally, I think that there is great need for one or more reasonably comprehensive texts on this topic to synthesize the more viable of the plethora of papers.

Humanist as I claim to be, I do not deplore this trend so far as it has gone. Quantification has increased, is increasing, and in my opinion ought not to be diminished but to stay—quantitatively—just about where it is now. It is an essential element with a valuable role to play; but it is not without its dangers. These are mainly: (1) a tendency to confuse ends and means; (2) a correlative naïveté which sometimes fails to distinguish between the trivial and the significant; and (3) a natural youthful ambition which to a point is innocent, or even laudable, but which beyond that point—hardly to be determined quantitatively—may

be excessive and lead to the Original Sin of academic life—
exclusivism or obscurantism. Be it noted that obscurantism
cuts both ways: usually, and usually rightly, associated with
a conservative view, it can yet be just as much a trait of the
radical and the progressive.

Ends and means

Confusion of ends and means is perhaps best seen in the
rather naïve resurrection of Lord Kelvin's famous or in-
famous dictum that 'when you cannot express it in numbers, your knowledge is of a meagre and unsatisfactory kind
. . . *whatever the matter may be*'.[17] The statement has
validity in a limited context, though even there it is little
more than a circular truism: 'It is important to count what
can be counted.' That it is more than this I absolutely deny;
yet because of its splendid Victorian self-confidence, it is
seductive, and hence can be seriously misleading.

Kelvin notwithstanding, there *are* matters on which precise quantified statements may be more meagre and unsatisfactory, and far less meaningful, than statements which
do not rest on statistical enquiry but of which the accuracy
cannot be impeached. I have illustrated this elsewhere[18]
from Madrid and Barcelona. Analyses, useful so far as they
go, can be made from the occupational structure of these
two cities, analyses which are statistically precise and valuable for a quantitative *description*. They are less meaningful—that is, they stand in more need of explanation and
interpretation, of outside support—than conclusions drawn
from the historical development of these two cities: Madrid
the creation of a consciously centralizing state power, Barcelona the focus of an intense regional separatism consciously opposed to the centralizing symbol and reality of
Madrid. Regional science here would certainly help to
point up the contrast, but it would completely miss the
point or essence, since this depends very largely on the intangibles of history and politics. From the point of view of
understanding regional realities in Spain, if we had to choose
there is little doubt—none in my mind—that we should
choose the non-quantitative approach in this case. Fortu-

nately we do not have to choose: each approach can illumine and support the other, and this should surely be our ideal.

Worse, perhaps, than this Kelvinian flourish are such statements as that quantified descriptions are the *goal* of scientific investigation. The goal of scientific investigation —of *all* scientific investigation, in which our individual investigations are as rills to the Amazon—is understanding of the Cosmos. To this end, quantified descriptions may be and often are very important means—sometimes essential, sometimes the only, means; *and yet, but means.* This is at least one dichotomy we must stick to. And one is tempted to add another; the difference between classifying and understanding, counting and judging! If we had full understanding, we should not need to classify, unless perhaps as a delegation or devolution to assist in presentation; as it is, we may well need to classify as an aid to understanding. But we should never mistake classification for comprehension.

Very naturally, those who have turned their attention to quantifying techniques and concepts—especially such things as 'nearest neighbour theory'—have been much influenced by developments in the study of biological populations, especially in plant ecology;[19] indeed, in some cases such studies seem to have given the initial impulse. One of the most brilliant pacemakers in this field is indubitably D. W. Goodall. It would be well if one of his most pregnant conclusions were better remembered:

> In any case, quantitative methods can never be more than an adjunct to *description*—they can never provide *interpretations*. Interpretation is a process in the ecologist's mind when he has fully surveyed the descriptive data, whether qualitative or quantitative; and, while quantitative descriptions may greatly facilitate or even guide these mental processes, they cannot replace them.[20]

'*They cannot replace them*'—worthy of letters of gold! Another point of Goodall's well worth weighing is that 'ordination'—precise designation by co-ordinates, as opposed to 'the bare statement of class-membership' in some 'stated region of the continuum'—can never be *wrong*, but it may be unnecessarily cumbersome.[21] This leads me to the second danger: the dogged analysis of trivia, the elaborate discovery of the well-known.

A la Recherche de la Platitude absolue

The meticulous exploration of the realms of platitude— painstaking, but a standard refutation of the dictum that 'genius is an infinite capacity for taking pains'—is no monopoly of quantifiers. We all know those careful qualitative descriptions of market-towns which take care to point out that the towns have markets. I recall a paper way back in the '30s which announced that the distant view of a prairie town of 150,000 people showed more tall buildings in the middle than one of 15,000. It seems to me that there is a distinct risk of expertise in a fashionable technique disguising an essential poverty of thought; and this is less easy to get away with in qualitative writing where there is no smoke screen of formulae. The *cognoscenti* have their own radar to see through it; the uninitiate may be completely bluffed.

In this field the most magnificent, the most sublime, examples come from sociology: such epoch-making generalizations (and this is not parody!) as that 'perhaps' people have more frequent, cordial, and intimate contacts with their personal friends than with those who are not their personal friends; or that while one usually marries someone of one's own creed and class, quite often he or she is of somewhat opposing temperament.* There are, I am glad to say, signs that this compulsion to *look* scientific

* Although this last conclusion on mate-selection was arrived at by impeccably quantitative methods—'With 15 variables [variably dichotomized and double-dichotomized] into 44 sub-variables, the complete interspousal correlation consists of 15 times 15 (= 225) submatrices containing 44 times 44 (= 1936) elements . . .'—it is perhaps not fair to quote it against respectable quantifiers, since the generalization is based on 25 university couples, a restricted sample not likely to be of practical use to colleagues with adolescent daughters. There are odder things in a study of campus petting.

171

('scientific' being equated with formulae) in sociology is working itself out. Common-sense and decent American English seem to be coming in again. But it is because I do not wish such gross idiocies to disfigure geography that I would sound a note of warning. Already there are premonitions of this Hudibrastic diseconomy:

> For he, by geometric scale,
> Could find the size of pots of ale;
> Resolve, by sines and tangents straight,
> If bread or butter wanted weight;
> And wisely tell what hour o' th' day
> The clock doth strike, by Algebra.[22]

One cannot, for example, be altogether happy about some of the recent work on business location; it is parody, doubtless, but equally doubtless not always extravagant parody, to say that some of it seems not much more than a mathematical demonstration that there are a lot of motels on the more touristy stretches of U.S. 66. One must discriminate and make due allowances; not all that looks naïve at first sight is quite so naïve when looked at more closely —though in some cases repeated reading substitutes circularity for naïveté as the offence. Some apparent triviality reflects a determination to take nothing for granted but to work everything out from first principles; but while this is an eminently proper way of thinking, it is rarely necessary in presentation, and it can lead to unhappy tautological expressions such as the 'inference' that 'highway-oriented functions are most successful when oriented along major highways'. That is just what 'highway-oriented' means, and one may question the argument or presentation that needs to spell it out; at the very least, it is open to misinterpretation. Nor, despite good will and some effort, do I find Berry's 'four conformations of business' a very novel or a very striking discovery.[23]

At the same time, it is likely that from the work of Garrison, Berry, and their associates[24] there will emerge some useful basic generalizations which would not be reached through straightforward empirical observation alone. But it is interesting to note how much does seem to depend on verification from field observation. This of course is as it should be; properly handled, the empirical and the theoretical approaches, the idiographic and the nomothetic, should support each other. The mistake lies in taking either for the one true and necessary way all the time; and, as we shall see, this mistake is being faithfully made. Nor should empirical checks of a theory be confused with substantive new knowledge, or its formulation equated necessarily with understanding, although it is in new and fruitful formulation that the real value of quantifying analysis chiefly lies.*

Considering the pressure for publication—almost any publication—which is a feature of the academic marketplace, it is not surprising that some essentially trivial material will be printed, some of it little more than raw data, or merely interim descriptions of experimentation which should not really have a place in a considered presentation. Quantified or not, the trivial we will always have with us; it is just rather more maddening when presented with a patronizing display of new method. In time, these essentially empirical quantifying approaches will find their true level—not a low one—and be recognized for what they are: useful tools, not universal keys to knowledge.

The sky's the limit

Finally, there is the danger resulting from vaulting ambition. Some of this is innocent enough, in its spirit even laudable, as for example in the rather startling 'Proposals to Develop Statistical Laws of Human Geography' by S. C. Dodds and F. R. Pitts.[25] At least the concept marks an advance on the crude law-making of the Semple phase, and has a certain curious charm. True, their Modest Proposal is not quite so breathtaking as Eugene Van Cleef's demand that 'geographers must observe every square inch of the earth's landscape',[26] but it does suggest the assembly and

---

* This seems an appropriate place to call attention to an apparent tendency to use 'empirical' as if it meant 'deductive' or even '*a priori*', and 'intuitive' to apply to *any* non-quantitative reasoning—even to 'intuitive inference', a contradiction in terms.

maintenance, over the next fifty years or so, of up-to-date 'geo-files' with cards for each and every 'unit' of the earth's surface—say each square mile (60,000,000 cards, plus or minus) or each 'township' of 100 square miles (600,000 cards). All would be fed into computers, and out would roll those lovely correlations which would at last, at last, give us 'laws of complete universality and high precision'. It would of course be better to use person-cards (say—but for how long could we say it?—2,500,000,000), each personal quantum of economic and social position correlating with the other data (altitude, soil, economy, climate . . . *ad infinitum*) on the respective unit card.

Well, if geographers were kings . . . Yet it would be imperceptive merely to dismiss this proposal as a delicious dream. The argument—and the objections—are carefully worked out, and even if we think that the actual proposal must remain in the realm of fantasy, the paper contains a residuum of sensible and useful observations. And paradoxically, once quantification were carried out on this scale, in a sense abstraction would be largely superseded: we would have an unsurpassable fund of empirical data, and the electronic tools for its analysis. And unless we could have a punched card for each and every human motivation —and changing motivations—there would still remain a vast field for interpretation. I confess that the prospect so dazzles me that I cannot but commend the spirit at least of these proposals.

It is otherwise when ambition co-exists with the pedantically elaborate discovery of the known by one single key, and the exclusivist assertion is made that this is the best, perhaps the only, way to discover it. I think that I am justified in taking as an exemplar a recent paper by J. Q. Stewart and W. Warntz: 'Macrogeography and Social Science'.[27] It begins by setting up an Aunt Sally called Microgeography:

> Complete spatial accounting is the goal of micro-geography. [Yes, on the Van Cleef or Dodds-Pitts line: but that is not what is meant.] An accepted triumph is the production of a map showing the precise location of each discrete occurrence

of the phenomena studied: the dot map is of course one of
the most valuable examples. Such denotations have unfortunately become thought of as alone constituting the 'geography' of the phenomena studied. . . .

Dear me! As if such a map were thought of as an end in
itself and not as a tool; as if one of the most recurrent problems of geographers were not how to generalize on maps,
rather than precisely spotting each discrete occurrence.[28]
Of course some geographers—and others—do go in for mapping for mapping's sake and produce pointless triumphs
in this line; but that any passably well-schooled geographer
has ever thought that such things 'alone' constituted his
study I very much doubt.

   The less critical and more substantive points in this macro-
geographical approach, the concept of potential of population, may have serious value as analytical tools, though
they have been criticized, in my opinion very cogently,
in papers by Lukermann and Porter of Minneapolis.[29]
Both point out some very questionable logical assumptions involved in the concept of an abstract undifferentiated
space—which seems the core concept of macrogeography
and regional science—when applied to the actual world of
phenomena distributed over the earth's surface. It is simply
not true, for example—and we can all see this—that accessi-
bility is simply a function of measured distance; yet this, or
something very much like it, seems to be predicated in the
general approach of macrogeography.

   I have not Lukermann's philosophical equipment, and
one cannot summarize his argument briefly. All I can do is
to apply the excellent empiricist touchstone 'By their fruits
ye shall know them', to assess the results put forward as
significant and the general temper displayed: neither is
very impressive. In fact, one feels rather as the little boy
in Andersen's story about the Emperor's wonderful new
clothes: 'But, Mummy, the Emperor hasn't got anything
on!' When one reads that 'a single, macroscopic, integrative
index potential of population, as the leading concept in
sociological intensity, introduces a powerful unifying con-

cept', one begins to wonder: another *single* key to turn *all* locks? These demands for a mechanistic all-embracing 'social physics' were heard long ago in sociology, where they now seem decidedly *vieux jeu*; are they now seeking refuge in geography?

What novel insights are in fact given in this distinctly assertive paper by Stewart and Warntz? The results are summated in a series of maps, and seem to me distinctly jejune, in part, perhaps, because the contour interval is very broad (it has to be, to remain 'macro'). They show, for example, the primacy of the metropolitan areas of New York, Chicago, and Los Angeles. Did these need showing?* (What would be valuable would be a much closer net to show the ranking of minor centres like St Louis and Birmingham; this however might be 'microgeography'.) There are two maps of potentials in 1860, which have no point at all unless it is intended—and the captions make clear that it is so intended—to illustrate relative strengths in the American Civil War. It is carefully pointed out that Figure 6 'indicate[s] Southern vulnerability to Northern sea power'. Winfield Scott grasped the point in 1861; even Jefferson Davis must have noticed it by 1865. That Stewart and Warntz in 1958 think it necessary to prove a historical commonplace argues a certain intellectual purblindness. It is true that, in conformity with the gradient of potential, 'the stiffest and most prolonged fighting' did occur in Virginia; but this was the result of political stupidity on both sides. One wonders how the gradient would have been interpreted had Sherman and the Western armies been given a free hand earlier. Of course the case is better if meant conversely, to show that the theory squares with an

---

* It is apparent from a comparison of Figure 3 in the *Geographical Review* article under discussion with the map on p. 22 of Stewart's chapter 'Potential of Population and Its Relationship to Marketing' (in R. W. Cox and W. Alderson (eds.), *Theory in Marketing* (Chicago: Irwin, 1950)), that the cartographical representation of results is affected, to an unacceptable degree, by the care and degree of generalization with which the isolines of potential are drawn. The relative values of Chicago and Pittsburgh are in fact reversed on the two maps.

acknowledged fact. But not much better: the point is too much of a truism to help greatly in a general validation.

This point is not made merely for debate. This approach, useful as it may be in the gross as suggesting certain rough approximations (in much the same way as Marxist theory does), is determinist in an unsubtle and unrefined manner. It completely neglects Goodall's warning: it mistakes description for interpretation, correlation for causation. The result is a serious misconception: it gives a misleading appearance of absolute historical inevitability.

One does not dispose of a theory by analysis of some ineptitudes. But when, as in the curiously infelicitous jingle with which Stewart and Warntz adorn their conclusion, they simply write off other approaches as demanding 'but little thought', we are entitled to look closely at their own style of reasoning. To me, it lacks logic and syntax.

Credo

This is, like it or not, the Quantified Age. The stance of King Canute is not very helpful or realistic; better to ride the waves, if one has sufficient finesse, than to strike attitudes of humanistic defiance and end, in Trotsky's phrase, in the dustbin of history. And if the quantifying trend carries with it—as I think it does—the danger of a devaluation of human idiosyncrasy, of local colour, yet it has also its hopes and opportunities: for a more verified and rationalistic perspective on the problems which confront us, as individuals and as a society, in this agitated age. It would be unfair and imperceptive not to respect the feeling that one is on an exciting new frontier of knowledge, that one may at last recognize and perhaps in the literal sense realize the whole rationale of human society. The Benthamites had this feeling, and before them the Encyclopaedists and the Hobbists, and after them the Marxists. It is almost certainly delusion, but a necessary sort of delusion: without this spirit we should still be cracking marrow-bones in caves.

Quantification presents an exciting new frontier, then, with rewards for the adventurous; but, conversely, has a frontier any meaning, can it even exist, without its core region? Here one comes back to 'earthbound analysis'. As Lukermann puts it,

> We turn, and not reluctantly, to the explanatory narrative which alone integrates our categorized subject matter into the scope of human experience. It is in this use of the circumstances of the particular that we make use of the generic content of science and create a geography.[30]

Whether we turn this way or not is perhaps a matter of archetypal attitudes, the perennial antithesis like that between Platonist and Aristotelian, between the sons of Hermes and Apollo.* The problem concerns us, first and foremost, as human beings, and each of us, in the last resort, must make his own choice, take his own steps, if indeed he has any free choice in the matter. As a determinist, I doubt that he has. But if 'freedom is the recognition of necessity', at least we may recognize it, and not beat ourselves to death on the enclosing walls. Within those walls there is as yet much scope for the play of individuality. I for one do not feel the death-wish so often ascribed to Western society at large by its open enemies or by faint-hearted over-intellectualized inmates.

This is a personal credo, for which I hope I may be pardoned, since it stems from the larger bearings of my theme —and we are shallow poor creatures indeed if we never stand back to look at them. More immediately, as geographers, as scholars devoted to a particular discipline, it may be helpful to reflect that we are not alone. In a kindred study the same problem arises—and the same vista. Professor La Nauze of Melbourne has evaluated the 'Butlin revolution'

---

* W. H. Auden, *Under Which Lyre?*—

> The sons of Hermes love to play
> And only do their best when they
> Are told they oughtn't;
> Apollo's children never shrink
> From boring jobs, but have to think
> Their work important . . .

This brilliant Phi Beta Kappa poem (1947) ought to be required reading for all aspirants or eminents in the academic world.

in Australian historiography which (I take some vicarious pride in saying so) has been hatched in my own University:

> There are no people in it, but there is growth of population . . . There is no elegant fun at the expense of the Italianate mansions of the 1880's; there is a statement which ten years ago might have been (but was not) guessed at, but which could not then have been based firmly on quantities: 'The building of cities [in the period 1861-1900] absorbed the greater part of Australian resources devoted to developmental purposes.'
>   . . . Let there be no doubt that the economist-historian is saying things important for political, social, and even cultural history . . . [But] history does not become statistics because the economist-historian insists that essentially quantitative questions must be answered quantitatively, nor would he claim that because all he has to say about religion is summed up in a table of figures headed 'Gross capital formation: Churches' that there is nothing else to say about the subject. . . . If the economist-historians should claim that, because it is impossible to measure them, exaltations, agonies, freedom and love have no place in the writing of history, it would be a case not for alarm or for jesting, but for pity. But they have not made, and are not likely to make, any such claim.[31]

How very similar that is to the position of geographers! 'People'—yes, we must keep them in; 'elegant fun'—yes, there must be a place for that. I wish, considering some developments in sociology, and, for example, Isard's claim of how to grasp the essence of a region, that I could feel quite so sure of La Nauze's last sentence—but in the last resort, whether *they* like it or not, there will always be innumerable enclaves of individuality not accessible to punched cards; always boys and girls to whom 'The Complementary Theory of Mate Selection' and its reference to 'a formal definition of love' in two volumes won't matter a damn.

Finale

To sum up a long and involved paper, which yet has omitted much, it seems to me fair to say that *so far* the effect of the quantifying trend has been intellectually stimulating; yet, as Preston James reminds us, we must ever be wary of 'the intellectually stifling effect of a clearly-stated but over-simple theory'.[32] The crux, as it seems to me, is this: quantification is in the end essentially classificatory rather than truly interpretative, though it is often an essential tool towards interpretation. If we forget this, and let it become master rather than servant, we may lay ourselves open to Collingwood's criticism of Toynbee:

> He has not undertaken any philosophical analysis of the way in which his [geographical] knowledge has been attained. He possesses enormous quantities of it, but he treats it as if it were something he finds ready-made in books, and the problem which interests him is only the problem of arranging it when collected. His whole scheme is really a scheme of pigeon-holes elaborately arranged and labelled, into which ready-made [geographical] facts can be put. Such schemes are not in themselves vicious; but they always entail certain dangers: notably the danger of forgetting that the facts thus pigeon-holed have to be separated from their context by an act of of dissection. This act, become habitual, leads to an obsession . . .[33]

Hartshorne also—with significant reference to sociology, a major victim—points to the tendency of enthusiasts in new and valuable techniques to lose their heads and maintain that

> . . . whatever is not amenable to analysis through such methods is not worth studying [there is usually a conventional disclaimer which deceives nobody]. . . . In a field in which the phenomena run the full range from cabbages to kings, from rainfall to religion, it would seem absurd to assert that all that is worth studying can be fully and correctly described in quantitative terms, or, conversely, that whatever phenomena can be described in quantitative terms are worthy of study in geography.[34]

Of course very few would be brash enough to *assert* these things; but not a few fail to notice that they *imply* them.

Hartshorne's words are unexceptionable as a general statement. But how shall we apply them in this special case?

Here I will once more—it is my last extended extract—fall back on Preston James:

> What can professional geographers and regional scientists do for each other? Geographers can perform their usual function of bringing people down to earth, by insisting that regions are real places where real people live and work in a particular kind of land and where transportation runs along real roads, not straight lines on a diagram, or arrows in an algebraic formula. Do not misunderstand me. The application of the statistical method to this aspect of economic geography has tremendous possibilities and might well rescue economic geography itself from the frustration of empirical description [and, conversely, rescue theoretical economics from its tendency to airy-fairiness]. I hope that there will be enough geographers ready, willing, and able enough to join with the regional scientists in cultivating this border field. . . . But geographers have also been ploughing in this field for a long time, perhaps with inadequate implements. The concepts they have formulated regarding regions and the method of regional analysis must not be disregarded or overlooked by the regional scientist. The real strength of this mating may lie in the bringing together of cartographic and statistical methods of analysis.[35]

Amen, so be it!

It remains only to draw some threads together, in the spirit of Hartshorne's 'reminder of the fact [so obvious; so often forgotten] that all sciences are but parts of a single body of knowledge'; all fields of study but parts of Cosmos. This paper is a plea for catholicity. So often we see dichotomies where there are really but groupings, perhaps not without overlap, along a continuum. And even where the dichotomies are real, they are so often—thinking of the earlier discussion of dualisms and triads, I would almost hazard 'always'—*dialectically and not statically* antithetic.

Humanist, quantifier, what you will—it is never wrong to plug your own line; it is almost always wrong to write off others. That horrible little word 'mere' and its analogues ('Oh, it's only on that level' and so on)—we should sit back and suspect ourselves whenever we use them. Whenever

N

we are tempted to use them about an approach, a concept, a technique, which has behind it *either* tradition and achievement *or* the vitality of a new thing, we should stop and think and think again. *Mere* description, *mere* quantifying, *mere* abstraction—each of these in a certain context may be valid; but the habitual and indiscriminate use of them writes one off as a *mere* obscurantist.

Referring respectively to Toynbee and Huntington, I once spoke of Myth and Statistic as being 'themselves but parts of Poetry and Science, which together make our vision of reality'.[36] I am glad to find that, in much the same way of thinking, Julian Huxley, who ranks on the scientific rather than the humanistic side (if we must refer things to this dichotomy), has said:

> One of the great needs of our time is to discover means for coping with the problems of quantity and value: after all, our most important experiences are qualitative, and when everything has been reduced to mathematics, something essential has evaporated from reality.[37]

For this task of developing a balance, geography holds a position of the highest strategic value, linked as it is (and no other discipline has quite so wide a spectrum) with the arts, the humanities, and the sciences, whether physical, biological, social, or 'in the field'. We have still new worlds to conquer, new allies to enlist; or, to be more modest and more realist, new contributions to make to the Grand Alliance of learning.

Toynbeeana

Toynbee and Huntington

A Study in Determinism

AT first sight it may appear strange to link the names of
Toynbee, who has been praised for 'putting Man back into
history', and of Huntington, usually and on the whole
rightly regarded as a thorough-going environmentalist. Yet
Huntington makes larger allowances to human initiative
than is often conceded, while the exalted idealist tone of
much of Toynbee's book tends to mask its large elements
of determinism. Both *A Study of History* and *Mainsprings
of Civilization* have as their central concern the tracing of
pattern in history; and that in itself implies a measure of
determinism. Naturally the spatial bulks larger in Huntington, the temporal in Toynbee; but as both take the world
for their parish and recorded history (and even more) for
their period, this distinction is rather formal.

Admittedly their differences are not slight. First, perhaps,
is the simple fact that Toynbee is a great writer and Huntington is not. At times indeed the writer in Toynbee runs
away with the thinker; a great part of his appeal lies in
beauty of style and, beyond that, in the immense and
ordered architecture of his work. Beside Toynbee, Huntington looks narrowly 'scientific', in the pejorative sense in
which the word is still used by some old-style humanists;
even, perhaps, a little parochial.

The strong and weak points of the two authors are complementary. Toynbee's special failing from a geographical
point of view is a looseness of touch, amounting at times
to positive misunderstanding; when dealing with the concrete facts of environment, which of necessity play a large

Reprinted from *The Geographical Journal*, Vol. 118 No. 4, 1952.

part in his work; but we can hardly imagine the author of *The Pulse of Asia* carrying the Eurasian steppe up to the Arctic Circle, as Toynbee does (I, 254), though it is true that he somewhere has the delightful slip of 'the Sikhs of mountainous Sikkim'.* Conversely, when Huntington treats of such immense movements of the human spirit as the great religions, his approach is far too external, lacking the sympathetic insight so often displayed by Toynbee. However this detachment really means less rather than more objectivity, since Huntington is so thoroughly inside his own movement, so emphatically a man of his own American Century. Toynbee also is a man of his time and place —Western Europe beginning to doubt its liberal humanism. But these very doubts mean that he is the more easily able to transcend his own outlook when occasion demands —or at least some occasions, for his lack of sympathy with some of his scapegoats (rationalists and revolutionaries, for instance) goes far to prevent him understanding some important makers of history. But, while Huntington pays sincere tribute to things of the mind and spirit, it is yet not altogether caricature to suggest that to him civilization is too much a matter to be measured by the number of cars and radio sets and public libraries. This vitiates much of his observation, despite its acuteness, of those numerous times, peoples, and places that do not readily fit into this scheme. Typical is the unquestioning acceptance of activity as in itself a good, with very little regard to what it is good for (299, 303, 328-9), culminating in the extraordinary tissue of good sense, half-truths, and plain fatuity with which he writes off Hinduism and Buddhism (288-91, 297-9).

Huntington's determinism is avowed, and clearly based too much upon a part only of the immense complex of

* References in the text are normally to the pages of Somervell's admirable abridgement of Toynbee, followed by the volume and pages of the original (where only volume and page are given, the passage does not appear in the abridgement); or to *Mainsprings of Civilization* taken as the culmination and summing-up of the forty years' work since *The Pulse of Asia*. Unless otherwise stated, environment means physical environment.

factors which have gone to the making of history; though
it should be added that he is aware of this, and it is his
disciples rather than himself who threw discretion to the
winds, particularly of course the winds of the cyclonic westerlies. By and large Huntington's mainsprings are biological and physical-environmental, Toynbee's psychical and
social-environmental. Essentially Toynbee hardly takes a
wider sweep through space and time than Huntington, and
his determinism is less explicit, in fact disavowed; yet it
none the less exists. His stated aim is 'the application of
the scientific technique, the elucidation and formulation
of laws' (47/I, 455-8), and I cannot see how one can altogether avoid determinism here. Laws imply at the least
chains of causation which may perhaps be short-term *sub
specie aeternitatis* but very long indeed in relation to the
life of human societies.* There is in fact implicit in
Toynbee's whole system (because it is a system) a sort of
determinism of stage, situation, or formula: Challenge-and-
Response, Rout-and-Rally, Withdrawal-and-Return, and
the whole apparatus of universal states and churches, internal and external proletariats, times of troubles and the rest.
It is true that the method is by no means so rigidly scientific as this rather esoteric terminology would suggest:
there is too much speculation on the inner meaning of
myths, and far too much argument from analogy.

Above all, at what may be called the major crises of his
work, Toynbee seems deliberately to turn his back on his
own logic. It is God, not Man, that he here puts back into
history. This is in a sense perfectly valid, since any view
which implies progress—or even pattern—presumably implies purpose also. But it certainly sorts ill with the general
logic of Toynbee's system (not to mention such asides as
the denunciation of 'theistic determinism' (448/V, 429-31)).
On the background of the generally naturalistic procedure,
too, such apocalyptic passages as the discussion of 'Transfiguration' (526-30/VI, 149 sqq.) appear to some readers at

* The well-known ambiguity of the phrase 'laws of science' is irrelevant here. The life of a 'law' may be short indeed; it is the idea of the
existence of real tendencies and pattern which is in question.

least as entirely unconvincing anomalies. Thus there seems to be a gigantic contradiction pervading the whole work, and the dialectic necessary to resolve it is over-strained.

The general impression is of a pattern in each author too rigid and, in Huntington at least, too much based on a part only of the relevant factors. This impression is of course subject to large qualifications for both writers, but on the whole I think it valid, and for Toynbee not necessarily disposed of by his own disclaimers. It is long since Hume pointed out, in a parallel case, that Bishop Berkeley proved so much too much that he produced a sceptical reaction precisely opposite to his own intent.

Many good judges, reading our authors, have felt that it is all a little too perfect, and that the sequences fall into place with a precision not quite warranted by the facts adduced. Then there are the facts which, in the nature of things, are not adduced: in Huntington especially there is no autonomy in the great movements of history, which are reduced to impersonal and even non-human forces and trends. But this assumes an inevitability for which we have no real warrant, however little we incline to see history as all made by the more or less irresponsible actions of great men, or however confident we may feel that, given certain relations of world-setting and of human material, the broad outlines of man's story would have worked out much the same despite local mutations.

Here we tread dangerously upon the verge of profound issues. Yet the problems of chance or free will or necessity must be faced in some fashion, though it would be folly on my part to proceed into them very far. Huntington seems to sum the position up when he states (292) that in our daily practice we all follow an intermediate position between absolute freedom and absolute necessity; a compromise perhaps untenable logically but pragmatically workable. These matters are not so irrelevant as may seem. It is not the function of the geographer to write philosophy; but, if he aspires to be more than a competent routine technician, it is certainly one of his responsibilities at least to be aware of philosophical problems which may bear upon his work. His attitude to this most fundamental general problem can hardly fail to have its effect upon his thinking on the more restricted question of geographical determinism versus possibilism.

Toynbee and geography

Some of the general doubts which a study of Toynbee raises have been indicated. They are largely inherent in his approach, in the attempt to ascertain a general scientific law, or laws, of civilizations. But the establishment of such a law raises a dilemma, since it clearly has a necessitarian cast which as clearly conflicts with an ideological preoccupation not always explicitly stated, but very definitely present. This is the altogether natural desire to find a way out for the Western world from the impasse into which it seems to have got on Toynbee's, or indeed on anybody's, principles; an impasse into which, if my reading of *A Study* is correct, it has not simply wandered, but to which it has come by the regular progression which he has traced through the other civilizations.

Yet here lies the deepest and most abiding interest in Toynbee's work; the actual pattern-making, brilliant as it often is, does not differ in kind from that of half a dozen thinkers before him. 'If the task of history is supposed to consist in ascertaining general laws governing the course of historical events, it is expurgated of three factors which are in reality of high importance: chance or accident, free will, ideas or the demands and conceptions of men.'[1] The real crux in Toynbee is his attempt to reassert at least the last two within the framework of his laws. That the attempt, despite the dazzling skill with which it is conducted, appears on the whole a failure cannot detract from its surpassing interest. It is only when we judge not by our own usual standard but by the highest—of which *A Study* is itself a touchstone—that we are entitled to pronounce the adverse verdict which I think must be pronounced.

But Toynbee is open to decided criticism on a different plane, that of empiric fact. Although Collingwood remarks, rather oddly, that what he takes to be Toynbee's fallacies

189

'only' affect fundamental principles and rarely distort his judgement in detail, from the standpoint of the working historian Geyl has made out a strong case not only against Toynbee's schematism, but also against the selection of facts on which such a system must inevitably be based, unless it is so surrounded by qualifications as to lose shape and identity.[2] Toynbee is not without defences on this score, but still it can scarcely be denied that in some contexts his selectivity goes much too far. Here we can refer only to the extraordinarily one-sided view of modern English history which is essential if his application to it of the formula of Withdrawal-and-Return is to make sense (235-9/III, 350-63 and 366-8). A footnote suggests that Toynbee himself had qualms here, and certainly to claim the Revolution of 1688 as a creative act rendered possible by isolation from continental entanglements reaches an extreme height of dialectic. It was perhaps tactful of Somervell to omit this instance from the abridgement.

Of more significance to our present purpose is Toynbee's handling of environmental concepts, which underlies his discussion of the origins of the earlier civilizations, and especially of the formula of Challenge-and-Response—a stimulating concept, but perhaps neither altogether novel nor paradoxical, except when so paradoxically applied as to be positively unsound. Toynbee here treads too confidently over ground which he has perhaps reconnoitred rather than surveyed. It is not a matter of passing reference, where slips might be condoned; scores of pages in the first two volumes (or about 13 per cent of the whole abridgement) deal with matters which are geographical or nothing. A preliminary caveat may be entered against the choice of sources. The general discussion of environmentalism is based almost solely upon Hippocrates, who after all wrote some little time ago, and on Demolins, who is set up in order to be knocked down again without a hint that Demolins is hardly an accredited representative of modern geography. On special topics Lattimore and Huntington are cited, the latter extensively, while writers such as Myres and Childe, from the marchlands of our subject, are also drawn upon. But apart from two references to Griffith Taylor and one to Bowman, I can trace no citations from any other geographers; the French school might never have been, though Vallaux and Febvre at least have surely some things pertinent to Toynbee's scheme.

These geographical pages include such views as that the Jordan is simply a smaller Nile; that the Nilotic environment is reproduced in the valleys of the Rio Grande and the Colorado; that the seventeenth century environment of New England was the hardest along the Atlantic seaboard of North America; that the aspect of the Roman Campagna after the decline of its agriculture shows us what the original 'dour' environment was like, and that the Danube basin has 'much the same distribution of climate and soil and plain and mountain' as that of the Hwang-ho.

I do not propose to traverse all these assertions in detail.*

This argument is in essence a back-handed attempt to dispose of environmentalism by attributing to it an automatic functioning that few, if any, geographers would admit. If the Nilotic environment is 'the positive factor to which the genesis of the Egyptiac civilization is due', then, says Toynbee, every other area with a similar environment should independently produce a similar civilization (58/I, 256). But this overlooks the fact that it is not possible to consider environment except in relation to that which it environs: always 'the environment of people (or species) X' is implied, and X is a variable even if the environment is not, which in fact it is. For Toynbee's dictum to work it would be essential to construct a 'model' (in the economists' sense) in which all variables except physical setting are reduced to uniformities, and moreover the variations in the physical setting are themselves merely and strictly repetitive. Toynbee rarely gives much weight to location, which in itself of course rules out the identities he postulates. But even granting this impossible identity of terrain and climate, there are still the vitally important differences of location in relation to the movements of peoples at stages

---

* [Two paragraphs are omitted here; their essential argument will be found on pp. 226-30 below.]

of culture capable of developing into civilizations, or in relation to the habitat of cultivable plants. These depend not only on current terrain and climate, but also on palaeogeographical changes.

It seems evident, also, that whatever the origins of the primary civilizations may have been, at a very early stage external contacts assumed an importance not sufficiently regarded in Toynbee's scheme of things. But waiving this, and again granting that the various great rivers of Africa, Asia and North America provided virtually identical environments (which is not true), for each to develop independently its own civilization would seem to demand that all would have to start with peoples at the same stage of culture at the same time. Otherwise we must assume a degree of isolation for which archaeology offers no warrant, but rather the reverse. This simultaneity is obviously ridiculous, so that even were Toynbee's assertion that the Nilotic environment reappears in the Colorado true, the fact that no civilization appeared in the latter proves nothing: it might be merely a time-lag.*

There are several strands in this misunderstanding of the physical environment. Probably most important is an almost complete lack of the sense of scale, surely a prime requisite of geographical thought, and it must be repeated that in these contexts Toynbee is writing geography and nothing else. The equation of Nile and Jordan is a glaring example.†

Toynbee regards the physical setting in a very limited way: he looks upon it as consisting of terrain, of climate, of vegetation, of soil, of a shape on the map. But in any given case only one or two of these factors is considered. The idea of the environment as an indivisible complex of all these factors, and more, hardly ever appears.

* This equation is so surprising that I quote the words of the abridgement (p. 58), which are practically the same as those of the original (I, 258): 'the most captious critic cannot deny that the environmental conditions offered by Egypt and Mesopotamia are also offered by the valleys of the Rio Grande and the Colorado.'

† [Some detail omitted here will be found on pp. 226-7 below.]

In general, Toynbee's attitude to environment seems two-faced. On the one hand it plays a considerable part in Challenge-and-Response, where the handling is at times brilliant and stimulating, for instance in the discussions of new ground and of overseas migrations. In this last context Toynbee goes so far in the direction of determinism as to approve the formula 'Drama . . . develops in the home country, Epic among migrating peoples' (106-7/II, 96). But on the other hand he seeks to minimize its role or to stand it on its head. 'We have been led to reject the popular assumption that civilizations emerge where environments offer unusually easy conditions of life, and to advance an argument in favour of exactly the opposite view' (80/II, 1-3). Not quite exactly; for taken literally this argument holds the startling implication that ice-caps and sand-deserts should be the seats of civilizations. Toynbee therefore retreats, as well he might. After many pages we arrive at the hazardous conclusion that there can be too much of anything, and that the maximum of hardness is not the optimum. Does it really need all this analysis to reach this unimpressive truism?

Two or three further comments may be offered. No serious student of environment would accept the view that Toynbee tilts at: for once we may follow him in accepting an illustration from myth, and assert that no one thinks civilization likely to arise in a Garden of Eden. In any case the words 'easy' and 'favourable' are not necessarily synonyms. Secondly, as Gourou points out, Toynbee's determinism is no less determinist for being a transposition of the 'popular view': 'Le déterminisme des conditions défavorables au lieu du déterminisme des conditions favorables, est-ce là un progrès?'[3] Much of the misunderstanding seems to spring from the statement that the physical environment 'taken by itself' cannot be 'the positive factor which . . . started humanity on the hazardous quest of civilization' (59/I, 270-1). But then in the very nature of things environment cannot be 'taken by itself' but only in relation to what it environs, in this case Man; a point to which we shall return. Further, why 'the' positive factor?

Does this not beg the question? For Toynbee the decisive thing is apparently the unpredictable reaction of man to an ordeal; and this ordeal, in the crucial initial cases, is provided by a change in the environment. This unpredictable reaction we may grant; but then this unknowable human positive is not positive, but only potentially so, until it is matched with the environmental change, and we are back where we started. No ordeal, no reaction, and the problem resolves itself into the ancient one of the precedence of chickens and eggs.

The flaws evident in Toynbee's treatment of environment do not of course invalidate his entire argument, though they are somewhat disconcerting at this early stage of the book. *A Study of History*, like most great systematizations, is not so monolithic as its author would like it to be. Most of the development of Toynbee's theme springs from different, largely psychological, bases; many of these may indeed be questioned, but they are not germane to this discussion. It is enough to suggest that on this important topic of environmentalism Toynbee's words are very far from being the last words; and in so far as his foundations are geographical, which is far indeed, they are undeniably shaky.

Huntington and history

Huntington's failings are numerous enough, and generally all too obvious. Science for him is emphatically quantitative knowledge, and almost anything can be measured if the right units can be found. So 'intermediate peoples, such as the Chinese, occupy intermediate places, with more cars than the pygmies, less than the Bulgarians'; and the context makes it quite clear that this is a scale of advanced or retarded civilization (6-7). Sheldon's psycho-physiological theory is taken over and applied to the analysis of religions, with results which Huntington admits to be speculative; spectacular might be a better word. Post-mortems on 'three groups of ten or more elderly Americans' provide the ratios of height, weight and length of bowel from which we may proceed to the view that the Buddhist ideal of contemplation 'might almost be called a glorified version of the visceratonic propensity to sit still and enjoy a good smoke after dinner'; whereas in Christianity cerebrotonic self-restraint keeps the mild virtues of visceratonicity from going to seed, at the same time avoiding the aggressive and domineering qualities 'which go with the mesomorphic body and the somatonic temperament' (46-51). Huntington has unfortunately to add that later Western Christianity has been more militantly somatonic; the implied compliment to earlier Eastern Christianity suggests that Huntington has not read his Gibbon: Conciliar history tells a different tale.

These, it must be admitted, are startling value-judgements, and it would be easy to compile an anthology of such excrescences. But the point is that they are excrescences, and can be excised without affecting the main arguments significantly. These arguments are indeed open to serious criticism, but on an altogether higher level. It is unfortunate that such excesses tend to obscure the very considerable amounts of solid observation and reasoning which underlie Huntington's major thesis, whether it is in the upshot tenable or not. Thus it is easy to point to the anomalies in the famous civilization-and-climate maps, though in our hearts most of us Westerners probably believe that the facts are as stated. The basis of their construction is subjective enough, and the way in which the statistical aggregates are used gives a picture sometimes at variance with direct impression in the field, as, for example, in India. Again, if the maps are taken too literally, it is facile to assume that much is liable to be non-suited by technological change; the high ranking of Norway, for instance, would have been impossible a century ago, before Ibsen and hydro-electricity. Such objections are true enough, and it must be admitted that at times, as in *The Human Habitat*, Huntington himself has given colour to them. Nevertheless they lose much of their point when we remember—what is too often forgotten—just how much Huntington claims. It is only fair to quote the limitations he himself lays down: 'The map of climatic efficiency has sometimes been misinterpreted as the basis for a theory that climate is the "cause" of civilization. This is a curious mistake. The map does not even indicate the existing efficiency in different parts of the world, for that is influenced also by heredity, stage of culture, diet, and other factors' (247). And in general Huntington insists on proper scientific caution, and on the rôle of cultural factors, to a greater extent than is often recognized.

Nevertheless, all allowances made, it remains true that his pattern is too much determined by physical factors, and gives too little play to the autonomous development of societies; development is indeed allowed for, but usually referred back to the environment. One reason at least for this lop-sidedness in Huntington is that he lacks what is at least as essential to the historian as is the sense of scale to the geographer, and that is sympathetic insight or empathy.

Before dealing with this major issue it should be noted that Huntington writes history at least as often as Toynbee writes geography, and here too a looseness of treatment is often noticeable. A good example, parallel to Toynbee's Withdrawal-and-Return of England, is the treatment of the Renaissance in *Mainsprings* (599-607). Here it is an uncritical acceptance of secondary authority which does the damage; but this itself seems to arise from a desire to make the historical sequence match the sequence of weather. So we find Cheyney cited to the effect that the 'dam' holding back social evolution burst in all Western Europe at 'practically the same time'; that cultural imitation is not a satisfactory explanation, and that in any case 'no testimony to such imitation exists'. It certainly does, for example, in architecture, town-planning or the displacement of traditional verse-forms—alliterative metres, *redondilhas*, and so on—by the *dolce stile nuove* and the formal stanzas and sonnets, spreading from Italy to Portugal and Scotland, and later even to Sweden. In England we need only think of Chaucer's debt to Dante and Boccaccio or Torrigiano's sculptures on Henry vii's tomb. However true (and it is abundantly true) Huntington's own dictum that 'a rational understanding of history requires a good knowledge of the changing physical background', one cannot but agree with Hartshorne's rider: 'and a sound knowledge of the historical events'.

But the fundamental historical weakness in Huntington is not looseness of detail but lack of sympathy. This is linked with the insistence on a 'scientific detachment' in which the observer himself is unwittingly taken as the norm, though this affects all the conditions of the observation and so vitiates it. There are hints that Huntington himself felt the inadequacy of his spiritual arithmetic: 'Unfortunately no widespread statistics are available for such qualities as idealism, altruism, honesty, self-reliance, originality, and artistic appreciation.' But this difficulty cannot be allowed to stand in the way: 'In general, however, these seem to be best developed among people who excel in more readily measured qualities, such as literacy, education, the use of libraries, and gifts for philanthropic purposes' (233). People like ourselves, in fact; flattering, but doubtfully true, and fatal to real objectivity. To understand any movement of minds and wills one must so far as possible get inside it and feel it, though this process must be checked by a return to a more general external standpoint. In retrospective thinking, failure to achieve this results in a thin empiric view of the contacts of great cultures, textbook stuff in which all that matters is who won, and in which the positive values which weave the rich texture of the past are at best resolved into clichés.

This essential quality of insight Toynbee often displays and Huntington signally lacks. The results are strikingly apparent in his discussion of geography and religion (281-306). Here we find a table ranking eight religions by latitude and by ethical content; the two orders are very similar. Christianity comes out on top, and one feels that only some lingering prudence inhibits a further latitudinal subdivision between Mediterranean Popery and Baltic Protestantism. We may sincerely believe in the primacy of Christian values; that said, how can we make a table of precedence for such complex and multiform faiths as Islam, Buddhism, and Hinduism?

o

Huntington goes on to suggest correlations between various ideologies and their environments, including the old question of the relation between monotheism and the Afrasian arid lands (292-3). This, especially as regards Islam, is something of a test case, and may be examined in some detail. It must be said that Huntington shows more awareness of fundamental difficulties than Semple before him or Whittlesey after, and he faces not unreasonably the problem of free will. We must agree with him that 'there is absolute determinism in one respect; the experiences of a walk through the jungle cannot be identical with those of a similar walk in the desert'. But this is the merest truism, and the argument which follows is not much better than Buckle's appeal to the immensity and malignity of the Indian environment to explain the grotesque imagery of terror in Hindu mythology—forgetting its lavish imagery of grace and beauty. The argument presented is merely the converse of Buckle's: 'out in the desert the things that man chiefly fears are big—winds, sun, cold, heat, drought'; * and while 'the desert man is as free as the jungle man to believe in spirits that inhabit stones, bushes, lizards, and beasts of prey, there is less incentive to do so.' Why? One might think that an isolated rock or bush, vital as a landmark, is much more likely to be the dwelling of some *genius loci* than a rock or bush lost amidst thousands of its fellows; and the rarer the lizard, surely the more potently significant. To return to Huntington's argument, because of this bigness of things it is 'natural for the primitive desert man to pin his faith to a few powerful gods who rule large areas. This does not compel him to believe in a single god, but it makes the transition to that belief easy and natural.' But look at the facts, and especially the question-begging word 'primitive'. So far as is known the first approach to monotheism took place in the far from primitive society of Ikhnaton's Egypt. The Mosaic dispensation may have evolved in the desert, after contact with Egypt, but Jehovah

* We are at least spared the clear skies and the glittering firmament on high which, in the cruder determinists, amply account for monotheism by reminding man of his own insignificance.

triumphed over a plethora of local godlings in Palestine, a country small, articulated and not 'big' in the sense implied by Huntington's description of the desert. How primitive was Hebraic society, in contact with Phoenicia and involved in the struggles of the great Empires of Egypt and Mesopotamia? Unfortunately it must also be admitted that there was plenty of animism in Arabia before Muhammad's time; and are we sure that there is none now?

One may perhaps agree with Huntington's summing up that 'it would be false to say that belief in one universal God necessarily evolved in a desert, but it is true that the evolution of such a belief is more probable there than in the jungle'; but the questions just asked suggest that many vital considerations are omitted by this mechanistic psychology. The fact that the three great monotheisms all issued from southwest Asia certainly challenges explanation—explanation at least of the 'secondary causes', not to prejudge the question of revelation. But, besides the fact that other religions contain monotheistic elements, it must be noted that the three are in a sense not three but one: Christ is the Judaic Messiah, Muhammad fulfils Moses and Jesus, Jews and Christians are also Peoples of the Book, and to the Christians Islam was initially just another heresy. This of course still leaves the question: why the one? On this all that can be said with much assurance is that such environmental influence as there may be is not so likely to be a direct matter of psychology as an indirect one of societies with a strong emphasis on discipline and experience, rendering appropriate a conception of Deity as a greater patriarch. On the general question one may ask how, on environmental principles, one can possibly explain the co-existence of essentially atheistic philosophies, such as early Buddhism and some Hindu schools, with polytheism and pantheism under the same skies and within the bosom of the same social system? The patterns are far too involved for any simple key to be of much value.

Huntington, it is true, knew Asia at first hand, and avoids the simple correlation of Islam and nomadism exemplified by Whittlesey, who speaks of Islamic law as integrating tribal government 'throughout the whole broad and uniform zone' of the Afrasian arid lands:

> Evolved in the desert, Moslem law eminently suits the conditions found there. It provides for whatever degree of political unity strong chieftains may from time to time assume over the scattered tribes. . . . The Koran is both the Holy Book and a guiding star for Moslem society. As a political instrument it is a standing and familiar negation of the concept of government held by sedentary populations the world over.[4]

Aside from the assumption, perhaps more bold than wise, that sedentary populations the world over have one concept of government, the sentence about strong chieftains hardly covers the Caliphate, a Universal State founded in the seventh century which could still be a subject of agitation in India in 1921. Above all, from about A.D. 700 at latest the great majority of Muslims have been either sedentary agriculturalists or urban traders as, indeed, was Muhammad himself.

Even in Huntington, the over-emphasis on the Afrasian arid environment, important as that is, ignores the fact that great faiths have their own life and growth. It would be strange indeed if a great movement of thought and feeling showed no powers of adaptation in a life of over a thousand years and in environments ranging from the Pyrenees to Yunnan, to Java, to Nigeria and to Mozambique. The great-uncle of Babur, the Mogul conqueror of India, 'evangelized' the Uzbeks, and tells us that he did not feel his task was complete until he had introduced cities and settled life; I think his authority equal to that of Semple, Huntington or Whittlesey. Then there are the rather difficult anomalies, on this narrow Islam-Nomad correlation, that the greatest Islamic states by population, Pakistan and Indonesia, are predominantly societies of settled cultivators. Probably the largest single blocks of Muslims in the world occupy environments as far removed from those of southwest Asia as could be imagined: the 40 to 50 million in Bengal, the 90 to 100 million in Indonesia. These anomalies, in Bengal at least, can be resolved without undue difficulty, by reference to the history; but this is what the sterner environmentalists rarely do, except in the loosest manner. There are without doubt links between environment and Islamic ideology; but they cannot be discovered simply by looking at Islam from outside, deciding (largely *a priori*, in accordance with a more general theory) what its principles should be on the basis of its assumed desert environment, and then regarding them as fixed for all time. This is a rigid materialism which far outgoes that of Marx, who allowed for at least some reflex action of the ideological superstructures on the economic driving-forces of history.

Here we are not dealing with mere excrescences, which could be amputated without much effect on the healthy functioning of the rest of the organism; these matters lie too central to the theme. If there were not more to be said, determinism would stand condemned. But there are reservations. It can hardly be denied that there are many sections of *Mainsprings* and Huntington's other books where he makes out a strong case. The analyses of short-term weather cycles and their effects on human activity contain trivialities, misconceptions, injudicious use of statistics, and dubious assumptions. Yet there is much in them which cannot be lightly discounted, and they form important contributions to the direct psycho-physiological influence of climate; it may be too early to make valid generalizations, but not to examine data and to suggest hypotheses. Elsewhere the argument may not be logically flawless, and yet it may be difficult to refute the findings as a whole, as in the discussions of the Puritan element in American society (98-126), of Icelandic culture (127-48) and of the effects of migration (68-97). I would stress again that he is not so one-sided as is often assumed. It is true that the weight he attaches to heredity can be discounted since he here evolves a theory of group qualities and aptitudes originally largely moulded by physical, especially climatic, influences, and so refers back to environment at a remove. Nevertheless the reader who puts prejudice aside will find not only much acute observation but also much good judgement, giving due weight to ethnic mixture, cultural contact and acculturation.

One could cite many supporting passages, in particular perhaps the closing pages of *Civilization and Climate* itself:

> Even if our hypothesis be fully accepted, no less importance will thereby attach to the other great factors which condition the events of history. Because a man dies for lack of air, we do not think that air is more essential than food, drink, warmth, the circulation of the blood, the reproduction of the species. . . . So it is with history. Even if our climatic ideas are correct, it will still be true that the ordinary events of the historic record are due to the differing traits of races, the force of economic pressure, the ambition of kings, the intrigues of statesmen, the zeal of religion, the rise of men of genius, the evolution of new political and social institutions. . . . Yet a comprehension of the part played by the climatic factor will enable us to explain some of the events which have hitherto puzzled us. Not all will be thus explained. . . .

And how pointless are Hanson's gibes, in *New Worlds Emerging*, in the face of Huntington's explicit assertion that his climatic hypothesis holds out most hope for the tropics themselves. 'If we can conquer climate, the whole world will become stronger and nobler'; these are the last words of *Civilization and Climate*, naïvely put perhaps, but far indeed from the crude necessitarian label given to Huntington by critics some of whom do not even bother to spell his name correctly.

In the last resort he comes very close to Toynbee: 'Means puts his finger on the crux of the problem when he says that in order to attain civilization people need not only a stimulating climate and raw materials well fitted to their work, but also "an indefinable factor" which is "apparently psychological" ' (398). Precisely the same passage is quoted by Toynbee (I, 273); to me at least Huntington's use of it seems more modest, more valid and more constructive. At his best Huntington gives us a large and noble vision of our earth as the link between Cosmos and the microcosmos, Man.

Towards a synthesis?

So far I have examined, in what may seem an unduly critical spirit, two antithetic philosophies of history which have yet a common significant character in that they both seek to establish a pattern and so are broadly determinist. Toynbee, on the whole at least, may seek to minimize, Huntington to stress, physical factors; yet even here they are but two sides of the same coin. The link between them I think is this: that however much they differ as to the role of environment, they both fall into the fallacy that there is or can be such a thing as environment 'taken by itself'. Nor are they alone in this; Mackinder says that 'human society is still related to the facts of geography, not as they are, but in no small measure as they are approached in the course of history'.[5] But the facts of geography are the facts as they are approached; there is no other geographical way of looking at them. This does not for one moment deny the objective existence of the world altogether apart from man. Before man was,

> the hills in order stood
> And earth received her frame,

and his exit from the stage may not be a very important incident in the cosmic drama. But this world without man is not environment, is not our world. The earth abstracted from man is a proper object of study—of the studies geology, geodesy, seismology, geomorphology and so on. These have the most intimate relations with geography; there should be no question of 'taking the ge out of geography'. But at least since Humboldt, if not Strabo, geographers have looked on earth not simply as a physical body but also as the home of man.

The frame of earth, then, is not in itself environment. It was there before man was, but then it was not human environment, because there was nothing human to environ. 'Environment taken by itself' is a meaningless phrase; without man environment does not exist. But we are fully entitled to make abstracts or isolates of the physical factors for study; it is obviously essential to do so. The danger is in setting up a false duality and so involving ourselves in insoluble or unnecessary questions of the chicken-and-egg order. There is also the danger, shared by possibilist and determinist alike, of anthropomorphizing Nature; those who talk glibly of 'co-operation with Nature's plan' do not often face up to the teleological implications of this phrase.

Insistence that there is no human environment without man is not in itself incompatible with the strictest determinism of physical controls. It is not necessary to demonstrate formally the error of that view; it is patent in our examination so far, and indeed the tide of geographical opinion is still running strongly against it. Perhaps too strongly, since it does not seem certain that 'possibilism' as often understood (or misunderstood) is the automatic alternative to a rigorous environmentalism. There may be a middle term, which one might call 'probabilism'; nor do I think that more than this is really implied by the original French masters, Vidal de la Blache and the rest. It must be remembered that they worked in an atmosphere steeped in precise methodological thought; English empiricism and American pragmatism may sometimes miss its undertones.

Let us take Febvre's famous assertion 'there are no necessities but everywhere possibilities'. I agree with what I take to be the meaning of this sentence; yet there are times when I feel that no single dictum has had a more disastrous influence on modern geographical thought and work. There could be no confusion if Febvre had added 'of which some are more possible than others'; probabilities, that is, rather than a vague assortment of free choices. Febvre himself mentions the negative necessity of not trying to grow pineapples in Greenland, and the much more important matter of commitment by one's choice: 'all possibilities are not compossibilities'. Clearly he did not mean to say that any possibility is present anywhere at any time, and Tatham is right in pointing out that sniping at possibilism on the pineapples-in-Greenland line is futile. Put so bluntly this is a truism; but in practice the emphasis on human initiative, correct in itself, has sometimes been given its head and has landed in thinking which is as intolerably woolly and vague as rigorous environmentalism is intolerably narrow and crude.

The repudiation of 'influence' in favour of 'relation' also carries with it the risk of a tendency to merely empirical description; this is perhaps a special risk attaching to the view of historical geography as simply 'the reconstruction of past human geographies'. This conception was a justifiable reaction against the view of historical geography as simply 'The Map of Europe by Treaty', past geostrategics, and perhaps a glance at trade-routes added. It has meant a great deepening and enriching of the actual content of the geography of the past. But at times also it has meant no more than economic history plus maps; by no means a valueless thing, but often overlooking political sequences and distributions which are themselves an integral part of the past geography, at once affecting and affected by the physical and economic geography of the times. A case in point is J. N. L. Baker's scholarly essay on the seventeenth century in *An Historical Geography of England to 1800*, an essay containing much admirable reconstruction. But nobody reading it would suspect that the century saw a civil war whose issue vitally affected our way of life, our very being as citizens of a constitutional monarchy. Nor can it well be maintained that this is 'not geography'; the distribution of allegiance is a geographical matter if ever there was one. Apart from the obvious significance of the Parliamentarian leanings of the ports and clothing towns, is there not a challenge to geographical enquiry in the fact that the very areas which supported the Crown (the North, the West, and Wales) were those which had most opposed the Crown of a century before—the century of the centralizing Tudor monarchy? To write anything on the English seventeenth century with the word 'historical' in the title and to say nothing of the Civil War* is simply to write Hamlet without the Prince. I do not think that Hartshorne has

---

* In fact these words occur twice—in the diagram, Fig. 65 where they are left in the air, entirely unexplained, and in a casual reference to the destruction of timber.

said the last word on this topic, though he himself seems to think so, when he claims that the question of the nature of historical geography is closed in favour of 'simply the geography of past periods';[6] unless indeed this phrase includes such political matters as those just mentioned, which seems far from Hartshorne's intent.

At bottom the extreme trend away from environmentalism seems to have an odd psychological motivation, a feeling that determinism means philosophical materialism, which is not necessarily so, and that it is thus disreputable or even immoral, which is even less so. To speak of 'controls' is doubtless nearly always illegitimate, but not, I think, quite always. This fear of controls seems to lead to a horror of admitting quite reasonable 'influences'. One almost suspects a kind of terrorism of what the French might say; but what if French possibilism were itself geographically determined? It would not be difficult to work out a plausible case, beginning with the Franco-German antagonism after 1870 and the obvious element of reaction against the suspected ulterior motives of Ratzelian political geography; and for that too there are excellent reasons along the lines of old-style historical geography.

This 'flight from controls' and yearning for a geographical free market are excellently illustrated in Gauld's *Man, Nature and Time*, in many ways an admirable book, one of the few which can be recommended to the intelligent student who wants a brief synthetic statement of what modern geography is about. Yet its acute *aperçus* are often left hanging in the air through failure to relate their data to the physical setting from which they cannot really be detached. One or two instances must suffice. Of the Eskimos we read (p. 144): 'What is striking is that so far from the elementary primitive economy which so severe an environment might suggest "they make use of the most elaborate devices known among primitive men, and their implements show amazing resourcefulness and ingenuity".' Apart from the confused identification of the economy, which is primitive and elementary enough, with technique, it is surely precisely because the environment is so severe that the adjustment has to be intricate and ingenious. It would indeed be striking if the Eskimo managed to survive without elaborate skills and devices.

More important, and indeed something of a test-case for possibilism, as Islam is for determinism, is the question raised by Gauld in these terms (p. 26): 'We might argue that a plantation economy based on slavery had much more to do with cotton-growing in the United States than any particular group of physical conditions.' This claim merely shifts the problem one stage backwards; it is justified as a protest against a direct determinism of 200 frost-free days automatically producing cotton-growing—if anyone but examinees ever thought on those lines; but as an explanation of the distributions it raises or begs more questions than it solves. Why did this plantation economy fix where it did, and not in New England or New York; or even near at hand in the Appalachians? Factors of social tradition— the aristocratic origins of the great grantees as against the yeoman, trading or artisan stocks of New England—play their part, and an important one; but no less important, surely, is the actual physical differentiation. On the one hand, in the Appalachians small-scale subsistence farming was at least favoured by the dissection and general isolation of the country; one might compare it with the dispersed settlement of highland Britain. On the other hand, in the tide-water counties, terrain—and water transport—favoured production of bulk cash crops. To get the best returns from such quasi-monopolies as tobacco and cotton, on rapidly expanding markets, large-scale working was clearly indicated. At this point the social factors enter decisively; given the social climate of the times, plantations and the rest follow. But these social factors after all operate only within given, if sometimes elastic, physical limits. To ascribe the dominant and initiatory role to plantation economy as such, is to mistake contingent effect for cause. There is no merely social answer to the question: why a plantation economy in the tide-water and not the upland?

We may go further by comparing the series of voting maps in the *Atlas of the Historical Geography of the United*

States with a series of physical maps of the South. I think that no reasonably unprejudiced person could deny that the political and physical distributions correlate so closely that it would require an impossibly high-wrought dialectic to escape the admission of a very strong influence one way or the other, by men or by mountains; and men did not make the Appalachians. Look at the great wedge of Republican votes, decade after decade, for President, for Congress, or in House divisions, breaking into the Democratic Solid South, and with very little variation in the marginal counties—just enough indeed to make a frontier zone rather than a boundary. Then think of all that goes with it; First Families of Virginia against poor Scots-Irish or Kentucky hillbillies; tide-water plantations against stony upland farms; slavery producing export staples against almost self-sufficient free labour; a tension of hill against plain culminating in actual secession when West Virginia cut loose from the Old Dominion to stand by the Union in the Civil War. It is of no avail to appeal to social origins as themselves an efficient cause of the distributions, since we then have simply to move backward to explain the distribution of men of various social habits, a distribution too closely correlated with terrain to be mere chance. Admitted that the Scots-Irish had not the Court influence to get great estates nor the capital to work them if they had, we have the converse that the grantees pre-empted the plains counties and, when they did secure title to large upland tracts, had too much sense to work them plantation-wise, but turned themselves into companies for the sale of land to free settlers, as for example did George Washington.

Here possibilism simply will not do; I think even 'control' is not too strong a word, not in the sense that the environment enforces an agrarian economy, but that if for historical reasons an agrarian economy is introduced, then some such differentiation as took place follows. This is one single case and certainly does not prove a general physical causation; but if it is granted, which I think cannot well be refused, then it establishes at least the possibility in other cases. I do not think, therefore, that the question of environmentalism is as yet finally closed, or is ever likely to be, except in the obvious sense that environment is not the answer to everything. This discovery should not blind us to the fact that in some ways and places it may still be a useful guide.

The upshot seems to be that neither environmentalism nor possibilism is adequate without large qualifications. As regards environmentalism, two things must be borne in mind: first, the appeal to geographical influences is safest by way of social structures. The direct psycho-physiological effects of climate on individuals after all work themselves out through social life, and in so far as there is an environmental influence on thinking, it is largely subsumed in antecedent tradition, which is a social matter. It is not only, though largely, because of different material features of the environment that the metaphors of erotic verse are likely to differ between, say, a young left-wing intellectual at Cambridge and a Gond in central India. Neglect of this principle led to many of the rasher and grosser exaggerations of the Semple school, forgetful of the fact that the psychology of the individual is modified when he is part of a group. Secondly, it is, as Febvre says, the idea formed of the environment which matters as much as the brute fact: the facts are as approached. Failure to allow for this leads directly to the major fallacy of projecting backwards present knowledge.

But the approach to the facts can never entirely escape the actual facts; this is the qualification of possibilism, at least as too often presented. The point may be illustrated by a passage from Collingwood. I do not know if he ever read Febvre, but all historical geographers will recall a remarkable parallel in the latter's discussion of this identical theme:

> The fact that certain people live on an island has in itself no effect on their history; what has an effect is how they conceive of their insular position; whether for example they regard the sea as a barrier or as a highway for traffic. Had it been otherwise their insular position, being a constant fact, would have produced a constant effect on their historical life;

whereas it will produce one effect if they have not mastered the art of navigation . . . a fourth if everyone uses aeroplanes. In itself, it is merely raw material for historical activity, and the character or historical life depends upon how it is used.[7]

This I think is overstated. It has its truth: a raw material is only a raw material if it is used, and it may be used in one way or another, or not used at all. Nevertheless, if it is not there, it cannot be used at all; there is a material datum to which the concept refers (it may be erroneously). The people cannot conceive of their insular position in any way unless they live on an island. In any event, whether the sea is barrier or highway it enforces special adjustments. Febvre also proves a little too much: 'England remains an island' not only as a matter of psychology, but also as a matter of logistics—the logistic problem provided by a 21-mile wide anti-tank ditch for which we have had cause to be grateful since Febvre wrote, and unfortunately may again. The use, of course, is largely a matter of social environment; but indirectly through society and technology there is an 'influence', the challenge or stimulus of the object as well as of the subjective concept.

If the arguments here put forward have any validity— admittedly they are very much matters of debate—we may find ourselves left with a considerable residue of determinism. Because Huntington set himself too high an aim it does not follow that all his work is vitiated by his failure to explain all that he wishes to explain. A new statement of determinism, more moderate, more supple, and more subtle than the old, is badly needed, even from the standpoint of the convinced possibilist. Our study in its modern form is still so young, and deals with so wide a range of phenomena, that it seems likely that an empirical approach is still necessary.

This paper has been in some sort a plea for the integration of history and geography, and, essentially, an attempted integration forms a large part of the work of the two authors mainly considered. It is true, as Hartshorne says, that this integration would be the portrait of reality, and that we can never attain it; but this is no more than the inescapable limitation of all human effort to interpret fully the world or any aspect of it; always there remains

> One thought, one grace, one wonder at the least
> Which into words no virtue can digest.

Hence selection, limitation, difference of emphasis, construction of isolates, are all necessary. But it is as well that now and then the effort to transcend particularisms should be made, and this, in their differing ways, Toynbee and Huntington try to do. There can be little doubt that some residuum of their thought will be absorbed into the commonplace of historiography; and, despite Toynbee's greater brilliance of writing and historical insight, it might be that Huntington's influence will be the more lasting, at least the more concrete and definable. This does not depend entirely upon literary quality; probably few geographers now read Humboldt, but fewer doubt his significance in the growth of our study.

The approaches of the two may be loosely, but perhaps not inaccurately, summarized as aesthetic in Toynbee, scientific in Huntington. I think that properly considered these are not mere opposites; like our authors, they interpenetrate. There is no art which has not its scientific element, be it only in technique; nor is technique alone adequate to the scientist if he is to attain his full stature. There must be an element of intuition, itself subject to the scientific analysis of psychology and not thereby devalued, any more than the beauty of a landscape is devalued by an understanding of the earth-processes which have moulded it. Perhaps the final limitation is that Toynbee broods too exclusively on Myth, Huntington on Statistic; but these are themselves but parts of Poetry and Science, which together make our vision of reality. Their apprehension as a unity is not yet, if indeed Man ever attains it.

Reflections on *A Study of History*

A Study of History is in scope nothing less than a complete rationale of human societies in their developed forms which Toynbee calls civilizations; 'complete' is a large word, and obviously not even Toynbee can put the totality of civilization into six or nine volumes, but there are very few aspects indeed which do not come within his grasp, from theology to costume. Whatever view be taken of its permanent significance, *A Study* remains most important for our own day both in its own right and as a symptomatic historical document: 'this is how history looked'. To erudition on a scale rarely paralleled Toynbee adds the yet rarer gifts of style and of a massive architectonic grasp: the swing and sweep of the work compel admiration from the most antipathetic critics. Yet it is open—as work on such a scale must always be—to considerable criticism in detail. More important is its general outlook, that of liberal humanism in its later phase of not unnatural doubt, the phase in which it looks back to older and less rational (or less well rationalized) schemes of values to secure some footing in a morally anarchic world. This seems slippery ground on which to build so towering a structure.

To analyse *A Study of History* in full detail would be fascinating but pointless, since critics competent to do so would be better employed on their own syntheses. But it is of interest to examine some of the methodology and assumptions underlying the work, and in particular to examine Toynbee's handling of geographical factors, which form a not unimportant part of the argument, and on the

Reprinted from *Historical Studies Australia and New Zealand*, Vol. 50 No. 20, 1953.

whole perhaps the weakest. In general the writer is conscious of the acute disparity between himself and Toynbee—

> Well knowing that, a puny Jonah, I
> The great Behemoth of the Schools defy;
> Whose learning, logic, casuistry's so vast,
> He overflows the metaphysic waste,
> But yet I hope some darts of mine will stick,
> And that, like Jonah, I shall make him sick . . .

In the field of the relations between physical environments and human cultures, however, he feels that he can meet Toynbee on not too unequal terms; and, as will be seen (whether the criticism is made out or not), this is of some significance in assessing, if not the validity, at least the use and interpretation of some of Toynbee's most striking concepts, notably that of Challenge-and-Response. The critical tone of this article should not be taken as a faithful reflection of the writer's total attitude to Toynbee; to draw attention to his many excellencies would be even more pointless than a page-by-page critical gloss, since these he who runs may read.*

The methodology

Toynbee's conception of what constitutes a 'civilization' is established in an introductory survey of the twenty-one societies, living and dead, which he considers as meriting the name. The ensuing discussion of the comparability of societies is a methodological vindication, by no means the only one but perhaps the most significant.

---

* The first figure in references is to the pages of Somervell's abridgement, the second to the corresponding volume and pages of the original. For convenience and brevity direct quotation is from the abridgement, but in all cases the argument has been checked against the original. Tribute must be paid to the surpassing skill with which the abridgement has been made; there is of course foreshortening of the original argument, but only here and there, and never on a large scale, is there any essential difference; and that mainly verbal. On the other hand, to return to the original is to be dazzled once more by the encyclopaedic scope of Toynbee's treatment. One hardly wishes it shorter, and yet Somervell's compression suggests a certain *longueur* in Toynbee himself.

213

The core of the methodology is found in the section headed in the abridgement 'History, Science, and Fiction' (43-7/I, 441-64). A distinction is drawn between the legitimate 'elucidation and formulation of laws . . . where the data are too numerous to tabulate but not too numerous to survey' and 'the form of artistic creation and expression called fiction which is the only technique that can be employed or is worth employing where the data are innumerable'.* In the sphere of human relations, then, we have

> innumerable examples of universally familiar experiences. The very idea of an exhaustive recording of them is an absurdity. Any formulation of their laws would be intolerably platitudinous or intolerably crude. In such circumstances the data cannot be significantly expressed except in some notation which gives an intuition of the infinite in finite terms; and such a notation is fiction (45-6/I, 452).

Yet sociology and psychology have fair claims to exist as sciences, not to be subsumed into an anthropology which deals only with primitive societies, which is the furthest concession Toynbee makes. Their exponents may at times appear platitudinous and crude, but in this century to write them off, as Toynbee virtually does, is itself crudity. Moreover, rather too much is proved. Many subjects lie open to similar objections and yet are clearly susceptible of scientific treatment. The student of palaeontology, for example, meets 'innumerable examples' of 'universally familiar' cephalopods, and it would be absurd even to think of cataloguing all the cephalopods which exist in museums, let alone those yet buried in the earth. Then there are, for example, the permutations of mineral assemblages in igneous petrology, in which magmatic groups might be compared to the major human social groupings. It is true that within each 'species' of human reaction to circumstance the

---

* The distinction between History, Science, and Fiction is first presented as a popular view; in the original, ten pages are devoted to tracing it respectably to Aristotle and breaking down these 'popular equations', only to find that 'they do nevertheless approximate to the truth' (I, 452), and are used as the basis of the discussion. The reader of Toynbee must sometimes be long-suffering.

range of variation is far greater than that within each species of cephalopod; but the analogy may not be unreveal-ing. And are not many scientific generalizations in some degree at least statements in finite terms of infinite, or all but infinite and hence practically infinite, series? The last quoted sentence does not seem able to bear all the weight reposed on it.

A corollary is important. 'The quantity of recorded insti-tutional relations that are relevant to the study of primitive societies will be much greater than those relevant to the study of "civilized" societies, because the number of known primitive societies runs to over 650, and the civilizations are at most 21' (46-7/I, 445-6). 'Relevant' is of course sub-jective, and the statement may be doubted on the grounds that it overlooks the greater internal complexity of the civilizations with their enormous (and as it were shifting) mosaic of class, religious, economic, national, and social institutions. Their far greater range in space (individually), in time (of observable record), and in the number of indi-viduals they include, gives room for a far greater range of permutations and combinations of personal and institu-tional relations than in primitive societies; it is surely the qualitative rather than the quantitative comparison which is significant, and even so Toynbee's quantitative statement seems invalid. The difficulty is hardly got over by the dog-matic assertion 'the known number of "facts" of the highest order' is just the twenty-one and no more; 'of the highest order' rather begs the question. The implications of an earlier statement seem to be slighted: 'nearly all individual lives that are of sufficient interest and importance to make them worth recording have been lived, not in primitive societies, but in one or other of those societies in process of civilization which are conventionally regarded as history's province' (44/I, 447). It is true that these are handed over *en masse* to biography, but one does not need to be a devotee of Carlyle's Heroes to admit that this partition is sometimes flimsy.

We may then feel that Toynbee lays himself open to two opposite objections: one, which he himself states, that it is risky to apply the scientific technique, 'the elucidation and formulation of laws', to a class of only twenty-one members; the other, that he under-estimates the innumerability of his data in personal-institutional relations, which on his own showing are only susceptible of 'fictional' treatment. Hostile critics (but not, despite appearances, the present writer) might say that this is precisely what they get; but even were this true Toynbee is not without a tenable defence. It is true enough that 'it is hardly possible to write two consecutive lines of historical narrative without introducing fictitious personifications' (44/I, 442-3), and beyond this all history worthy the name must draw largely on the shaping spirit of imagination, in the etymological sense of the word. This hardly excuses, however, some of Toynbee's almost incredibly anthropomorphic personifications of societies. And the dilemma remains: either way some of the main theses of the book may prove to be precariously based.

Where the method leads

This methodological discussion ends with the assertion that *A Study* is an attempt, admittedly risky, to apply the scientific technique; and certainly there is no lack of formulation and classification, of esoteric terminology and a general air of systematics. But these are the mechanics of scientific method, not its soul. The fact that Toynbee has a philosophy of history, which, for all its avowed empiricism, has at times an *a priori* aspect, has apparently been a stumbling-block for some critics; but this reproach is beside the point. It is difficult to conceive of anyone being so foolish as to devote himself to so vast a synthesis without some preconceptions to start with, and however inadequate such philosophies may seem, the way forward is by trial and error, and to abandon the search is a counsel of despair. Even Toynbee's selectivity, so severely handled by Geyl, might be admitted within limits; any philosophical history will almost inevitably burke some awkward facts and inflate others more convenient to the theme. As for inconsistencies, one is lucky to avoid them in an article, let alone six large volumes; and they are remarkably few and unimportant

216

except for what may be termed the deliberate ones, when at the great crises of his argument Toynbee turns his back on 'science' and embraces intuition: in the discussion of the parallels between Hellenic 'Saviours' and Christ Himself, of transfiguration, and of the prospects of salving Western Christendom, which by all Toynbeean laws broke down irretrievably generations ago. These will be regarded as beautiful but aberrant excrescences or as magnificent acts of faith, according to the reader's temper.

Toynbee's philosophy may or may not be acceptable *per se*; the real rock of offence to many (including the present writer) is the somewhat rigid schematism to which it gives rise. The sequences seem too good to be true, and at times they seem to be reached by a selective interpretation of the facts which goes rather beyond reasonable latitude. Again the formulae, Challenge-and-Response, Withdrawal-and-Return, and the like, fall too pat and become stock responses. For all the apparatus of scientific nomenclature, a larger part than the avowed method warrants is played by intuition, by brooding on myth, and by argument from analogy, surely the most dangerous of all the idols of thought. When we find Spengler's method denounced as 'to set up a metaphor and then proceed to argue from it as if it were a law based on observed phenomena' (248/IV, 11-13), our enjoyment of the epigram is tempered by a sudden vision of Satan rebuking Sin. A few examples must suffice; but before endeavouring to compile an anthology of apparent error, the writer would emphasize once more that if in some aspects *A Study of History* is a source-book for what Karl Pearson called 'a neglected branch of education—the study of fallacy in concrete examples', it is also very much more than that. Like Nature in Alfred Austin's poem, if Toynbee does indeed sin, he sins upon a larger scale because he is himself more large.

To begin with, the rich fund of illustration by anecdote and allusion has its own dangers, and at times its use seems almost disingenuous. Disputable points slip in as a lawyer slips in a prejudicial rumour: 'according to the legend' such-and-such 'is reported'—but then used as if it were undoubted fact, for example the destruction of the Alexandrian library (518/VI, 111-12). This looks perilously like hedging, wanting the weight of the instance without openly affirming it. Arbitrary lay-figures are set up and knocked down again, having been gratuitously provided with an aim suited to the argument but hardly proven.

We have repeated interpretations, often brilliant in themselves, which simply do not follow from nor bear out the sweeping idealist dogmas with which they are linked. Such is the discussion of technics and civilization (193-7/III, 154-74) which is not exactly in a vacuum but yet seems loose from its moorings. As a minor illustration we may note that, while the main idea of the discussion of Palaeolithic cultures (197/III, 172) is just, the facts as presented are woolly or worse: the 'immense psychic revolution' of the supersession of Neanderthal man *was* in fact attended by very notable advances in technique, and we need not, indeed cannot, 'on the technological classification confound the sensitive artists' of the Aurignacian cave-pictures with the 'Missing Link', as Toynbee does.

There is, too, what appears to be a remarkable confusion between an idealist view of the springs of social action and the anthropomorphic praise or blame of societies *en bloc*. 'The source of action' in a society 'is never the society itself, but always an individual' (533/VI, 175). Yet the arrested civilizations of Nomads and Eskimos have failed through 'the idolatrous worship of a technique . . . Their single-track lives have condemned them to a retrogression towards an animalism which is the negation of human versatility' (327/III, 79-88). The imputation of free choice is really rather monstrous; these peoples find themselves in such and such an environment, in which by much effort they maintain remarkable cultures, and Toynbee himself of course pays a tribute to the great original achievement of planting and maintaining a human society in such environments at all. Yet, being there, how else can one live in a semi-desert but by shepherding, on the edge of the Greenland ice-cap but by hunting and fishing? And on the other hand, why should they abandon such signal gains in the struggle against hostile nature? Would not such defeatism be an even worse human retrogression? And in any case is there really so much evidence that Nomads and Eskimos are really so un-adaptable? After all, neither group is monocultural and neither lives in a uniform environment. The classical igloo and the classical 'pure' nomad cultures were always re-stricted and are now dwindling; and that the changes in culture implied by this have come by outside contacts is not to the point, since it needs no Diffusionist bias to recog-nize that such contacts have been among the primary fac-tors of cultural change in practically all societies that have ever existed. A reading of Codrington and Febvre[1] suggests that for the Nomads at least it is Toynbee's view of them, and not their own way of life, which is single-track; and this despite the very real contribution which Toynbee makes in his long analysis of the great nomadic incursions, their causes and their effects.

Yet Toynbee on occasion can be completely mechanist: 'On Marxian principles we must expect that, if a Russian peasant is taught to live the life of an American mechanic, he will learn to think as the mechanic thinks.'* About the works of his tractor, yes; but who proposes that he shall lead such a life? The tractors on a *kolkhoz* may be the same as those on a mid-West farm mortgaged to the local bank; are the social life and organization the same? One does not need to be a Marxist to regard this as an over-simplification; the aim of the Five Year Plans was not just 'to transform the old Russia into a new America'. Of course Toynbee admits this verbally, but he regards—or regarded!—any ulterior motives as 'a strange dream to be dreamed by states-men for whom a materialist interpretation of history is an article of faith'. But here he sees *only* technique, and not the whole socio-economic situation: the very ground on which he elsewhere disposes of economic determinism. Thus he rather unnecessarily asserts that the abandonment of Roman roads was not a cause of the breakdown of the

---

* 205-6/III, 200-2. 'On Marxian principles' is put in as a supple-mentary *argumentum ad hominem*, and not by antithesis to Toynbee's own view in this context.

Roman Empire (but who is so simple-minded as to think it was?) and cites with approval Rostovtzeff's rejection of the economic explanation of the decline (256/IV, 41-2). This was due to 'the failure of administration and the ruin of the middle class'; but if the latter is not economic (as well as social) what is?

The elasticity of the English language is not infrequently stretched to breaking-point. One ambiguity—the use of the word 'breakdown' for the initial false step which sets a civilization *on the road* to breaking down—evokes a spirited defence from Somervell, from which 'it will be seen that, when the term is used in this sense, some of the most fruitful, illuminating, and celebrated achievements in the history of a civilization may come after the break-down, and, indeed, in consequence of it'. Quite: one sees (with altogether undue effort) what is meant, but what would we say to a student who used plain English words with this Humpty-Dumptyish licence? And why not find some term, however clumsy, which means what it says? But indeed Toynbee often indulges a penchant for Pickwickian usage:

> When in connection with Western civilization one sees a *pax oecumenica* assigned to the years 1797-1814 and 1528-1918, one is inclined to ask if words have the same meaning for Professor Toynbee as for the rest of us.[2]

This wresting of language is sometimes combined with a wresting of the actual historical sequence to make it square with the formula; this is perhaps most strikingly seen in the discussion of England's 'withdrawal' from continental entanglements after the failure of the medieval adventures in France and the defeat of the Armada (235-9/ III, 350-63). This has been faithfully dealt with by Geyl: 'The Glorious Revolution is indeed a fine example of the great deeds which England was able to achieve by her seclusion! Have William the Third and his Dutchmen been forgotten?' Apparently so: there was indeed 'a partial and temporary return to the continental arena, under the brilliant leadership of Marlborough' (who doubtless commanded at Minden, Fontenoy, Vittoria, Waterloo, and the Crimea), but on the whole from 1588 to 1914 'the avoidance of continental entanglements was accepted, without further question, as one of the fundamental and perpetual aims of British foreign policy'.* One wonders what the elder and the younger Pitt thought they were doing. The aim may have been at times accepted, but rarely without question, and more often as a meaningless slogan which would go down well, though British statesmen (as distinct from the leader-writers of the *Daily Express* and their forebears) knew it for an impossibility in fact. On the few occasions when we did hold more or less aloof our isolation was not very splendid and at times perhaps enforced rather than sought; 'non-intervention' had an ugly ring long before the Spanish Civil War, in 1863-4 for instance, or in relation to James I and the Palatinate. In fact we avoided continental entanglements by the not very direct method of intervening in nearly every major crisis and not a few minor ones; once more there seems a decidedly Pickwickian sense to be attached to the phrase 'withdrawal from the general life of Europe' or from 'the trammels of a regional society'. This holds for arts as for arms: can anyone really see the age of Dryden (or indeed of Shakespeare) as fitly summed up in such terms?

The recurrent Toynbeean device of shooting up an Aunt Sally is notably well illustrated by his treatment of 'British' Diffusionism: the iteration of the adjective fits in with the general polemic against a narrowly occidental view of history (in itself absolutely correct) and is perhaps a trifle prejudicial. Toynbee's general refutation of Diffusionism is unexceptionable, and indeed common form; but the materialist bias ascribed to the Diffusionists is surely gratuitous. It is of course perfectly true that civilizations are not built up—solely—of such bricks as sewing-machines and rifles; nor is it the Diffusionist view that they are.

---

* 'This statement requires some qualification in regard to English foreign policy during the period A.D. 1689-1815' (Toynbee's footnote) —over a third of the total span. And, on a point of detail, why not twenty years earlier, the period of the Triple Alliance and its reversal?

Further, one cannot but feel that Toynbee's antithesis between the ease of exporting Western material techniques, as against the incommunicability of the spiritual flame of the Western poet or saint, is a little too facile. Has it not often been just the abstractions of thought and feeling which have most easily made the rounds?—goods undoubtedly of minimal bulk and possibly of highest value, to use the cliché of economic geography. One thinks of the rock of Tangtse, beside the hidden Tibetan lake Panggong, with its medley of Buddhist and Nestorian inscriptions attesting that faiths, more than merchandise, have been the traffic of these savage mountain ways. In our own day there is the wide acceptance of Aldous Huxley (for instance) in the East, or of Tagore in the West; and if these are thought rather dubious 'goods', is it not a commonplace that the true mystics, wherever found, speak like unto like, just because they are largely divorced if not from local colour at least from local mundane reality? *Ex Oriente Lux*; and conversely the greatest Tamil statesman of our day perhaps takes no less pride in his translation of Plato's *Apology* than in his place in the councils of his country. The ideologies suffer their mutations, of course, but so do the techniques; and in any case this is hardly the right end of the stick with which to beat the Diffusionists.

Finally, there is a fine promiscuity in the selection of authorities in fields other than Toynbee's own—and not necessarily subsidiary fields, since geography at least lies at the heart of much argument on the genesis of civilizations. The results are at times diverting. We find Mr Gerald Heard described as 'a modern anthropologist', in what Toynbeean sense is difficult to determine since the passage cited (199/III, 183-4) is an odd mixture of sociology and archaeology, though it contains, as Toynbee says, 'a finely imaginative touch' in describing Anglo-Saxon dykes as the frontiers of the Iceni. Mr Heard turns up again as a sort of palaeo-biologist, suggesting (in Toynbee's words) that the 'armour' which saved the primitive mammals *vis-à-vis* the dinosaurs 'was not physical but psychic' (329/IV, 427). The truth in Heard's arguments is surely a commonplace of evolutionary theory, but that it may not be the whole truth is suggested by the cloudy rhetoric in which it is embedded; the antitheses seem too pat to be more than half-truths. It is difficult to take entirely seriously 'the principle that life evolves by sensitiveness and awareness; by being exposed, not by being protected; by nakedness, not by strength; by smallness, not by size'.* Certainly these are elements to be reckoned with; yet if the development of a spinal cord and a brain is to be considered of any importance, we cannot entirely overlook the connection between increase of size in terrestrial animals and the strong vertebral framework which it called for. The dinosaurs, like the Eskimos and the Nomads, doubtless did stray into 'the blind alley of over-specialization'; one certainly cannot accuse Toynbee of ending in this particular *cul-de-sac*, but some of the addresses whence he gets information are in dubious streets, and he rivals the dinosaurs in bulk.

After Mr Heard as a representative of almost everything, we have M. Demolins as the representative, presumably, of modern geography. His narrow determinism, which is probably subscribed to by no geographer of repute in his own country, by hardly any in Britain, and by very few in America, provides ample ammunition for a short annihilation of environmentalism (199/III, 193-4). But there are few modern geographers who have not played this same game, which has now become too easy; and Toynbee's failure to notice, let alone to understand, the outlook of modern students of the physical environment—apart from Ellsworth Huntington—vitiates a part at least of the discussion of Challenge-and-Response, which cannot but rest largely upon a consideration of geographical factors. To these we may now turn.

Toynbee's geographical concepts

At least seventy-five pages—about 13 per cent—of the abridgement are taken up by essentially geographical matter: the question of the relation between human soci-

* What's wrong with earthworms?

eties and their physical environments. A general caveat
might well be entered against Toynbee's cavalier approach:
environmental questions have been studied in a scientific
spirit for at least 150 years, since Humboldt; it is thus something of a shock to find as the chosen spokesman of environmentalism a Greek of the fifth century B.C. (55/I, 251-2).
Remarkable as the work of Hippocrates is, it is surely
absurd to test the validity of a concept by analysis not of
its developed forms but of one of the earliest known statements of it, some 2,400 years old; we do not go to Lucretius
for our views on atomic structure. Demolins has hardly
enough weight to be worth citing as a witness; Huntington
is more to the point, but his views are very largely repudiated by the present generation of geographers. In the
writer's opinion this repudiation has gone too far, but there
can be no doubt of its existence. But in any case, as Gourou
remarks, putting the question as if environment created a
human society is quite beside the point:

> Comment une civilisation supérieure, qui est un ensemble
> complexe de faits humains, pourrait-elle être produit par
> un milieu naturel qui est un ensemble complexe de faits
> physiques?[3]

We are invited to reject 'the popular assumption that
civilizations emerge when environments offer unusually
easy conditions of life' (80/II, 1). Nothing is easier; very
few, if any, serious students of environment would sub-
scribe to so simple a view, which incidentally involves
the assumption that 'easy' and 'favourable' are complete
synonyms. The emphasis of modern geography is on opportunity and stimulus; nor are even the surviving determinists immune from this tendency. It is less easy to follow
Toynbee in favour of 'exactly the opposite view'; hence
'stimulus' rather than 'challenge', though this is admittedly
a mere matter of verbal emphasis. At the same time Toynbee's paradox itself leans rather far in a determinist direction; to cite Gourou again,

> Le déterminisme des conditions défavorables au lieu de déter-
> minisme des conditions favorables, est-ce là un progrès?

In practice, of course, common sense breaks in, and Toynbee shrinks from his own extreme formulation: 'there is a mean range of severity at which the stimulus is at its highest, and we shall call this degree the optimum, as distinct from the maximum' severity (146/II, 260, 290-1). Exactly; but does it really need these pages and pages of intellectual travail to produce so meagre a mouse? As Geyl puts it, a blow on the head may stimulate one to fisticuffs, but it may be so hard as to knock one right out; 'this has a less impressive sound, but does it not convey precisely the same meaning?' It is fairly clear, without much research, that on an ice-cap or in a rainless desert no civilization is likely to arise since no human beings can permanently live there (on their own resources at least); and that if there were ever a Lotus-land which offered food and drink for the asking (there never has been out of Eden) there would be no point in taking the not inconsiderable trouble of building a civilization.

Nevertheless, though the result be so jejune it may be that the way to it, if rather roundabout, is in itself worthwhile. And indeed it often is; the concept of 'old and new ground', for example, is most stimulating and admirably presented. But often also the track lies through a tangle of misrepresentations of the physical facts on which, after all, the argument is based: misinterpretations serious enough to throw doubt on the validity of the conclusions, not mere slips. Fundamentally Toynbee is here writing as a geographer. But the sense of scale in space is absolutely essential to the geographer; without grasping the fact that a hundred square miles of marsh is not, from a human point of view, merely ten times ten square miles, but is qualitatively different, it is impossible to reach a right evaluation of the challenge provided and the response required. This sense, as fundamental to the geographer as the 'placing oneself in the movement' is to the historian, Toynbee quite simply lacks. Moreover his view of the physical environment is as a rule too narrow, confining itself in a given case to but one or two of the complex of factors, climate, soil, location and the rest, which make up an environment. And he sees entirely non-existent uniformities, as when he speaks of the Eurasian steppe as extending to the Arctic Circle (I/254).

The treatment of the crucial case of the early Afrasian civilizations is not untypical. To establish the thesis that 'the special environment offered by the Nile in Egypt is the positive factor to which the genesis of the Egyptiac civilization is due' we must show that 'in every other separate area in which an environment of the Nilotic type is offered, a similar civilization has independently emerged' (58/I, 256-8). We might suggest that 'every' and 'independently' leave out important matters of location and timing, and indeed beg a lot of questions; but more decisive is the comparability (or even implied identity) of various riverine environments. The environmental theory is valid in the Euphrates-Tigris region, 'but it breaks down completely in the case of the much smaller but similar Jordan valley, which has never been the seat of a civilization'. In part probably simply because it *is* much smaller, not offering (were it otherwise favourable) the minimum base for the production of the large surplus necessary for the development of a civilization. But in fact the Jordan is far indeed from being just the miniature Nile which Toynbee thinks it. It rises in the lee of Lebanon, in an area with a rainfall of some 25 inches a year; but this area is very limited, and Tiberias has only 18, while evaporation in the lower valley is equivalent to about 180 inches. It has only one per cent as much discharge as the Nile; the stream itself is sunk nearly everywhere between steep banks; the terraces above are in the lower half largely formed of disintegrated limestone, fertile soil but terribly thirsty; and (according to Zionist sources!) at least a third of the valley is 'ridged . . . entirely unsuitable for cultivation', while the soils in the lower third are highly saline. The contrast with the Nile floodplain, enriched by the basaltic silts of Ethiopia, could hardly be more complete. Irrigation has been and is practised on a small scale here and there, mostly at the debouchments of tributary valleys; but the grandiose schemes for a Jordan Valley Authority rely on water from Syria or even the Mediterranean. Above all, there is nothing in the least comparable to the annual Nile flood. Yet Toynbee can speak of the Jordan environment as 'the same' as that of the Nile, or as one 'in which the required conditions are fulfilled equally well on a miniature scale'! As a matter of fact, even the Euphrates-Tigris environment is only generically, not specifically, kin to the Nilotic.

Again we are told that 'the most captious critics cannot deny that the environmental conditions offered by Egypt and Mesopotamia are also offered by the valleys of the Rio Grande and the Colorado'. One does not really have to be very captious. To begin with, hardly any of the basin of the 1,750 miles long Colorado has over 20 inches of rain; contrast this with the 40-80 inches of the Blue and White Nile catchments in Abyssinia and Uganda. The topography of the Nile and the Colorado basins is different in the extreme; the Colorado is much more broken, but there is nothing like the staggered series of tributaries above Khartoum, with the Blue Nile ponding back the White and prolonging the period of high water. The vegetation cover of the more humid parts of the Nile basin, and its lakes and marshes, are far more efficient regulators of run-off than the vegetation of the Colorado. In the Nile basin rainfall is either almost non-existent or falls fairly steadily in well-defined seasons; in the Colorado as a whole there is more rain than on the lower Nile, but much of it falls in irregular violent downpours, and erosion is intense. The Rio Grande approximates more nearly to the Colorado than to the Nile, though it is not a very close approximation. Neither the Colorado (obviously) nor the Rio Grande offers anything like the potentialities for navigation which are found on the Nile, with its peculiar advantage of the Etesian winds blowing upstream; and the role of the river as a highway (which Toynbee does not so much as mention) was only second to its value for irrigation in the development of Egyptian civilization. In both the Colorado and Rio Grande there are doubtless some broad and general analogies to the Nile; but they are far from 'offering the environmental conditions' of Egypt, and the differences are very significant from the cultural point of view. The most fundamental are that the Nile has a unique advantage in its flood-régime, and that in the Nile basin 'the coarse stuff is caught in the sunken fault-block depressions into which the upper Nile flows' (the fine and fertile basaltic silt of the Blue Nile passes on) while the Tigris and the Colorado, fresh from the canyon, have been well styled ditch-chokers.

It may even be suggested that on the human side also Toynbee's comparison breaks down. The history of modern development in the Rio Grande and Colorado valleys is not one of 'miracles' but rather a melancholy story (until very recently) of reckless exploitation and bad planning, made worse by the violent changes of channel, from which the Nile is almost immune, owing to its peculiar physiography. The full irrigation possibilities of these American rivers have not yet been developed, and in places there has been actual abandonment of irrigated areas owing to silting and erosion consequent on over-grazing on the watersheds. And, even if the Pueblo culture was not autochthonous, it had at least taken the first steps to civilization: 40 of the 150 miles of ancient canals in the Salt River valley are incorporated in the modern system, and the bold massing of the pueblo has been an influence, and not a bad one, on modern building in Arizona and New Mexico.

But it is in the attempt to reconstruct the primitive environment of the Lower Nile that the lack of a sense of scale and the neglect of all factors of environment except terrain (in a most limited sense) and vegetation are perhaps most strikingly shown. The reconstruction assumes that the Lower Nile floodplain closely resembled the present condition of the great Sudd swamps of the White Nile around the Bahr-al-Ghazal (71/I, 302-15). With a remarkable heroism the founders of the Egyptiac civilization met the challenge of desiccation by 'plunging into the forbidding Sudd'. Ecologically the marshes of Lower Egypt and the Delta may well have been similar to those of the Bahr-al-Ghazal today; but there was indubitably one difference of fundamental importance: size. The Nile floodplain is only some ten or twelve miles wide, and has firm sites as bases for settlement on either side; nor would it have been unknown as a fishing, hunting, and fowling ground to the inhabitants of the little valleys on the uplands which, as desiccation set in, became oases and perhaps thereby fostered the beginnings of settled agriculture. In any case, you can see right over it from the scarped valley-sides. On the other hand the vast marshes of the Sudd are 100 to 150 miles across in any direction. Obviously there is a difference in tractability between the two; on Toynbee's 'determinism by unfavourable conditions' one might expect the Egyptiac civilization to emerge from the Sudd proper. Moreover, the narrow view of environment which Toynbee takes leaves out of sight such an important factor as the presence on the Lower Nile, and the absence in the Sudd, of ample and excellent tool- and building-stone; not to mention, at a later stage, the readily accessible copper and other minerals of Sinai. Without these things it seems unlikely that there would have been an Egyptiac civilization.

Things are little better when we turn to the less debatable (because less ambiguously documented) North American continent in the colonial phase. Victory in the competition for exploiting rights went to the New Englanders, who had the hardest environment (96/II, 65-73). It is arguable, to be sure, that the victors were first Virginians and later New Yorkers, and in any case a whole host of factors is left out, among others the sort of support from and links with the metropolitan base, and the social factors involved in this. But the matter here is the environment. 'Taking all in all—soil, climate, transport facilities, and the rest—it is impossible to deny that the original colonial home of the New Englanders was the hardest of all.'* Once more, denial is a duty rather than a right. The climate of Lower Canada is far harsher than that of New England: open to polar air masses over the land, away from the moderating influences of the sea, the agricultural base of French colonization has January mean temperatures of 10-13°F., against 25-28° in New England. Summer temperatures are more relevant to

---

* The formulation is Somervell's rather than Toynbee's, but it is warranted by II, 70.

agriculture: they are 64-68°, but the growing season is shorter: 120-150 frost-free days against 150-180. The amount of useful soil is more limited, and soils on the whole poorer than in New England. As for transport, it is true that the St Lawrence is navigable for ocean-going vessels for 1,000 miles, as far as Montreal, but for four or five months of the year it is ice-bound; and above Montreal there are eight sets of rapids with a total fall of 226 feet before Lake Ontario is reached; and beyond lies Niagara. Climate, soil, transport; in every aspect the claim fails. But it is not even consistent: later (147/II, 294) we find that New England is actually within the optimum climatic area of the eastern seaboard; in Maine we have diminishing returns, and the Maritime Provinces of Canada are worse still! This can hardly be squared with the preceding arguments; and if the Maritimes are themselves worse than southern New England, what are we to say of Quebec, with its far more extreme climate and relatively less good soil than New Brunswick and Nova Scotia?

It is hardly necessary to go into further detail. Throughout these geographical pages we find repeated failures to take into account the elementary findings of the study on whose subject matter the argument rests. Locational factors, for instance, vital as they are, are often neglected; mere shapes on the map are married to the standard formulae: for instance 'the challenge of the sea' in Japan, where in fact the sea was a moat defensive, opportunity, food, riches, almost anything rather than a challenge in the Toynbeean sense.* Again, it is consistently assumed that a landscape exploited and then abandoned by man simply reverts to its original condition: the 'latter-day wilderness' of the Roman Campagna 'has reproduced the pristine state of the forbidding landscape which was once transformed by Latin and

* It may be noted that, while the discussion of the culturally 'stimulating effect of a sea-crossing . . . in the course of a Völkerwanderung' is valuable, generally valid, and very well worked out, Toynbee can think of only six examples (104/II, 86-7). It is, perhaps, fairly clear why his six examples do not include one of the most obvious: the Vandals. . . .

Volscian pioneers into a cultivated and populous country-side' (84/II, 17). But the state of the Campagna in Livy's day or in ours is not evidence as to its state before it was settled by agriculturists; it is not very likely that it was any more 'dour' than most areas of central Italy. Within the time-span of civilized societies it is only rarely that anything like the original vegetation cover would succeed by reversion to natural processes after the balance of the natural climax vegetation has been destroyed; and indeed one might almost hazard the generalization that the last state of an area once tamed and then abandoned is more often than not worse than the first, from the point of view of human occupancy.

Admittedly this is a specialist view, and it would be the height of unreason to expect all the arguments in so immense and wide-ranging a study to have equal weight of documentation and equal validity. But it can hardly be maintained that a discussion of environment is marginal to the problem of the origins of civilizations or to such themes as 'Challenge-and-Response'. In a matter so germane to so much of Toynbee's initial argument, it is surely legitimate to suggest that more acquaintance should be shown with the work of those who have sought to unravel the complicated strands which link man to his home, the earth. Such geographers as he does quote—they number five—belong mainly to the determinist school whose findings are definitely not accepted by the great majority of modern geographers; yet the subject is not an esoteric one, nor are Humboldt, Reclus, Vidal de la Blache, Febvre, Mackinder entirely obscure names. Huntington, Hippocrates, and Strabo are essentially Toynbee's geographical authorities; is it too harsh to suggest that this is a lapse from the standards of scholarship?*

* According to the index, Huntington has 26 citations, Owen Lattimore and Griffith Taylor 3, Demolins 2, Isaiah Bowman 1. Of these Demolins hardly counts, Taylor is usually regarded as far too rigid a determinist, and Huntington as little better; though this is perhaps unjust. The index, though not quite complete, is remarkably thorough, even including passing quotations from Gray's *Elegy* and from *The Ancient Mariner*.

Conclusion

It would be unfair to suggest that his exceedingly shaky geographical foundations invalidate Toynbee's general conclusions, dependent as these often are on sheer psychological analysis of impressively documented human situations. Yet it is perhaps symptomatic of a certain looseness or even recklessness of thought, displayed also in the too frequent reliance on argument from analogy. To examine the psychological and philosophical bases of *A Study of History* would lead the writer into metaphysical heavens where his footing would be as unsure as is Toynbee's on the physical earth. But one may at least draw attention to the lapse from detachment when Toynbee considers the chance of survival for Western civilization. There is a conflict here between the demands of the seemingly inexorable pattern and the natural desire for a way out; in so far as *A Study* is scientific, all the marks of breakdown seem glaringly displayed, but by an act of faith there may be reprieve. But this act of faith, while certainly not insincere nor merely verbal, yet seems constrained: it is significant that even in the abridgement its discussion is couched in a rhetorical, almost apocalyptic, tone; eloquent prose, but one has an uneasy feeling that the structure is as stable as a house of cards. The more sober estimate of Geyl's concluding section seems infinitely preferable, offering a surer basis for action and unity.

It is, indeed, not very easy to discover what Toynbee really does believe in: in progress, but not in 'the superstition of Progress'; in reason, but not in rationalism; he blows hot and cold on liberalism; he is avowedly anti-determinist, and yet the general cast of his work is a necessitarian one; he stands perhaps for so nice a calculation of the golden mean, so careful a looking before and after, that the springs of action are relaxed. Really, it would be only fair to tell us what, finally, is his message; that he has one we can hardly doubt, or his massive work would be only a melancholy monument to nothingness, and it is assuredly not that. But doubtless this is to be the theme of the concluding volumes, though one may think that it is already foreshadowed in the sixth; and as for that, *credo, quia impossibile.*

To those who cannot do this, who cannot accept brooding on myth and seductive analogy as substitutes for objective weighing of fact, Toynbee offers—and they are no trifling gifts—the sheer pleasure of reading him, an inexhaustible treasury of historic situations which as units are often magnificently analysed, an irritant stimulus to rethinking their own postulates. For these we must be grateful. But on the whole *A Study of History* appears to one reader, and perhaps to more than one, a house of many mansions, all imposing, many beautiful; but builded upon sand.

A Fragment from the Apocrypha

WE have seen, in an earlier section of this Study ('The Mimesis of Genetics', *supra,* Annexure D.c(xiii) to Part IX, vol. XV, pp. 543-620), that in the life-cycles of those twenty-one societies which I have agreed to call civilizations there is traceable some sequence of temporal and spatial growth and decline, corresponding, at least by analogy, to the evolutionary development of animal organisms. From a Time of Troubles emerges the early flowering of a civilization and its attempted organization into a Universal State. After an adult life-span of about two centuries the Universal State, which may indeed have suffered breakdown long before it has reached its apogee, is overwhelmed in a *Völkerwanderung* of the external proletariat it has unwittingly fostered, and is subsumed into the less grossly material avatar of a Universal Church. At this point in our enquiry, however, it may appear that our analysis, valid enough to a superficial view, as it may appear, is as yet incomplete.

For, as we contemplate the vastness of the record which provides the raw material of our Study, embracing as it does, for the single exemplar of our own Western Christian species, nothing less than the whole accumulation of historiographical erudition stored within the walls of that grandly Palladian edifice which stands, with a sturdy classically-ordered rhythm and self-confident disregard superbly aloof from, and indeed by its mere presence rebuking, the squalid debris of a civilization in decay, the sordid boarding-houses and still more sordid pseudo-intellectualist *soi-disant* minds and loves of Bloomsbury—to wit, the British Museum—it is surely more and more borne in upon us that to our sequence must be added another, and we may well think a culminating, component: the Universal History.

A Fragment from the Apocrypha

In fact, just as the close-knit vertebrate structure of the Universal State falters and disintegrates, to be left as a material heritage to its genetically-apparented simulacrum the Universal Church, so in turn the firm doctrinal and dogmatic outlines of the Universal Church soften in the dissolvent tides of a new time of intellectual troubles, fostered from within by the sapping subversion of that internal intellectual proletariat which it has itself mistakenly nurtured in the venerable, or at least venerated, halls of universities forgetfully betraying their pristine role as defenders of sound religion, no less than by the malicious assaults from without of the external intellectual proletariat, so fittingly symbolized, as I have suggested in the preceding sentence, by the glittering but spiritually shabby shallowness of Bloomsbury. Yet, in this desolate and fluctuant waste of so-called thought, a desperate endeavour is made by some hardy and dedicated spirits to arrest the process of deliquescence, to rear some dyke, though but of inflated prose, against the encroaching inundations of reason and science. The Universal Historian comes into his own.

The attempt of course is not foredoomed to success. And indeed the dustier shelves of our great libraries are littered with the voluminous elaborations of those whom I may, with not too much of ὕβεις, style my progenitors: broken-backed Leviathans of learning stranded on the shores of forgotten *Weltanschauungen*. The reader's indulgence is craved, for a few moments, while we survey, with utmost brevity, the more notable of such attempts.

First perhaps we must salute the *clarum et venerabile nomen* of the (mis-called) Sophist Protöinbeeus of Tiathamhoys (*balbutiebat* 241-193 B.C.). ...

[Here 37 pages are lost]

Turning now from the times of the absolutist Sage of Malmesbury to that far later and much agitated phase of our Western civilization which succeeded to the abortive *pax oecumenica sive napoleonica* of A.D. 1797-1815, we find, perhaps surprisingly, a thinker representative both of an

235

internal and an external intellectual proletariat, in his double capacity of Doctor of Philosophy of the University of Berlin and of a but recently self-externed member of that Judaic subterranean intelligentsia, which flourished, albeit pallidly, as it were as a subtle internal secretion within the complex physiology of European thought. I refer, as is indeed obvious, to that markedly Zealotic Millenarian Karl Marx (*denuntiabat* A.D. 1844-1884). For Marx, Teutonic metaphysics, in its speciously attractive raiment of Hegelian dialectic, did at least provide the architectonic scaffolding whence he emptied his vials of prophetic vituperation, legacy of his consciously repudiated but ever internally active Hebraic *haereditas*; but from this incongruous mating stemmed a dogmatic intolerance, a too-rigid schematic categorization, from which succeeding Students of History could take warning, if not indeed refuge, in History as Fiction.

His compeer Oswald Spengler (*obscurabat* A.D. 1914-1936)[1] overlaid, perhaps to excess, the finer insights and subtle perceptions proper to the attempt to elucidate historic law in a scientific spirit with metaphysical and rhetorical exuberances. Moreover the Spenglerian method, replete as it is with the mechanical apparatus of scientific methodology, and seminal as it has been—in no case more sublimely procreative than in begetting the more purple passages of the present Study—not infrequently declines into the logical fallacy of setting up an analogy and proceeding to argue from it as if it were scientifically demonstrated truth: an error from which this Study is I trust most conspicuously free.

Of this Study indeed, indubitably (I would think) taking a just place in the sequence and tradition here outlined, it is difficult for even its author to speak with due and

---

[1] The British-Israelitish conflation of these two, with perhaps an additional cognomentative element from Herbert Spencer (*obtundebat* A.D. 1850-1903), into the material myth of Marks and Spencer may be disregarded as a characteristic example of the tendency of the more perverse and eccentric side of the British genius to construct empiricist eidola.

entire detachment. This is not the place to emulate the elegance of Gibbonian autobiography, to equate that evening in the Roman Forum 'when the bare-footed Fryars were singing Vespers'[2] with the, in appearance, more mundane and secular pavement of Buckingham Palace Road, considering both these sites as haunts of the *genius loci* generative of great historical work. Of that indeed in another place.[3]

Yet there is indeed one outward and visible sign—or, to borrow the word of the Romish Cardinal who is yet one of the glories of the English Church and of English prose (*convertitur* A.D. 1846)—one 'note', albeit negative, which may, without undue presumption, be taken as imputing its rightful place to this Study: the converse of the phrase in Holy Writ, 'Woe unto ye when all men praise ye.' The crowd of detractors rude of whom the Puritan arch-poet complained has not spared any of the great Universal Histories of the past; nor, in this day and age, is it to be reasonably expected that a modest superiority to the archaic pedantry of mere fact should be spared by those blind mouths whose lives are given to, whose livelihoods are drawn from, the peddling of accurate but petty detail: the dates and results of campaigns, the actual composition of armies and of doctrines, the true course of isotherms and of rivers.

To all such, whether they hail from ancient Utrecht or from remote and youthful Canberra, the philosophic student of history may, for once, reply by an analogy—a method, after all, not disdained by Plato, still less by the yet more untrammelled sages of Neo-Platonism. And our analogy is drawn from attested history, recorded by that glory and shame of Renaissance France, the Tourainian Founder-Abbot of Thélème (*bibebat* A.D. 1495-1553).

It is related by Rabelais of the King of the Pichricoles that, with a sublime confidence in his own ardent genius, that enlightened monarch cheerfully set out to execute complex amphibious operations, leading non-existent

[2] *Miscellaneous Works of Edward Gibbon* (London, 1796), pp. 127, 129.

[3] *A Study of History*, Book XIII D, Vol. X, p. 139.

armies by unknown routes, and fully assured of nothing
but his own incomparable artistry in war and the discovery
at various staging-points of all but limitless supplies of the
headiest wine.[4]

May that magnanimous spirit, superior to, when not
oblivious of, the brute facts of geography, logistics, and
history, ever remain, as he ever has been, the great exemplar
and model for the Universal Historian.

[4] *Premier livre des faicts et dicts heroïques du noble Pantagruel,*
Ch. XXIII.

Finis Coronat Opus?

*The Intent of Toynbee's History** is a collection of papers read at Loyola University in 1955: in five years the editor could surely have tidied up the clumsy and ambiguous phrasing of some contributors. He has failed to do even elementary justice to D. M. Robinson's paper on Toynbee's Graeco-Roman world. Robinson was around seventy-five years of age when he wrote it, and died before he could revise; but that hardly excuses such a muddle as a list of important characters in church history which includes William Land [Laud], Thomas Crom[well], Kitchen of Standof [Count Zinzendorf?], and that famous pair 'Nicholas Farrar, Little Gidding'; nor does one see what the devil (the phrase is appropriate) William Rufus is doing in this galley. As for the 'bare mention' of Mahomet, Toynbee could have replied that a bit further down the index one finds Muhammad. All this does not look well from a University whose name after all suggests some slight ecclesiastical flavour.

There is an agreeable introduction by Toynbee himself, *Reconsiderations* in miniature, but the book proper makes a poorish start with three typical pieces of historiographer's history: there are good points pro and con, but the gross effect is not very profound or stimulating. After this, however, the book gets into its stride. The essay by von Grunebaum on Toynbee's treatment of Islam asks some very searching questions and has a very acute analysis of what the author calls, in excellent phrases, Toynbee's 'elastic doctrinairism' and 'contrived stylization of historical fact'.

Reprinted from *Australian Outlook*, Vol. 16 No. 1, 1962.

* *The Intent of Toynbee's History: A co-operative appraisal.* Edited by Edward T. Gargan. Chicago, Loyola University Press, 1961.

Hans Kohn on Toynbee's Russia is disappointing, but M. A. Fitzsimon's collation of Toynbee's outlines of American history may be, as its author says, outrageous and tribal in method and approach, but does bring out the way in which Toynbee doesn't see, or isn't interested in, events in themselves: as von Grunebaum puts it, civilizations or societies 'are described merely in terms of what they did or underwent, never in terms of what they were'. This seems a weakness in a student of history; and yet, perhaps, Toynbee might reply that this is precisely the difference between history—Ranke's 'what actually happened'—and a Study of History.

The most rewarding essay is perhaps that by Edward Hardy on Toynbee's universal churches: well-written, extremely fair, and much to the point. Eric Voegelin's analysis of 'Toynbee's search for truth', though written in a rather repulsive jargon, is probably the most radically searching, as it is the most devastating, of these critiques. Its point is essentially that put forward by Oscar Halecki in the last essay—put crudely, that Toynbee should return to the Church—but it is far superior to Halecki's somewhat superficial *propaganda pro fide*. And yet, when Voegelin reproaches Toynbee with a 'dilettantism with regard to questions of reason and revelation, philosophy and religion . . . that could easily be overcome by anyone who wanted to overcome it', is it not a failure of empathy to assume that all is so easy? Nor, incidentally, does it square with the standard Christian reproach that agnosticism is 'the easy way out'.

The first impression of Toynbee's own book is very promising.* The sweet reasonableness, which at times over the volumes has worn a little thin, reasserts itself; the modesty of the enquiring student seems less conventional; there is throughout an air of candour and co-operation; preconceptions seem less fixed, dogma less assured; argument from analogy is generally kept well in hand; the

* Arnold Toynbee, *A Study of History*: Volume XII, *Reconsiderations*. London, Oxford University Press, 1961.

strident rhetoric and apocalyptic visionings which marred portions of the earlier volumes are markedly absent; the personalia no longer embarrassing. Here and there Toynbee even laughs at himself, and we can laugh with him even when the joke is on us—the obvious pun on this reviewer's name has never been more neatly and pointedly used, and who could resist such an epigram as 'criticism, unlike grace, is sure to abound anyway; its economics are, indeed, those of abundance' (p. 642)? It must be said right away that a great deal of this first impression survives a closer reading: even Geyl is to some extent disarmed. And yet, and yet . . . the old Adam is still there, though his sins are now more venial.

These are of course, as Toynbee puts it, 'Effects of Being What One Is'—and not only the irreverence towards pretensions to uniqueness and the disregard of scholarly caution which he ascribes to this cause and for which he makes a good case, sometimes a very good one (pp. 620-57). There are also the far-fetched similitudes, the digressions of doubtful relevance, the longueurs: at one point (pp. 375-6) there are 25 lines, about 20 of which are needless on this level of debate, to express a correct preference for 'Hellas, Hellenic' over 'Greece, Greek'. Then there are some startling omissions: one can hardly imagine that 'a Student of History' is unaware of *The Idea of History*, and yet Collingwood, whose few pages on Toynbee are trenchant and penetrating, gets four mentions, none of them direct references and only one, where Collingwood happens to be on Toynbee's line (p. 439), material. One is staggered to find pages on water control and social organization, with special reference to early Chinese history, without any mention of Wittfogel: yet apart from earlier articles, *Oriental Despotism* appeared well before several works which are cited, and however much one disapproves of it, one cannot well ignore it in this context.

Were it not for the transparent good faith with which the book is written, one would be tempted to speak of sleight-of-hand or evasion in some places, where what has happened is simply a failure in rigorous criticism of his own argument, a failure of course to which everyone is liable. Thus the vigorous and largely correct denunciation of the 'apathetic fallacy' (an excellent term) and of the habit of using analogies and metaphors from natural science when treating of human affairs (p. 32) is not backed up by any specific reference to their use by historians, and so loses its point; it is significant that there is not a single example cited to back up a characterization, approaching caricature, of one type of modern historian (p. 634), and surely politeness is no excuse for failing to give verification.

Toynbee's defence is, of course, facilitated by the fact that he has been assailed from so many directions that some of the criticisms cancel out; he is also not infrequently able to avail himself of a *tu quoque*, as for example in the matter of selection of facts. But here he misses the point that this is a matter of degree; one might indeed say that whether the topic is geographical environment, Jews, selection of data, or simply the proportions of a book, Toynbee seems to have but a poorly developed sense of scale. It is true that it is impossible to write any extended history without some preconceptions, without some use of metaphor, personification, and reification of abstractions, and without letting the demands of structure and thesis affect both the selection and the ordering of data, which must therefore be to some degree subjective. But these truisms are no adequate defence to the charge against Toynbee that he goes so far in these directions as to throw doubt not on his good faith but on his critical competence and judgement. Indeed his own defence on this point seems half-hearted, perhaps because he is fundamentally not interested in the essential nature of past situations, only in the part which they play, or can be made to play, in his pattern. On the question of England's withdrawal from European affairs, with its notorious ascription of the Revolution of 1688 to this detachment from the Continent, he says simply: with Geyl's help 'I believe I could produce a revised version of my thesis that would be acceptable to Geyl himself' (p. 266); but his hint towards this *tour de force* is unconvincing, and he makes no reference at all to the equally telling criticisms, by Geyl and others, of his specific narratives of Italian, American, and other national or even macro-regional histories. The concessions, such as they are, are merely verbal, and do not come to grips with fundamentals.

At this point a reviewer who is himself discussed at some length in *Reconsiderations* finds himself in a dilemma. It is manifestly immodest, and unfair both to the subject and the readers of his review, to turn it into polemic for his position; yet if he says nothing, he appears to let his case go by default. I do not propose to argue with Toynbee on the main point, further than to say that, while he scores one or two palpable hits, his rejoinder turns largely on a shift of meaning between 'civilization' and a Civilization in his sense of a member of the twenty-one civilizations (p. 320). It is more modest (and more effective) to cite Geyl: where Toynbee deals with some of my criticisms, 'the debate goes a little deeper' and Geyl can ask 'Does he realise that in these admissions the condemnation of his great work is implied?'[1] My case can rest under that aegis, but for one point where I feel entitled and indeed bound to protest against an imputation of intellectual arrogance. It is not in the least true, as Toynbee very strongly implies (p. 635), that I think Hippocrates an inadequate exemplar of environmentalism simply because he lived twenty-four centuries ago. No doubt 'the capacity of human minds to think about this problem was not inferior in the fifth century B.C. to what it is today'—nor, in passing, is there *a priori* any reason to think it superior, a point which, one feels, is often overlooked by classicists. But my reason for dissent is far from arrogant: I disagree that 'the stock of information accessible by that date was already sufficient for that purpose' for the simple, modest, but all-sufficing reason that I do not think the data available *now*, after twenty-four centuries, are adequate for a definitive judgement on this question. This unfounded imputation merely serves to conceal the fact, undeniable and not attempted to be denied, that Toynbee has not even begun to consider a great body of scholarship very relevant to some of his theses.

But this is not an accusation of bad faith: it is simply that his answer seemed natural and adequate to Toynbee.

At least this is a reply of sorts. Sometimes Toynbee simply cites fundamental criticisms and stays not for an answer: for instance, he blandly quotes, but does not attempt to meet, the protests of Trinkaus and Frankfort that, for all his disclaimers, he has really not broken out of his Hellenistic and Western shell and that his images— 'arrested civilizations', 'the cliff above', and so on—betray 'an evolutionistic as well as a moral bias . . . completely under the spell of a nineteenth-century Western outlook' (p. 583). There is perhaps some exaggeration here, but there is also more than a little truth, which wouldn't matter so much if it were not for Toynbee's frequent lecturing, at times petulant, of purblind Western secular historians, his gross exaggeration of Western *hubris* (these days, anyhow), and his repeated claims to an oecumenical view.

The better things in *Reconsiderations* are not few, although (as one might expect) they often have little directly to do with the formal defence. One can agree, without very much reservation, with the spirit and conduct of such discussions as those on the relativity of the observer's approach (pp. 47-68), on the increase in quantity of data (pp. 105-14), on world government (pp. 309, 525-6, 619-20, and elsewhere), on post-Colonial dictatorships (p. 545), on the alternatives of striving for sainthood and a 'conditioned' termite-existence (pp. 564-8), on whether there is a 'Master-Activity' in human affairs (pp. 658-63). While much of the long discussion of Hellenic and Sinic 'models' (pp. 170-209) is tedious, and a little of it seems to me confused, there is an extraordinarily good and suggestive parallel (pp. 465-6) between a hypothetical Christian-Syriac development under Zenobia and the Islamic-Arabic development which actually took place under Muhammad: an 'if of history' which convincingly explains why Islam *appears* such a drastic solution of continuity, and is itself a model of how to use a model.

These are the things in which Toynbee has always excelled; and it is perhaps a pity that they are so welded into a system which seems so much less valid as a whole. In truth the system is not so monolithic as its author would wish (such is the habit of systems); but—to vary the metaphor— the precious stones are embedded in such a mass of over-burden that it may be difficult to quarry and preserve them: perhaps Toynbee has written too lengthily to be lasting. After all, *Capital* might not have been so explosive without the detonator of the *Manifesto*. But, whatever one may think of the execution, one must salute the courage which could undertake and carry out a work so vast in scale and so grand in design. And tribute is also due to the dignity and even nobility of Toynbee's personal credo, shown above all in the confrontation of Job and Epicurus (pp. 638-40): even so benighted a rationalist as this reviewer could not read this passage without being moved and exalted.

And yet, the final words must be ambivalent. The critics of Toynbee include men whose integrity and capacity for tough thought cannot be gainsaid; their criticisms have been neither few nor trivial: they go to the roots. There is something touching in the spectacle of a man stressing so often and so strongly, and in such good faith, his willing-ness to stand corrected, and then meeting fundamental challenges with merely verbal responses, meaningless con-cessions, ratiocinations which turn in upon themselves and end where they started. The only really radical criticism Toynbee has accepted is his own, resulting in the shift from civilizations to higher religions as the foundation-stones, the Alpha and Omega of the enquiry.

Artist, poet, prophet, rhetorician, what you will, playing with a sort of divine carelessness with the materials of history; but only episodically a historian. There is much of value, no doubt, in the spillover of this diverse aesthetic activity; but taking it as a whole, I will repeat myself: 'a house of many mansions, all imposing, many beautiful; but builded upon sand'. Only a temporary structure, replies Toynbee (p. 647), and 'when the spate has come and gone, the site will be clear' for a better one—and the sooner the better. Can he really, in his heart of hearts, feel this or wish it? Is it heroism, is it folly, to build on such a scale

245

R

and yet avow a wish that the work shall be ephemeral? Unparalleled humility, or self-deception? These questions are asked with all respect, with sympathy and with humility. One may reasonably expect that at any rate a few stones will be built into the foundations of structures less grand, but more solid. And that, perhaps, is as much as any scholar can hope.

RETRATO : DE : EMANVEL : GODINHO : DE : EREDIA :

Manuel Godinho de Erédia

Quest for Australia

Prologue, A.D. 1545

From the poop of the junk Father Vicente could see the
walls of his little chapel, the new-cut coral rock gleaming white through the crowded columns of the palms. The
Mission had been remarkably successful: the chapel itself
was tangible evidence, an invaluable base which would give
prestige to the catechists who must carry on the work until
a resident priest could be appointed. That perhaps would
not be very long, so much beyond expectation was the
achievement of these first few months. The joyful tidings
of the Gospel were already known and indeed influential
in the back-country; for not only had the King and Queen
of this port of Machioquique been baptized, but their up-
country cousins of Supa and of Linta had left their palaces
and come to live permanently in the little town, so that
they could continue to receive instruction from the catechists and to live in communion with the Christians of
what would surely be a most flourishing Mission, so strongly
based was it already.

And this royal family of Supa and Linta, Juan Tubinanga and his Queen re-named in the Faith Dona Archangela: how firmly grounded were they in their new belief!
The daughter too, especially the daughter, Dona Elena—
for so young a girl, barely fifteen, how eager for holy dis-
course, how edifying an example of devotion! Surely their
influence could not fail to win for Christ the whole of this
large island, to make of it a centre whence Christendom
could spread in ever-widening circles; perhaps (who knew?)

Reprinted from *Meanjin*, Vol. 16 No. 2, 1957.

as far as the mysterious Isle of the Papuans itself. Or even beyond that, if there were a beyond. . . .

But here, in lively procession beneath a brightly coloured canopy, came King Lapituo of Machioquique and his Queen Tamalinda to take formal leave of the Father. It rejoiced his heart to see that the procession was headed not by heralds and armed men, but by the Cross and—already —a small company of choristers. Father Vicente could not see Juan of Supa nor Dona Archangela, but doubtless they would form their own company. He must hasten ashore to greet them.

Just then Father Vicente became aware of a certain commotion, almost a turbulence, at the tail of the procession: loud confused shouting, a disorderly rush of men from the palace—armed men, brandishing spears and naked swords. The royal canopy swayed and sagged unevenly to a halt; the Cross and the choristers hesitated, advanced a few paces, and then huddled into an irresolute group.

Then Juan Tubinanga appeared, striding hastily with a complete disregard of royal decorum. He almost ran to his cousins, shouting as he came near. The Machioquique pair seemed astonished at his furious gestures; then the canopy was furled abruptly, the Queen and her ladies turned back, and Juan and Lapituo came forward. The armed tail seemed now to have swallowed the head of the procession, the crowding warriors had hustled Cross and choristers aside.

On the point of stepping into the sampan for the beach, Father Vicente paused in the junk's waist, trying to take in this abrupt change from peaceful festivity to riot. 'We'll find what the trouble is first,' said the mate, and let the little boat drop astern.

By now the crowd had spread out along the beach, definitely menacing, and a few were making as if to run the canoes into the water. Through the general tumult Father Vicente could catch a repeated name: 'Vessiva! Vessiva!' But that was Dona Elena's pagan name! He looked around: the two merchants of Malacca were obviously urging the master to up anchor and away; they wanted no risks with a good cargo of spices and sandalwood. The master glanced, half-deferential and half-deprecatory, towards Father Vicente, but looked away hastily as the Father made a move towards him.

There was one trained soldier in the tiny company, a man well enough fitted to take charge in an emergency like this, when a bold front might avert violence long enough for reasonable explanations. On the other hand he might be over-hasty—the Father had noted signs of impulsive temper—and the last thing Father Vicente desired was that any blood should be shed, unless, it might be, his own. But curiously enough Juan de Erédia, who had never before been backward in danger, was nowhere to be seen. Perhaps that was as well: this was a Christian field, and it was for a soldier of Christ, one moreover directly commissioned by Francis Xavier in person, to command; if need be to become the proto-martyr of the new Mission.

But at this point an arrow whistled overhead, the master jumped to activity, the anchor-cable was cut and the sails shaken out, and the little junk stood out of the bay; a couple of men with lighted match at the stern-chasers was hint enough to keep the canoes at a respectful distance.

As for that soldier of fortune Juan de Erédia, perhaps he had not felt himself the best man to take over this particular crisis. He was below, with Dona Elena. . . .

One may reasonably surmise that strong words passed between the Father and the soldier on the passage back to Malacca. They put as good a face as they might on the affair; but it was small consolation for the probable ruin of the Mission, that this hopeful convert Dona Elena made it very plain indeed that she had been a more than willing party to her own abduction. Father Vicente agreed to put into his written report the words 'married, or at least betrothed'; but he took good care, as soon as they reached Malacca, that Juan and his Elena were properly married, 'conformably to the Council of Trent'. There the matter rested.

251

1623

The very harassed Viceroy of the State of India was writing to the King. He inherited a great name, this Viceroy D. Francisco da Gama; but a little and a shrinking State. It was 1623, seventy-eight years since those still-heroic days of Father Vicente's triumphant Mission and his dejected return bringing back, to his own reluctance, a perhaps too-forthcoming convert. Now Dona Elena's son was dead, and since he had figured, frequently, in the official correspondence, the matter should be reported. . . .

Yes, there were plenty of references on the files. 'For years Manuel Godinho de Erédia has been sending me these papers of discoveries. . . .' And again, 'Manuel Godinho de Erédia is still sending me memorials of discoveries, as Your Majesty will remember he did to my predecessors for years. . . .' And again . . .

Well, he was dead now, and an end to his endless Memorials. Perhaps it would be enough simply to state the fact. Or perhaps a final summary, some judgement on the matter would be in order, lest some busybody on the Council of India should enquire why, given the poor state of the Treasury, nothing had been done about those vast potentialities in gold and spices of India Meridional. . . .

The Viceroy wrote, 'As for these papers of discoveries, I always thought that there was very little to them, no reason for putting any capital into the project—and still less now that we have so little. . . .'

That was the official epitaph on the magnificent obsession of Manuel Godinho de Erédia.

1956

Three hundred and thirty-three years later again, and I held in my hands the maps where Erédia had plotted the evidence on which his dream was based. Mere chance had given me the clue, the very day before I left London, and now the truly Illustrissima e Excelentissima Senhora Lygia da Fonseca Fernandes da Cunha said simply, 'Erédia? I have them here.' It had been a long trail: Sydney, London, Amsterdam, Lisbon, Rio de Janeiro; but there they were, boldly pricked out, those sailing routes from Java and Flores and Timor to the Isles of Gold. Some of the detail was admittedly disturbing; it was indeed rather shaking to read the legend 'Isles of Women who fight with arrows in the manner of the Amazons'; it did not square with my notions of the Australian aborigines.

But putting everything together, there seemed little doubt that behind all the fantastic scraps from Ptolemy and Marco Polo, behind all the chaos and the legend, Manuel Godinho de Erédia had something solid on which to base his persistent claim to be the pre-emptive Discoverer and Magistrate of India Meridional, which is the Isle of Gold, the Great Southland, Terra Australis, Australia. . . .

It does not of course really matter a damn whether or not 'Willem Jantszoon may have been the first To set a boot-print on our shores': for practical purposes the history of Australia is correctly reckoned from 26 January 1788. But the proto-history of the discovery has all the fascination of a detective story studded with false clues and with suspects who have regretfully to be dismissed. Except for another Portuguese, Quiros, and perhaps not even excepting him, there is no stranger figure in the whole gallery than Manuel Godinho de Erédia. He might perhaps be best described as magnificent raw material for Arnold Toynbee or Rex Ingamells, had either ever heard of him.

Erédia (or Herédia, as his name is often spelled) himself tells us the story of his parents' runaway marriage; or rather, for he had some of the instincts of the historian, he inserts into his *Declaration of Malacca* a properly attested account of the Macassar Mission, from which (with a slight addition of what I trust is local colour) my opening scene is drawn. Father Vicente's misadventure was in 1545, and it is pleasant to record that, although naturally much scandalized by the elopement, the Machioquique folk less naturally remained Christians, so that twelve years later Dona Elena succeeded in restoring friendly relations with her outraged family; though from some phrases in the document I strongly suspect that this was very largely at the instigation of the merchants of Malacca. There is a pleasant touch too in

Erédia's concluding remarks about his mother, although even here his obsession is plainly displayed:

> And I mention this baptism here, as it closely concerns me, as the legitimate son of D. Elena Vessiva, since God permitted that she should be baptized from idolatry, to bring me into the service of God and of the Crown of Portugal and Castile, with the new discoveries of India Meridional. And of her piety she did not wish to use the arms of Supa and Machioquique, but rather the starry heavens, as a dweller in their blessedness and glory; since by reason of her works and charity and continued devotion it is to be presumed that she enjoys that heaven which she blazoned.

I imagine that Manuel Godinho invented these arms for her: certainly heraldry was one of his many interests.

Manuel Godinho was the fourth child of the marriage, born in 1563. His father came of a family of Spanish hidalgos, settled in Portugal as a result of backing the wrong side in a dynastic dispute. A recent Portuguese writer, Quirino da Fonseca, makes the most of Manuel Godinho's affiliations:

> The father, in whose veins ran the ardent Aragonese blood, could not resist the advances—certainly attractive, though perilous—of a Malay princess. Since the romantic fact of the desire of an impetuous soldier for a Malay princess might well mean his losing his head—spiritually and materially— he decided to abduct his lover.

This is engaging language for a communication to the Academy of Sciences; but Erédia's complex ancestry endowed him with 'considerable capacities, which would have marked him out for distinction, had he lived in a less depressing milieu' than Malacca in the days of Portuguese decline. With this estimate I agree.

After studying at the Jesuits' school in Malacca, Erédia spent four adolescent years at their seminary in Goa. Here he gained a sound classical education, certainly in Latin, possibly even some Greek. Jesuit education had also intensely practical aspects, and Erédia became a rather uneven mathematical geographer, a good draughtsman and cartographer, and a more than competent surveyor, with at least enough skill in engineering to be entrusted with the design and execution of fortifications. Among the scores of maps, plans, and heraldic blazons in a fascinating MS. of his, recently discovered by Senhor Jorge Faro of Lisbon, there is a map of Goa which is one of the earliest representations of a city in strict plan, instead of by the method standard in his day, that of street-profiles in perspective. And according to Paul Wheatley of the University of Malaya, Erédia's survey of Malacca, both text and maps, kept far ahead of any similar work done in the region for at least two centuries after his day. He was certainly an admirable recorder of things which came under his direct observation, as is shown for instance by the delightful, and accurate, drawings of native boats and of plants which adorn the *Declaration of Malacca*. In matters of survey and cartography, therefore, Erédia is worthy of considerable respect.

It was probably soon after he left the Goa seminary in 1580 that Erédia developed the grand passion of his life, the quest for Nova India Meridional.

In Erédia's conception, India Meridional was approximately in the position of northwest Australia—and incidentally in that of the 'Jave la Grande' of the mid-sixteenth century Dieppe maps, which must derive from a Portuguese source (but that is another sub-plot in this complicated whodunnit). But in detail Erédia's ideas are an extraordinary jumble of borrowings, basically from Ptolemy, Marco Polo, and the Italian Ludovico di Varthema, who travelled extensively in southern Asia from 1502 on; all this shot through with more local legends. There is little point in trying to disentangle his confused conflations. His credulity and lack of critical power are only rarely mitigated by passages such as that in which he indicates, politely but firmly, that SS. Augustine and Lactantius, though Fathers of the Church, were quite wrong about the Antipodes. This of course had been common knowledge among the educated for centuries, but in view of Erédia's pronounced respect for ancient authority, it is noteworthy that here he goes out of his way to assert an independence.

In some respects, however, Erédia was remarkably up-to-date. The Faro MS., as I may call it, incorporates the discoveries of Mendoza, Quiros, and Torres; and the last of these at least is surprising since, although it is scarcely true that Torres' voyage was completely forgotten until the British discovered his report at the taking of Manila in 1762, knowledge of it was obviously restricted. It is also at first sight surprising that Erédia knows of Dutch discoveries almost as soon as they are made; but for some time he held a position, at least quasi-official, as cosmographer to the State of India, and its duties could have included military intelligence.

Erédia must be absolved from the charge sometimes loosely made against him, that he claimed to be the literal discoverer, the actual finder, of the land which appears on his maps with an outline very suggestive of Arnhem Land (and again of 'Jave la Grande'), and is inscribed: 'Nuca Antara discovered in 1601 by Manuel Godinho de Erédia by command of the Viceroy Aires de Saldanha.' The map however also shows very clearly, in the appropriate relative position, 'Land discovered by the Hollanders and called Eendracht or Concordia.' From Erédia's own accounts of his life and work it is clear that the Nuca Antara inscription was designed simply to assert his claims to it as lying within his sphere of projected discovery. This pre-emption was based on the facts that Erédia was firmly convinced of the existence of numerous islands, or even a landmass, roughly corresponding to the northwest of the actual Australian continent, and regarded himself as possessing priority rights in its exploration, by virtue of his royal patent to prosecute the discovery; not of course that all this would stop the Hollanders!

This commission, granted in 1594 by Philip I of Portugal (more familiar as Philip II of Spain) nominated him as 'Discoverer of India Meridional'; that is, it gave him priority rights to discover it, and, as was customary, appointed him Adelantado or Chief Magistrate of any lands that he should find. This was standard form; but one of the few things unmistakably clear in Erédia's writings is that he never sailed to India Meridional and never claimed to have done so, and the confusion on this point is only in the minds of later commentators chewing over citations of citations. In fact the burden of Erédia's later work is one of continuous lament at the constant frustration of his endeavours to turn his dream into reality. For that the times were out of joint; there was 'no reason for putting any capital into the project, and still less now that we have so little. . . .'

At the turn of the century, however, it must have seemed to Erédia that his hour had come, for he obtained what seemed important new evidence on the problem—evidence such that Aires de Saldanha prepared to act on the 1594 commission. It is at this point too that Erédia becomes of real significance to the question of early knowledge of Australia, knowledge not only pre-Dutch but pre-European. For in addition to his jumble of classical and medieval citations, ranging from Solomon's Ophir and Tarsis to Polo's Veach and Maletur, he imports a new element: direct reference to specific Malay voyages.

We must remember his half-Malay origin; remember also that, while not without the prejudices of his faith and time, he was a man of real intellectual curiosity, as is shown not only by his range of reading, but by the regional sections of the *Declaration of Malacca*, which are more than library or hearsay compilations, but are based on his own fieldwork—the direct (and carefully illustrated) descriptions of a man with his eye on the ground.

This *Declaration of Malacca and of India Meridional with Cathay* exists in Erédia's own MS. of 1613 in the Bibliothèque Royale at Brussels, and was published, with facsimiles of its fifty-odd maps and drawings, at Brussels in 1881-2. The fact that there is no reference whatever to it in the standard works on Australian discovery of Arnold Wood and Ernest Scott is a minor puzzle in this chaos of interlocking puzzles; unless indeed we ascribe it to pure ignorance of a not very excusable kind. Neither Wood nor Scott seems to have made any serious attempt to tap the numerous Portuguese sources bearing on the proto-history of Australian discovery; but even so, Erédia had been discussed perhaps more often outside than inside Portugal—in French and in English—when these Australian authorities wrote.

The three tracts or short treatises which make up the *Declaration* are of very unequal value. The first, the regional survey of Malacca and parts adjacent, is good first-hand stuff; the third, on Cathay, is rubbish. The second, which most nearly concerns us—it deals with India Meridional—is betwixt and between.

This second tract opens with an essentially Poloesque chapter on India Meridional in general, replete with the confusions of Java Major and Minor which are the despair, or one of the despairs, of students of the problem. But Erédia adds remarks on trade between the two Javas; and while one cannot swallow the identification of a land of spice and gold with aboriginal Australia, there is the curiously precise detail that contact between the two was broken for 331 years, until 1600. Where would he get 331 years, if not from Malay sources? Deliberate imaginative invention? But it is evident from his work that Erédia was no conscious faker of his evidence, but passionately convinced of its truth. And indeed he specifically refers to 'those verses and ballads and histories of the Empire of Mattaram'. The son of a Macassarese princess should have been in a better position to draw on Malay tradition than most men.

However, in 1600 a small craft from Luca Antara (the name is from Polo, and the indiscriminate use of Luca and Nuca seems mere clerical error) was brought to Java by storms and currents, and so excited the curiosity of King Chiaymasiuro of Damuth (probably at the extreme east of the island) that he decided to go and see for himself. As a conscientious historian, Erédia reproduces a letter of Chiaymasiuro describing his voyage, a weird document indeed, and (more soberly) a legally attested certificate from Pedro de Carvalhaes, a councillor of Malacca who was at Surabaya at the time, and met Chiaymasiuro.

After a twelve days' voyage, Chiaymasiuro reached an island full of gold and spices, inhabited by a people who except on one point—love of gaming—could not be identified with Australians, old or new, by the wildest and most imaginative dialectic. They wear fillets of gold in their hair, use a curved kris like that of Bali, and spend their time in sports and recreation, being especially addicted to cockfighting. Obviously, Chiaymasiuro did not get out of Indonesia. Yet one can hardly doubt that some southeasterly voyage was made. Pedro de Carvalhaes' certificate speaks of the event as being common talk in eastern Java, and is quite specific; he himself had the story from Chiaymasiuro at first hand. While he made his statement 'because the discoverer Manuel Godinho de Erédia asked this information of me, for the benefit of his voyage, and because it is for the service of the King', this seems no reason for a responsible official swearing to a pure invention. Rather the reverse, looking to the last clause.

More fantastic in some ways, in others more convincing, is another certificate from the obliging Pedro de Carvalhaes, concerning a small craft from Ende (Flores) which was caught in a typhoon and, unable to make Savu or Roti (which close the Savu Sea to the south, between Soemba and Timor), was driven to a large unknown island—promptly identified by Erédia with Polo's Luca Veach. The people once more seem to be Malays, though their weapons are tipped by fishes' teeth. The island was surrounded by reefs and a narrow belt of thick seaweed, so that the boat's people had to cut a passage to reach the shore; this does not look like an invented detail.

This island lay to the south of an uninhabited 'Pulo Cambin', which has been identified with the present Kambing or with the Ashmole and Cartier Reefs—and these are only 220 miles from Australia and still visited by Indonesian fishermen, who habitually set up temporary camps on them. The standard Portuguese reference on the toponymy of the Discoveries regards the latter identification as 'precarious', but it seems much less precarious than that with Kambing, which is not uninhabited and lies only 12 miles from Dili, capital of Portuguese Timor, where the Portuguese had been established since about 1520.

Moreover, in the Carvalhaes narrative there are further uninhabited islands—perhaps the Seringapatam Reefs?—between this Pulo Cambin and Luca Veach. This seems to rule out absolutely the Kambing identification, since such details cannot possibly be made to apply to a place north and in sight of so large and well-known an island as Timor.

Unfortunately, at this point Pedro de Carvalhaes enters the realms of fantasy. Not only do the voyagers pass the Isle of Women (Polo again), but on Luca Veach they see a positive mountain of gold, the gullies on its flanks gleaming with the metal. Just possibly one could pass this off as an exfoliated dome of some highly micaceous rock, and the gold which they took on (as much as the boat could carry) as pyrites. But then a cursory examination in the bazaar would dispose of anyone trying to pass pyrites for gold, and yet Carvalhaes says that after a further storm in which all the gold not needed for ballast had to be thrown overboard, there was still enough left to be the source of all the gold circulating in Savu!

By one of the abrupt turns with which the student of Erédia is familiar, we re-enter a more normal world of affairs. At this time Pedro de Carvalhaes was captain of the Portuguese fort at Ende and was advised of the matter, in all its glittering detail, by

the most honourable and powerful natives of that Christendom. . . . And on this information I immediately ordered the purchase and fitting-out of two oared vessels, provided with the necessary stores and pilots and seamen of Ende, to make the voyage to Luca Veach. And the vessels being ready to weigh anchor and set sail, then the Fathers of the Preaching Order [Dominicans], as Vicars-General of that Christendom and Administrators of the South, requested of me, with much insistence, that I should in any case prevent that voyage, because the Christians, as ignorant of the navigation and without knowledge of the latitudes, without doubt would certainly meet their perdition and death in that Ocean. And from respect to this solemn demand of the Religious, I undid the design, and did not execute that rich voyage to Luca Veach, or the Isle of Gold. . . .

This was not the only time in the Portuguese story in the East that worldly men proposed and the godly disposed otherwise; there was for example the tragi-comedy of Buddha's Tooth, a hostage worth excellent commercial treaties with the monarchs of Kandy and Pegu, but at the behest of the Archbishop of Goa solemnly pounded to pieces with pestle and mortar: no trafficking with idolatry! But to Erédia, Pedro de Carvalhaes' loss was his gain; these certificates which he furnished in Malacca in 1601 warranted a new—and this time a successful!—approach to the authorities.

Erédia had other evidence in his files, plenty of it: a number of other voyages, voluntary or storm-driven, which fetched up at isles which had in common that they were isles of gold. Some of his accounts are wild romanticism, derived from Malay or Arab legends and songs, the probable source of Polo's Isle of Women. Others can be rationalized to some extent: the great depopulated cities and fortresses of stone, eight days south of Luca Antara, might well be some bold headland of the Kimberley region— even with good field-glasses and from the stable deck of a modern ship it is sometimes difficult to distinguish massively stratified rocks from masonry, and indeed one profile in *The Australian Pilot* looks so genuinely artificial that the ship's officer with whom I saw it could scarcely be persuaded that these battlements and gateways could not be the work of human hands. But what are we to make of the ship *São Paulo*, which in 36° south, sailing many days to the east, came to the Isle of Wax, so named 'from the many pieces of wax which they found on the shore, marked with different Arabic letters'? Or of the 'ship of Holland, which, with a tempest in 41° south, found that Terra Firma of the South, where they found many Portuguese, sons and grandsons of others who were wrecked on the coast, and had arms and artillery in their possession, but went naked and unkempt'? From Erédia's world-map, if that is evidence, these would seem to be tales of shipwrecks respectively on St Paul or Amsterdam, and Kerguelen or Crozet.

Rather more serious (perhaps) is 'the case of Francisco

261

S

de Resende with the Malacca junk, which after taking on a cargo of sandalwood at Timor, was driven by a typhoon to the Southland', where the natives prevented them from landing. But once more—again and again this seductive but destructive detail—these natives came into the water up to their waists, to exchange gold. . . .

Probably one element in this mass of dubiety was the tendency of the Malay imagination (perhaps as long ago as Polo's day) to push further and further south a land which their hearers often identified with the Golden Chersonese of Ptolemy. As Ferrand points out in his study of the medieval kingdom of Sailendra or Sri Vijaya (based in Sumatra), for a long time both Portuguese and Dutch overlooked the genuine, if limited, local sources of gold owing to an obsession, carefully fostered by the Malays, with the Isle(s) of Gold known to exist some 300 leagues south or southeast of Sumatra. This *Ilha de Ouro* crops up incessantly in the documentation (not only in Erédia); and at least it serves to demolish completely Arnold Wood's airy assertion in *The Discovery of Australia* that there was no motive for any Portuguese advance beyond the Moluccas.

Even without this element of Eldorado-round-the-corner, what more motive did the men of a self-conscious age need but the memory of the voyage, but a few decades back, by which Columbus had gained certain, indefeasible, immortality? And indeed we know that in 1518-19 and again in 1521 Portuguese expeditions set out from Malacca to go south of Sumatra and find the Ilha de Ouro. One was lost; of the other we do not know what it found, if anything; but it seems likely that here was the origin of the remarkable similarity of 'Jave la Grande' on the Dieppe maps to the general lie of northwestern Australia. At all events, with all the fabulous accretions, there seem to be too many hints of a 'Southland' in the Portuguese literature for us to dismiss the Dieppe outlines, as Wood and Scott do, as the result of 'voyages of imagination'; and indeed on several points these authors can be convicted of faulty reasoning from inadequate or inaccurate premises. Erédia cannot have known of the Dieppe maps, and seems indeed to know nothing of the earlier Portuguese voyages, which is puzzling. But he was following up another trail, starting from the other end of Indonesia.

Certainly the evidence he collected enhanced his credit with the authorities. His two most recent and specific reports depended on Pedro de Carvalhaes' certificates: and in judging whether any credence can be placed on them as evidence for a pre-Dutch knowledge of Australia, we must remember that he was a man of some position and would not wish to risk it. One can of course assume that he was simply shooting a line, playing up to Manuel Godinho's probably notorious monomania with a tavern tale. But would a councillor of Malacca sign, and swear on the Gospels, to a joke, and a joke which would be immediately investigated by a man with a passionate personal interest in the matter, and one in good standing with the Viceroy? Fantastic as what Carvalhaes says is (in part), his manner of saying it carries some conviction. Twined thick with legend, there was yet something in the way of fact to go upon; and so at this time we find Erédia nearest his heart's desire. In all probability that would have led him to Australia—in command of an expedition with competent pilots, he himself a first-class map-maker and a good reporter of what he saw.

The documentation must have included an exemplar of the 1602 map in the Biblioteca Nacional at Rio de Janeiro, on which Erédia had marked his interpretations of the actual tracks of three Malay voyages to the south. They seem realistic enough, and one of them starts from Timor and seems to end somewhere on the Kimberley coast. The voyages of 1518 and 1521 had gone to the south of Sumatra and Java, a rather hazardous navigation (the south Java coast is still avoided), whence perhaps their lack of success or (if that of 1521 came to anything) of follow-up. But Erédia knew, what is obvious from our maps today, that Flores or Timor would be a better jumping-off place. He made careful plans to use the local monsoons, and after harbouring for the bad weather in Timor, Ende, or Savu, 'in August or September [a month or so early for good winds] with the name of God the all-powerful to undertake the discovery of the fortunate Isle of Gold'.

About 1602, then, the prize seemed at last within Erédia's grasp. Not only had he the precious royal nomination as *Descobridor e Adelantado da Nova India Meridional*, but two successive Viceroys had approved the project and the second, Aires de Saldanha, had actually appointed ships and men. All was set for the great enterprise; but this time it was the ungodly who disposed otherwise.

> Being in Malacca, waiting ready to go into the South, to effect the voyage to India Meridional, the land of gold, there happened the wars of the fortress of Malacca with the Malays, so that the military personnel of the enterprise had to stay in Malacca, for the defence of that fortress, and the Hollanders blockaded the embouchures and passages of Bali and Solor, without which this fortunate voyage could not be effected. . . .

The rest is anti-climax to a climax which never happened. Erédia himself played his part in the wars, designing the fortifications of Muar and harassing the Malays with a flotilla of small craft. Between times he explored the hinterland, mapping the country and locating deposits of gold (of course), silver, mercury, tin, and iron.

But he did not as yet give up hope. The enterprise was only reserved for the time when peace and tranquillity returned to the South; then he would 'go to take possession of that land to incorporate it with the Crown of Portugal and to open up the trade of Luca Antara with Malacca, for the good of the customs revenue'.

The Crown and the Cross were never far separated in his mind. While he was in the hinterland of Malacca he had a vision of a cross in the sky, clear evidence of heavenly favour for his design; pathetically, he had this set down in detail and properly attested by Father Belchior Figueira of Malacca. It is probably to this that he refers in a moving passage of a letter to D. Francisco da Gama:

> Since I am no more than a servant and instrument for effecting this discovery of gold, and my conscience torments me to

undertake this discovery since God has favoured me therein. And therefore I cry to Your Most Illustrious Lordship that you may cast your eyes upon me for such great good, in which Your Most Illustrious Lordship will have a great portion. . . .

But the sands were running out, for Erédia and for the Crown which he served with such devotion. The Dutch talons were firmly set into the dying Portuguese dominion. 'Trade supports war and war supports trade' was the avowed motto of the Hollanders, and before this virility of a young bourgeoisie there was no hope for the outmoded State of India, headed by such poor faded figures as Erédia's da Gama, an unworthy descendant of the great Vasco. Portugal had lost heart even in the homeland with the subjugation to Spain, by a mixture of dynastic accident and dynastic lunacy, in 1580. Liberation in Lisbon by the revolution of 1640 was offset in the East by the Dutch capture of Malacca itself in 1641, after a very gallant defence.

By the time his home town fell Erédia had been dead for eighteen years. But his hopes must have died before him; though he continued, by a not uncommon sort of conditioned reflex, to send each new Viceroy those Memorials of the advantages of the discovery, those reminders of past promises: doubtless the old bore was a figure of fun to everybody except the clerks who had to listen politely. In 1610 he applied for the position of Cartographer-General, to be told that there was no need of such a post. Not that the bureaucracy was unkind: the King wrote to the Viceroy, 'As for the business of Manuel Godinho de Erédia, there is nothing to be done about it for the reasons you have given; but I recommend that you should favour him in accordance with his capacities, etc.' And so, like Quiros, he died probably as much from the heart-sickness of hope deferred as from anything else. For the state which he loved was itself sunk in the dark apathy of despair.

The *Declaration of Malacca* contains two drawings which bring the man before us in all his frustrated romanticism. One is the Arms of Nova India Meridional: a scutcheon with a dove displayed, a branch of greenery in its beak—the dove of Noah's deluge, as is shown by the motto: *columba venit portans ramum*. The other is his self-portrait: a coat of arms, more authentic-looking heraldry than his own blazons and so probably the arms of Erédia, is in one corner. He himself stands in doublet and gown, with short beard and close-cut hair, a high forehead and a look of weary dignity and melancholy puzzlement, a suggestion of a Laputan sage. But his right hand rests on a globe, the thumb firmly indicating the two Javas and Luca Antara, the land of his dreams.

Surely this ever-fantastic, ever-frustrated creature deserves a sympathetic memory. His work is in large part a medley of incurable romanticism, mystical credulity, uncriticized fable; yet there can be little doubt that it includes a nucleus of solid fact. If he never discovered India Meridional for himself, he devoted his life to the assertion of its existence and the amassing of evidence to support that assertion; at times, at least, he got near the truth; and in the last resort perhaps only bad luck robbed him of the fame he so ardently coveted. With capacities both for imaginative creativity and for solid painstaking work, with a limitless faith in and devotion to his ideal, in another place and time he might well have left his name as something more than that of an odd obscure dreamer in a forgotten corner of a dying Empire. In his queer confused way, he was a believer in Australia before Australia was.

Note: Apart from Erédia's own *Declaracam de Malaca* (MS., 1613, printed Brussels 1881-2, source of all quotations unless otherwise indicated), the essay is based mainly on: O. Martins, 'Godinho de Herédia', in *Portugal nos Mares* (Lisbon, 1889; fourth edition 1954); Q. da Fonseca, 'A participao dos portugueses . . . no descobrimento da Austrália', *Mem. da Acad. das Ciências de Lisboa* (Coimbra, 1937) and J. Faro, 'Manuel Godinho de Erédia, Cosmográfo', *Panorama* (Lisbon, 1955).

I should like to express my thanks to Senhor Faro, to Senhora Fernandes da Fonseca of the Biblioteca Nacional at Rio de Janeiro, and to Senhor Alexandre Marques Pereira, of the Sociedade de Geográfia, Lisbon.

Terra Australis – Cognita?

I. INTRODUCTORY: OPEN QUESTION, OR CLOSED?

> Willem Jantszoon may have been the first
> To set a bootprint on our shores, but he
> Disqualified himself by being Dutch
> From celebration in our history . . .[1]

JANTSZOON or Torres, Hollander or Portingall—the point of priority is perhaps merely a trifle *sub specie aeternitatis* and on the Theatre of the World. But it has a natural interest for Australians, and as an exercise in historical detection it is engagingly replete with hopeful clues which lead nowhere, dark sayings which cut both ways, and suspects who have to be let off, till it all ends in a dismal verdict of Not Proven.

It is then more than a little surprising that the only full-length work on the Discovery written by a professional historian should be Arnold Wood's printed lectures, which are not documented to the standard which might reasonably be expected in dealing with so complex a problem.* The subject is a mere incident in the history of Portugal

Reprinted from *Historical Studies Australia and New Zealand*, Vol. 8 No. 29, 1957.

* All references to Wood are to *The Discovery of Australia*, London, 1922; his earlier papers in the *Journal* of the Australian Historical Society are substantially reproduced in it. Lest the remark above seem harsh, let me draw attention to the 'Authorities' at the head of each chapter: no dates, few indications of editions used in a sphere where this is of exceptional importance, and such delightfully vague references as 'Motley's *Dutch Republic*', with on the other hand citations by volume and page of a work succinctly given as 'King' and nowhere referred to by title.

and the Netherlands, not even that for France; and yet the footnotes to this paper would suggest a different story.

Disregarding sectarian romanticism, the standard view still seems to be that of Arnold Wood and Ernest Scott: that the *Duyfken*'s landfall in 1606 was not only the first recorded, but the first to take place. This may indeed be true; but the evidence suggesting that the Portuguese had some fairly definite knowledge of Australia long before 1606—perhaps by 1526—is cumulatively stronger than Scott and Wood were willing to admit, though it must be admitted in return that it adds up to no more than fairly strong probability.

Neither Wood nor Scott appears to have had any first-hand knowledge of Portuguese sources, in itself a serious limitation; nor did they always make as careful use of the material available in English and French as they might have done. Moreover the problem is one of historical geography (on any definition of that much-defined term), and as such is concerned with the nature of places as well as with men and their documents. Disregard of actual geographical conditions at times robs their arguments of much of their point; this is notably true of their remarks about Java. Again, the documents of this branch of historical geography are largely maps, and neither of our authorities seems to have had much expertise in the highly technical history of cartography. I cannot claim such expertise myself, but a general geographical training does at least assist in weighing cartographical evidence.

Wood simply turned a lecture course into a book with very little editing—which makes it the more lively but the less viable as scholarship. Scott's interest in exploration as such seems to have been much keener than Wood's, but it is difficult to resist the impression that to him this pre- or proto-history, so untidy and so difficult to pin down, was a necessary nuisance to be got through before the real matter-of-fact of precise dates and documents was reached.* Both

* As Scott put it in his address to the 1926 meeting of ANZAAS at Perth, 'If we would get rid of obscurantism in connection with the history of Australian discovery we should take our stand on the solid

could not but realize that it was essential to go into that part of earlier cartographical and nautical history which concerned Australia, but that part in turn was but a part of their historical interests: their hearts and minds were more deeply involved elsewhere. Wood indeed surrendered to the charm of medieval speculation about the Antipodes, but he pays if anything too much attention to the hangover of Ptolemaic geography, which had very little effect on Portuguese geographical thinking; otherwise of course they would never have tried to round the southern extremity of Africa, which was non-existent on a Ptolemaic view. But all this, and especially the easy game of making fun of Cosmas Indicopleusthes, is very little relevant, and is indeed misleading in attaching far too much importance to the very few educated medievals who were flat-earthers.

Their history is nautical rather than navigational, their geography often rather naïve 'outlines'. Hence maps to them are simply shapes on paper: their more purely intellectual origins may indeed be faithfully analysed, but the bearings of the three-dimensional facts of geography on actual discovery, the complications involved in plotting them—these are incompletely apprehended.

One has of course a natural tendency to discount the significance of evidence which one cannot evaluate fully for oneself, and this may account in part for scepticism as to Portuguese claims. The converse is true, and this may well affect my own thinking. It certainly affected Collingridge, whose advocacy of Portuguese priority was unrestrained and uncritical; Wood's reference to him ('groping in a fog, we are both guessers') is a gesture of courtesy from professional to amateur, and as such perhaps too consciously modest.

---

fact that nothing is known of this country until the Dutch came upon it in the 17th century.' Just so: and for three and a half centuries 'nothing was known of North America until Columbus came upon it in 1492'; but the Norse discovery is now a matter of historical fact, and although voyages later than the sagas are not precisely documented (the evidence is not unlike that presented in Section IV below), there can be scarcely any doubt of their occurrence—and this without reliance on the dubious Kensington Stone. Surely obscurantists are those who *close* questions.

One can well understand a sceptical reaction to Collingridge's exaggerated claims, but Wood and Scott veer too
far in the other direction. Few serious students would be
willing to dismiss the Dieppe maps so summarily as Scott
does when he remarks that the 'Dauphin' map

> was long believed to have been prepared from some unknown
> Portuguese original, and to afford proof that Portuguese
> navigators were acquainted with part at least of the coast of
> Australia between 1511 and 1529; but closer examination has
> dissipated that belief completely.[2]

That the Dieppe maps afford *proof* is a prejudicial over-
statement; but the more closely they are examined, the
stronger is the case for a Portuguese original, and one might
almost say that the only thing likely to be dissipated would
be Scott's competence to judge.

It is the object of this essay to suggest that some serious
reconsideration is needed. Since Wood and Scott have been
criticized above in general terms, it seems best to begin
with an examen of some points where they seem to me to
go astray; and this may relieve the more positive discussion
from being too much cluttered up with polemical asides.

It should, I hope, be obvious that adverse criticism of one
sector of the work of Wood and Scott neither implies nor
is meant to imply any depreciation of their contribution to
Australian historiography in general. Even in this field, it
would be difficult to better Wood's elucidation of the wan-
derings of those romantically vagabond lands which seem
to have been invented for the despairing puzzlement of the
student—Pathalis Regio, Brasil Inferior, the Javas Major
and Minor, and all the misbegotten progeny of Polo.

II. EXAMEN

1. *The south coast of Java*

Both Scott and Wood make much of the fact that little
was certainly known of the south coast of Java during the
sixteenth century; *a fortiori*, nothing at all could be known
of lands still further south. This does not follow, and as
the point is revealing of the geographical and linguistic

limitations of our authorities, it may be examined in some detail.

Scott says specifically that the Portuguese 'were acquainted only with the north coast' of Java, basing himself on a quotation from Diogo do Couto, who is not named but cited as the writer of one of 'the few [!] books written by Portuguese travellers during the 16th century'.[3] Do Couto's *Decadas da Asia* is not a travel book at all, as Scott implies, but a formal history of repute; as the reference does not appear in editions of Scott's book before 1922, its proximate source is obvious. As quoted by Scott following Wood following Collingridge, do Couto says that the south coast 'is not frequented by us': not quite the same as the gloss. The verb he uses, *tratar*, is not given as 'frequent' in standard dictionaries; what do Couto means is either 'we [Portuguese] do not trade with' or (rather less likely) 'we [editorial] do not treat of' the south coast. Actually these come to much the same thing—an admission of ignorance—but the bold glossing of an unchecked quotation is a little disturbing.

Wood, if not more specific, is at least less cursory; and he gives a show of documentation—that is, he tells us from whom he borrows his quotations. One may protest, however, that 'Diogo do Couto, writing about 1570' is a damned inadequate reference to a book which in the 1778-88 Lisbon edition runs to thirteen volumes totalling 5,996 pages—admittedly little ones.*

Not a word in Spanish or Portuguese sources, says Wood (adding a saving 'so far as I know') to suggest knowledge of anything south of Java, except one passage in Galvano [Galvão]; but 'a good many which suggest ignorance'. These turn out to be: the sentence from do Couto just discussed; another from Barros; and an extract from Themera (1558) 'quoted by Major as representing the best Spanish opinion of the time', but actually translating what seems little more

* The do Couto reference is *Da Asia*, Dec. II Liv. iii Cap. 3—p. 165 of Vol. IV* (so numbered) in the edition mentioned; all references to Joao de Barros and his continuator do Couto are to this edition (in Mitchell Library). Luckily the sentence cited is in the first of the do Couto volumes!

than a confused piece of Marco Polo from one Johannes Bohemus—a distinctly suspect source for serious knowledge of its date. The rest of the 'good many words' from Spanish or Portuguese are—Wood's recollections of Fra Mauro (1459) and Friar Odoric (*c.* 1330)!

As a *pièce de résistance,* however, we are introduced to Linschoten (who, incidentally, did *not* 'visit the Far East'; he got no nearer to it than Goa):

> If we are to believe this very intelligent and well-informed Dutch traveller, the natives of the North coast of Java did not even know whether their land was an island, or was a tip of the great Southern Continent . . . reaching to the neighbourhood of the Cape of Good Hope.[4]

But this is a most unlikely, almost an outrageous, interpretation of Linschoten's words, which in the 1598 translation quoted by Wood run:

> . . . touching the breadth, it is not found, because as yet it is not discovered, nor by the inhabitants themselves well known. Some think it to be firm land and parcel of the country called *Terra Incognita,* which, being so, should reach from that place to the Capo de Bona Sperance, but as yet it is not certainly known, and therefore it is accounted an island.*

Surely 'Some think' = *on dit*; 'some people', not 'some of the natives'; this is the straightforward reading, and it is surely illogical that the Javanese should not know that they lived on an island, and yet be aware of the Ptolemaic *Terra Incognita,* which to them must have been *Inaudita*! In any case, it is not the Javanese but the Portuguese view that matters here, and contemporary Portuguese writers speak of Java as an island as a matter of course.

This reliance on second-hand quotation may have been

---

* The punctuation of the Dutch text ('. . . *noch vande selfde inwooders bekent, sommighe presumeren dat het vast land is* . . .') oddly enough would have supported—slightly—Wood's reading more than either the translation he used or that in J. E. Heeres, *The Part borne by the Dutch in the Discovery of Australia 1606-1765,* London and Leiden, 1899, p. 2. The interpretation here suggested was confirmed by enquiries in the Netherlands.

unavoidable, but it might at least have suggested a little more caution in commenting on quotations out of context and unchecked. Conversely it results in passages relevant to the thesis being overlooked. Much more to the point than Wood's citation from Barros, with its tales which remind him of Friar Odoric (and such tales were deliberately spread by the Portuguese to warn other navigators off), is a passage in which the author states definitely that the Portuguese had not yet sailed along the south coast. But he gives good reasons for this and for the lack of contact between north and south: the mountains run the length of the island and, 'according to the natives, all the coast of that part has few harbours, by reason of the great inrush [golfão] of the South sea'.[5] It will be seen that Barros gives very little support to Wood's theory of Javanese ignorance of insularity.

One need not dispute the fact that the south coast of Java was indeed very little known and less frequented. But that this is neither remarkable nor remarkably important can be seen from the further fact that it is still relatively true— as is suggested by even a small-scale atlas map. Steep-to, with very little coastal plain and even today with only one port of any significance, it is moreover a lee coast on a grand scale, with deep water close inshore—a type of coast dreaded in sailing-ship days, as lack of soundings gave no warning of its proximity when visibility was poor, and, worse still, no holding ground. Only in January do the winds blow at all steadily from the north; for the rest of the year they are from east round to south-west, and the latter direction is the prevalent one in what was the normal 'open' sailing season: and they fetch across the immense width of the Indian Ocean. References to lack of survey or landward inaccessibility, and phrases like 'so far as is known', occur on almost every page of the Admiralty *Pilot* dealing with this coast:

> This coast is bold and precipitous, less indented than the north coast, and is exposed to a heavy and dangerous swell which rolls in at all seasons; this coast is little frequented . . . steep rocks and rugged points, covered always with breakers,

and the whole having a barren and desolate appearance . . . although in some cases a less forbidding beach and a decreased depth may be found, yet they very seldom afford a fit spot for anchoring, by reason of a heavy swell which breaks unceasingly on all exposed points, or rolls into the bays and havens. Notwithstanding this, the south coast of Java is not altogether destitute of places of refuge.[6]

When I mentioned this point to the Director of the Maritime Museum at Amsterdam, his response was immediate: 'A terrible coast—*that swell*!' If this is the mental association of an officer on a modern warship, it is little wonder that Portuguese and Javanese craft gave this coast the widest of berths. We do not need to recall the legends of Friar Odoric; we do need to pay some attention to geography when writing of problems in historical geography.

2. *The question of motive*

Having treated this matter with an air of pained surprise ('the strange ignorance of the South coast of Java, which is a matter of singular importance in our story'), Wood goes off on the opposite tack:

> Nor does it seem to me that there is the least reason to be surprised by this apparent ignorance. There is nothing whatever suspicious about it. It is what we should have expected.[7]

This not for the solid geographical reasons just set forth, but because (i) the ships and men available were few—which is true, but not enough; and (ii) once the Moluccas and their spices were reached, 'There was little motive for further exploration'—or, more strongly, 'everything that we know of the ideas and habits of the Portuguese and Spaniards in this period makes it highly improbable that these discoveries should be made'—again because of difficult navigation, shortage of men, and 'lack of motive for voyages of detailed and scientific survey'.

Although, as befits one using a lecturing technique, Wood is not afraid of a certain dramatically subjective presentation of his argument (for example, in the equation of Quiros and Arias with Don Quixote) one feels that there is here a very marked failure of empathy. There is no reason at all to think that the Dieppe maps Wood is here discussing, if not 'the product of voyages of imagination', could only be produced by 'detailed and scientific survey'. The introduction of the last phrase begs the question; although, as we shall see, there is some evidence that they were sought for, accidental reconnaissance could easily account for the outlines shown on these maps. This being so, then from 'everything that we know of the ideas and habits of the Portuguese and Spaniards in this period', it is abundantly clear that very little motive indeed was needed to set them off exploring.

And why not? When d'Abreu reached the Moluccas it was only twenty years since Columbus had achieved an indefeasible immortality; it was an age both self-conscious and adventurous, there were still new worlds to discover—and perhaps only very academic people would think more motive necessary in the age of Eldorado.

Not only was Eldorado just around the corner as a general thing, but in this case there was a specific Eldorado—the Isle(s) of Gold which were well known to lie south or southeast of Sumatra. It seems likely that Malay and Arab traders deliberately misled the Portuguese, and later the Dutch, as to the true source of the gold locally circulating, to head them away from limited but definite local deposits,[8] but the account given to Diogo Pacheco in 1518 was seductive enough:

> more or less south of that port of Barros [Baros or Barus, in Sumatra], at a hundred-odd leagues, there was a chain of shoals and reefs, in the midst of which was an island, not very flat, and full of palms along its shores, in which lived many black people, with whom they exchanged gold at the water's edge . . . who gave a great quantity of gold for some cloths of Cambay. . . .[9]

The same story is told by Erédia a hundred years later, and we shall return to Barros, both port and author; for the moment it suffices that there was motive for voyages south of Java.

3. *Manuel Godinho de Erédia*

The omission by both Wood and Scott of all mention of a man who had been formally, if falsely, proclaimed the first European discoverer of Australia is surprising; the more so in that on one point at least his silence could be interpreted as an argument in support of their thesis that Portuguese claims were fallacious. They might be entitled to dismiss Manuel Godinho de Erédia as a crank, a Quiros *manqué*, though it seems likely that there was something definite behind his queer confusions; but it is extraordinary that he is not even mentioned as a curiosity—one would have thought him admirable raw material for Wood's effective half-romantic half-colloquial style.[10] It is not a matter of linguistic difficulty or unavailability: when Wood wrote, Erédia had been discussed perhaps as often in English and French as in Portuguese, and even mentioned by Tenison Woods in 1865.[11] Most of the more relevant works are in the original Mitchell collection, and Rainaud's 'perhaps, was most useful' of all Wood consulted.[12]

Erédia certainly did not discover Australia, nor did he claim to have done so in a literal physical sense. But he is decisive as to the question of motive (were more decision needed!); and he presents some evidence, confused and in part dubious as it may be, of Malay voyages to a Southland. He has thus a definite, if small and ambiguous, place in the proto-history of Australia. Moreover, from Wood's own point of view, his silence as to previous Portuguese voyages, his ignorance of the Dieppe maps or their original, are arguments (though in my opinion far from conclusive) against a pre-Dutch discovery.

III. THE PEDIGREE OF DIEPPE

Sooner or later any discussion of the proto-history of the Discovery must grapple with the problem of the Dieppois maps of 'Jave la Grande'. Their dates and general features are so well known that it should not be necessary to particularize them, but a few suggestive points may be examined.[13]

To begin with, it does not seem necessary to gamble on all or nothing, to adopt Wood's completely negative verdict ('brilliant geographical romances') or else to go to the other extreme of maintaining that the maps represent detailed knowledge of the coasts from Cape Leeuwin north about to Cape Howe (or beyond), as is claimed for example by Collingridge and Gago Coutinho.

The essential fact is simple, and difficult to explain away: six world and nine regional maps produced in northern France between 1540 and 1566 show a large land-mass with a rough approximation to the trends of the Australian coast, and in the right latitudes—though the meridians are much too wrong to be explained by the well-known difficulty of determining longitude. It seems futile, and is unnecessary, to attempt to match each cape and bay with corresponding real features; as J. A. Williamson points out, though Jean Rotz's version, in many ways the best of the series,

> is not a good map . . . its eastern and western coasts bear a greater resemblance to the true outline than do the coasts of the Americas in La Cosa's Spanish map of 1500, which embodied the results of numerous voyages of discovery.[14]

Rotz is allowed on all hands to be an unusually conscientious cartographer, careful to distinguish between the known and the hypothetical: even so, his outlines of the inner arms of the Baltic are extremely inaccurate, of northern Scotland diagrammatic and almost Ptolemaic; and when one has noted this, there seems little point in trying to locate Port Jackson or Port Phillip on a Dieppe map. All too often students of these maps never lift their eyes from Jave la Grande.

The pedigree of Dieppe is undoubtedly Portuguese, as is shown by the more or less bastardized Portuguese toponymy of most of the series. The only serious argument for a French origin is, I think, Hervé's, based on a rather vague remark in Fonteneau's *La cosmographie avec l'espère* (MS., 1544): 'so far as I have seen, it [Jave la Grande] is a mainland'. On the face of it, this does not imply direct knowledge: but the full passage seems a curious mixture

277

T

of Ptolemaic ideas and a claim to first-hand experience of Antarctic latitudes. However, rather than fall into the trap of glossing a passage unseen in the original, we may let it pass, and note only that Forsyth indicates that if not actually Portuguese, Fonteneau must have been in Portuguese service, and that Hervé himself lays more emphasis on 'a secret document emanating from the archives of the Portuguese Crown' as the main source.[15] Wood, admitting a Portuguese origin, forgets his 'voyages of imagination' and regards the originals as 'made for the use of Portuguese seamen, and according to the best Portuguese knowledge'.[16]

Scott postulates a Catalan original, for which he offers no scrap of evidence except that 'the figures [on Desceliers' map] are very like the decorations which at this period Catalan mapmakers used'.[17] It is not clear which of the three or four maps by Desceliers is meant—their decorative style varies considerably—but decorative portulans were no Catalan monopoly. There is not even a hint of Catalan or Provençal maritime enterprise anywhere near these regions, unless we think that 'Cap de Grace' on Guillaume le Testu's map of *c.* 1555-6 recalls his alleged birthplace Grasse in Provence and so are 'fondés à admettre que des marins provençaux, parmi lesquels se trouvait peut-être Guillaume le Testu, ont à une date antérieure à 1555 abordé à quelque point de la côte australienne'—always assuming that he *was* born at Grasse and not (as was in fact the case) at Havre-de-Grace in Normandy! But this map is last but one of the series, the rest of which are firmly Norman; and le Testu omits Jave la Grande altogether from a map of 1566, which seems an improbable thing to do had he been there. If therefore a Portuguese source be ruled out, the logical claimants would be the Dieppois with their long tradition of distant voyaging.*

* Shown e.g. by their alleged priority in West Africa, or by Gonneville's voyage of 1503-4—probably to Brazil, although encyclopaedias still occasionally refer to it as possibly reaching Australia, a claim totally discredited and abandoned by serious students. The Norman brothers Parmentier were in Sumatra *c.* 1529, which may indicate the channel by which the information on the Dieppe maps reached France.

But once more it helps to look beyond Jave la Grande. Jean Rotz was a Dieppois, probably of Scots descent (= Ross); yet in the Atlas he presented to Henry VIII of England, which contains two maps of Jave la Grande, the coast of England itself carries a number of straight Portuguese forms, amongst others:

agulhas (The Needles)	*a bosco*	(New Forest)
antona (Southampton)	*cidade velha*	(Old Selsey?)

Not of course that Henry the Navigator's men discovered Hampshire or that the Dieppois never reached it; but why should Rotz use Portuguese names on a coast within a hundred miles of his home town—unless he was basing his Atlas on a Portuguese original?

There is more positive evidence that the toponymy, though not without difficulties, leaves no place for any but a Portuguese origin. Particularly significant is an obviously garbled place name on the north coast of Java (which is practically coterminous with Jave la Grande on the Dieppe maps). This name appears variously as Agnada Dollim, Guada Allim, Agnada Dallom, and Agoada Dallom. Inexplicable as it stands, it becomes clear when we find an expanded version on a map of *c.* 1513-14 by Francisco Rodrigues: 'agoada de Joham lopez dalluim elle descobriu daqui ate Japara' (i.e. 'watering-place of J. L. d'A. who discovered from here to Japara'); and we know that in 1513 João Lopes de Alvim made a close examination of this coast. This is not of course evidence that the Portuguese discovered Australia, but it seems to demonstrate indisputably that the source of the Dieppe maps is Portuguese.

These points seem to me quite decisive, even without the Portuguese flags which adorn Jave la Grande on the first and last of the Dieppe series, Desliens' maps of 1541 and 1566. These bring us to a stumbling-block which Scott triumphantly fell over: the vignettes liberally scattered over some of the maps, notably those of Vallard (1547) and Pierre Desceliers of Arques (1546, 1550, 1553).

Taken literally, these are fatal: this is not Australia. But even here we can distinguish between the sobriety of Rotz's mere generalized landscapes of hilly savannah, and the glowing romantic exuberance of Desceliers' detailed, even finicky, miniatures, bright with the amazing richness of medieval illumination. It is all very fantastic if you look at it with a literal eye, but quite in order as generous crafts-manship—which is what it is meant to be. Useless to complain that in the weird fauna we look in vain for so much as a wallaby, or that those strange rites never were in Australia. Yet this is just what Scott does: 'These figures cannot be representative of anything seen in Australia.' Quite true: but if (once more) we look beyond Jave le Grande, to Brazil or South Africa, we find pictures just as unrepresen-tative of anything seen in those parts, and even Scott would scarcely argue that these countries had not been visited before 1530. But indeed we do not need to go so far afield. A closer look at Desceliers' map shows that each of these scenes has a label—easily legible even in Collingridge's reproductions—and these refer to such places as Pegu, Sumatra, and Ceylon. 'Taken literally', as Forsyth puts it, Jave la Grande is used simply as so much space for the legends. What becomes of Scott's 'closer examination'?

In other directions Scott is just as unhandy:

> [the map-maker] did not like the look of Ptolemy's plain line, so he serrated it. [a] He actually attributed names to the teeth of the saw as if they were real capes. . . . [b] There is no continent stretching from Java to South America on the one side and to the south of Africa on the other.[18]

As to these points: (a) imaginary lands might often be tricked out with a conventional topography, 'to give an air of verisimilitude to an otherwise bald and unconvincing' outline, as on Wytfliet's imaginary Terra Australis of 1597; but these maps produced in academic studies do not carry a complete suite of place names. If the names on Jave la Grande are invented, why should a Norman or a Catalan or a German desk-geographer invent in Portuguese—even if poor Portuguese? and (b) from the Ptolemaic tradition nothing would have been more natural than to link up any discoveries in the Australia-New Guinea area with the

Magellanic Land, Terra Australis, or Brasiliae Regio—in their more Antarctic versions.[19] But this continent of Scott's is precisely what the Dieppe maps (except Desceliers' of 1550) do not show: they hedge on this point, leaving the southern ends of the coasts hanging in the sea, when they do not run off the edge of the map. The fact that so obvious a linkage is as a rule not made is if anything an argument in favour of the pro-Dieppe hypothesis. What motive had Rotz to insert a baseless fiction in the Atlas presented to Henry viii? If he desired to impress, that could have been done quite as easily and as well on the lines of Schoener or Orontius Finaeus, with a large inflation of the traditional Terra Australis.

Even if others of the Dieppe school were more reckless than Rotz, it seems illogical to assume, with Wood, that 'if one large part of the coastline is admitted to be imaginary, the suspicion that the whole is imaginary becomes irresistible'.* For the maps of the time are strewn with coasts part known and part supposed. Leaving aside real fantasies, such as what might be styled with great convenience the Polo Archipelago ('Beach and All That'), and confining ourselves to a continent partly known, Schoener's globes of 1515-20 show an island South America, with a strait near Panama and a very broad channel from Atlantic to Pacific about 40°S (15° north of the Straits of Magellan). This divides 'Brasilia sive Papagallis terra' (shown reasonably correctly from the voyages of Vespucci and others) from 'Brasilia inferior', a conflation of Patagonia and Antarctica; but the complete west coast of the continent, certainly not seen by any European, is shown, though marked 'Ultra incognita permansit'. Note the *ultra!* And had Quiros' alleged 200 maps come down to us, they would surely have shown a land-mass covering the Coral Sea; does this mean

---

* I agree however with Wood as against Major that it is incredible that most things from Cape Leeuwin to Bass Strait should be known, but not the Cape York Peninsula; but I do not think that this can be generalized to apply to the west coast at large. Nor did Flinders, whose judgement may surely be allowed as good as that of Professor Wood or Professor Spate or indeed any professor whomsoever.

that his landing on Espiritu Santo was imaginary? On the west coast at least, as Wood admits, there is some reason to agree with Flinders: 'the direction given to some parts of the coast approaches too near the truth for *the whole* to be marked from conjecture alone'. The italics are mine; Wood quotes this sentence but does not appear to see its full import.

There is however the difficult problem of the longitudes. If the land-mass is Australia, the maps have shifted it bodily westwards until Jave la Grande is impacted into the real Java, separated from it only by a narrow channel. Such a shift would put Arnhem Land adjacent on the south to Java, and Cape York to Sumbawa. The north coast of Java is accurate enough, but to the south accuracy is vitiated by the juxtaposition of Java and the great mainland of Jave la Grande.

This would seem an impossible error for a Portuguese cartographer to make. Not to repeat the earlier discussion of the south coast of Java, Rodrigues' map produced after the Moluccas voyage of 1512 shows a much better outline of Java—doubtless in part from indigenous sources—than any other map of the century except perhaps one by Alonzo de Santa Cruz (which I have not seen) of 1542. It seems likely that Rodrigues' map was 'official' and secret, while the vaguer outlines of Pedro Reinel (*c.* 1517) became standard in the 'public' cartography of the century, to Linschoten and beyond.*

The effect of this westwards shift is of course to block up the Timor Sea, so that the approach to the Moluccas could only be across the Pacific (and Magellan's route was so difficult that it was soon superseded by direct voyages from Spanish bases on the American west coast) or by the Straits of Malacca and Sunda (and here the officers of the King of

---

* Be it noted: (1) *The Book of Francisco Rodrigues*, with his maps, forms part of the same codex as Pires' *Suma Oriental*; (2) Ramusio, who translated the *Suma*, was unable to obtain a complete transcript and states that if the author 'wanted his book to be seen, he was forced to take away all that part which towards the end deals with the Moluccas and the spices'.

Portugal must be reckoned with). The effect was thus to bar out all but Iberian seamen. From this, Collingridge goes so far as to suggest collusion between Spain and Portugal—in itself a most unlikely thing in the years, critical both for the Moluccas dispute and our immediate problem, before the Treaty of Saragoça in 1529—since 'both nations had something to gain by showing the sea-way blocked' by linking Java with the (Antarctic) Terra Australis so that, as in Ptolemy's day, the Indian Ocean would be land-locked on the south, but for the Cape entry. But, as we have noted, it is one of the virtues of the Dieppe maps that they mostly do not take this easy course, so academically orthodox as to be almost obligatory. Moreover, del Cano in the *Vitoria* had sailed across the Timor Sea, as is shown on Ribeiro's map of 1529, so that the Spaniards knew the truth on this point. Hence Collingridge is forced to his hypothesis of collusion, and for once we can agree whole-heartedly with Wood:

> As for the *motive* of the Portuguese map-maker, it seems to me that if his aim had been to discourage Spanish voyages, he would, like so many others, have drawn an *empty* Pacific. . . . These Portuguese maps . . . might have persuaded [the Spaniards] of the existence of a great Southern Continent, a large part of which, at any rate, was shown even by the Portuguese to be on the Spanish side of the line . . . there seems no evidence either that the Spaniards were acquainted with these maps, or that the Portuguese ever sought to make them acquainted.[20]

The Portuguese had few or no scruples about faking evidence if it suited state policy; and had this fake or error of the longitude been to their advantage they would have publicized it. They did not, and the presumption therefore is that they did not commit it. Since no hint of Jave la Grande appears in the 'public' cartography of Portugal, the original charts, if Portuguese, must have been kept on the secret list. The question is bound up with the delimitation of the Spanish and Portuguese hemispheres, but this affects the question of secrecy rather than the longitudinal shift in itself: for it would be quite impossible to take all of Jave la

Grande out of the Spanish sphere without trespassing too far into the already fairly well-known parts of the Indian Ocean, while the more limited shift actually made on the Dieppe charts would be pointless, as it could not possibly deceive the Spaniards after the *Vitoria*'s voyage in 1521-2; and, as we shall see, 1522 is a likely date for the first Portuguese voyage south of Java. There was an alternative: to keep quiet and to shift the dividing line itself. Hence perhaps the silence of Galvão as to a 'southland', which so puzzles Wood: he was after all Governor of the Moluccas, and only seven years after Saragoça he had to report the visit of a Spanish ship from Acapulco, with the promise of more being prepared 'to be sent to China and the Lequeos [Riu-kius] and Molucca, and to discover another new world'.[21] Better say nothing!

But if Portuguese seamen could not possibly confuse the north coast of Java with that of Arnhem Land by accident, and had no motive to do it on purpose, a Frenchman with no local knowledge could have done so. The Parmentiers, who were in Sumatra about 1529, have been suggested as possible intermediaries. This is plausible at first sight, but would they not have made a better job of it, since they could hardly have failed to hear of the *Vitoria*'s voyage?

To me it seems more likely that there were two sources involved: a map of Java, perhaps after Rodrigues (to allow for 'Agoada Dollim') but possibly with an indeterminate south coast; and a map of Jave la Grande by itself. Whatever reserves may be held as to a general policy of secrecy, there can be very little doubt that in a case like this, of new coasts which it might be possible to hold *incommunicado* indefinitely, such maps could only be obtained surreptitiously; there were strict regulations for their issue to and return by captains and pilots; and indeed we have seen the evidence of the *Suma Oriental* codex itself. But Lisbon was full of spies, and an illicit 'borrowing' for a night or two (for a consideration to the confidential clerk, of course) and the consequent hurried copying, without benefit of tracing paper, might well account for the distortion evident in the Dieppe maps. No doubt also, as Williamson suggests, a

Portuguese renegade, perhaps a New Christian who found the kingdom too uncomfortable, might have smuggled copies out; there were many such in the larger ports of western Europe.[22]

There remains one more difficulty, which I feel to be a strong one but which I have not seen in the literature. Giving largest scope to the policy of secrecy, one cannot see that it could have applied when the Crown of Portugal fell to Philip II of Spain (I of Portugal) in 1580. The administration was, it is true, kept entirely separate from that of Spain, and no doubt patriotically resentful officials would be in no hurry to dig out ancient documents—in the general slackening of the springs of Portuguese life at this time it would be no wonder if files were innocently 'lost', and sometimes really so; while the Spaniards might not have been so eager in the search as they would have been at the time of Saragoça fifty years earlier. Still, if there really were Portuguese originals of the Dieppe maps (and this seems so certain to me that perhaps 'mystery' is a better word than 'difficulty'), it is strange that no hint of them came to light at this time. Erédia's ignorance is not perhaps surprising, but Quiros, Portuguese by birth and with a passionate concern for the Southland, would surely have left no file undisturbed, no archivist unpestered, and it seems extraordinary that he should not have heard of information so superbly fitted to his purpose.

Notwithstanding this very puzzling silence, it seems fair to sum up, with Williamson, to the effect that while it is difficult either to accept or to reject the hypothesis that the Dieppe maps represent a definite discovery, the more difficult course, if we examine the evidence closely, is to regard the sudden appearance of so definite an outline as mere fantasy. The maps are hard to explain on any view, but, everything considered, the simple process of sweeping them away as 'the products of voyages of imagination' leaves even more to explain than accepting them as imperfectly representing an imperfect knowledge of Australia obtained from Portuguese sources, or perhaps from Asian sources via the Portuguese.

IV. FROM TORDESILHAS TO SARAGOÇA

The Papal award of 1493, as amended by the Treaty of Tordesilhas in 1494, did not divide the world 'like an orange': although the sphericity of the earth had been firmly established for centuries,[23] nobody had been to the other side of the globe and there was little point and less possibility of making a precise demarcation of the utterly unknown. There was also an escape clause covering prior discovery and possession.[24] But once the Portuguese reached the Moluccas in 1512, and even more when Magellan's ships *Vitoria* and *Trinidad* reached them from the Spanish side —via the Philippines—the question became acute.

There can be no doubt whatever that the Portuguese were in general better informed of the true dimensions of lands and seas than were the Spaniards who, under Columban influence, held far too long to the gross under-estimates of distance (expressed of course in exaggerations of longitude in degrees) of Ptolemaic geography. This superior information gave the former considerable advantages in negotiation; thus Columbus' claim to have reached Asia, or near it, 'favoured the acceptance of the Portuguese proposals in 1493 and 1494', thus securing a solid footing in Brazil.[25] Moreover the King of Portugal was first in possession of the Moluccas—though it was a nearer thing than is generally realized, as the Portuguese hold was really only secured by the building of a fort at Ternate in the interval between the *Trinidad*'s departure and her return.[26]

The Badajoz discussions were abortive, but the Treaty of Saragoça (1529) was in effect a diplomatic triumph for Portugal—though largely because of Charles v's European tangles—and its major provision may well have much significance for our problem. This was that a line of demarcation should be adopted from pole to pole, defined by laying off 19° on a bearing NE by E from the Moluccas,* and drawing a meridian through the point so obtained.

---

* '. . . una linia de polo a polo, convjene a saber del norte al sul, por huum semicirculo que diste de Maluquo al nordeste, tomando la quarta del este, diez y nueve grados. . . .'

But this meridian would be considerably to the east of the true anti-meridian of the Tordesilhas line—perhaps as much as 14°, so that the Portuguese 'hemisphere' was 187° as against 173° for the Spanish. Why?

To Portuguese writers it seems obvious that there was something to hide—namely Australia. The placing of the line 12° or 14° east of its proper position would bring all of the continent west of Mount Gambier or Melbourne within the Portuguese sphere, without any need for a westwards shift such as that on the Dieppe maps. In the north the Spaniards knew too much, once Magellan had reached the Philippines; but in the south it was still possible silently to stake out a claim. Considering the quasi-secret expeditions which both parties sent out 'for the rapid exploration of the island world of south-east Asia', one may well ponder Jaime Cortesão's summing up:

> . . . it is difficult to imagine that the Portuguese had not reached the northern shores of that continent. . . . Does not this singular coincidence of this belated Castilian project ['para descobrir outro novo mundo'] with a hidden reality indicate the leakage of a secret discovery, and the suspicion on their part that the lands discovered were outside Portuguese sovereignty, according to the Treaty of Saragoça? The silence of the chroniclers and the documents . . . would have a completely logical explanation in the series of facts, both causes and effects, of the Treaty of 1529.[27]

One may feel that there is here some special pleading—and Jaime Cortesão is the leading theoretician of the 'policy of secrecy' (which is further discussed below); nevertheless Saragoça is a significant element in the problem, and one neglected in Australian writing.

The likelihood of a chance discovery by a ship off its course was much less for the Portuguese than for the Dutch. The centre of gravity of Lusian power was to the west, in India: the continuing element of a crusade against the 'Moors'; the need to cut off Turkish aid to the Muslim rulers of western India by controlling the sea-gates of Aden and Ormuz; the early grasp of the local and locational advantages of Goa as the metropolitan node of the 'State of India'—all these combined to set up a geopolitical pattern in which Malacca was an advanced base and the Malacca Straits the normal entry into the Archipelago. The Dutch, arriving later and for four decades unable to take Malacca itself, used the Sunda Straits entry, which they guarded by founding Batavia in 1619. When we recall the good reason for avoiding the seas south of Java, it is not surprising that it was left to the Dutch to pioneer the route running before the Westerlies from the Cape and northing in about 100°E —which was bound to lead sooner or later to a landfall in New Holland by captains miscalculating their easting. Nevertheless there were at least two Portuguese voyages which should be discussed in this context: one, that of Gomes de Sequeira, accidental; the other, by Cristovão de Mendonça, deliberate. The chronicles then are not absolutely silent, though in the former case their voice is perhaps incoherent, in the latter abruptly cut off.

Very specific claims (in my opinion fallacious) have been made for the involuntary voyage of Gomes de Sequeira in 1525, concerning which there are at least four quasi-contemporary accounts.[28] There is no doubt that Sequeira was blown some 300 leagues east from Celebes, fetching up on an island 'of some 30 leagues'. Admiral Gago Coutinho is convinced that the route was *south*-easterly across the Arafura Sea to Cape York Peninsula. The most serious point in favour of this interpretation is the representation on a chart by the Genoese Gastaldi (1554) of two groups of islands east of Timor—'Insul. de Gomes des quera' and 'Ins. des hobres blancos'. These correspond well enough to the Tanimbar (Timor Laut) and Aru-Kei Islands respectively, and Barros states specifically that Sequeira marked the position of the islands named after him on a chart, while the people were

> of a brown colour, rather white than black, with smooth hair and beards, simple folk who showed that they had never seen other men, and whose speech the Malay interpreters did not understand.

However, they could indicate to Sequeira that gold was found to the west of the island! Irrespective of its accuracy, Gastaldi's chart is clear evidence of an isolated borrowing from a Portuguese original now lost: the relevance to the Dieppe question is obvious.

Coutinho's argument is that Sequeira was driven between Timor Laut and the Aru Islands; Cape York is about the right distance and in a storm-driven voyage like this the discrepancy with Gastaldi's position is not perhaps very material; only rough approximations are possible. There were also any number of cases in which a mainland was mistaken for an island and *vice versa*. But the Admiral seems to want too many things both ways at once; and finally blows himself up by pointing out that the Kimberley goldfields *are* west of Cape York. . . .

Armando Cortesão bases himself rather on Galvão's account; Galvão became Captain of the Moluccas only ten years later and would surely have been in a better position to get accurate accounts of such a chance voyage than were Barros and Castanheda in Lisbon. Galvão says that the voyage was *north*-easterly; and from a study of the winds Cortesão shows, I think quite conclusively, that the island of Gomes de Sequeira was in all probability Palau.

Finally we may consider the voyages of Cristovão de Mendonça and his predecessor Diogo Pacheco—the former being the just-faintly-possible True Discoverer. All that we know about them comes from Barros; but this is much less suspicious than seems at first sight, since if the topic was on the secret list—and this is inherently most probable—then Barros as the official historiographer would alone have had full access to the documents.

We have already mentioned Pacheco's voyage of 1518 to Barros, reconnoitring for the Isle(s) of Gold. Barros lies on the west coast of Sumatra, at about 2°N (opposite Nias), and Pacheco returned to Malacca by the Sunda Straits. Next year (1519) he set out again, but somewhere south of Barros (and definitely on the west coast) he was wrecked: in João de Barros' words, 'o primeiro dos nossos que perdeo a vida por descobrir esta jhla douro'. But as Armando Cortesão

U

points out, if he was the *first* to lose his life in the quest, there must have been others.[29]

Of Pacheco's voyage we do at least know the end; of Mendonça's only the beginning. In 1520 Diogo Lopes, Captain-General and Governor of India, received royal instructions to

> entrust some person with this journey to discover the Isles of Gold, beyond Sumatra, of which we wrote before, since many persons who had travelled in those parts of India gave great hopes that they could be found.[30]

Accordingly Cristovão de Mendonça was sent 'on the voyage which we shall mention later'. But all that we learn later is that in mid-1521 Mendonça was at Pedir and Pacem (at the northern end of Sumatra) on his voyage, but, as the monsoon did not then serve, he went on to Malacca, presumably to await the favourable monsoon towards the end of the year.

The expedition was important enough to be given three ships; the odd thing is that Barros is normally meticulous in telling of the disposal of ships at the end of a voyage, so that his silence in this case is distinctly suspicious. A mere loss could well have been recorded, as was Pacheco's; but Mendonça turns up later as Governor of Ormuz.

At this point it is probably desirable to come to closer terms with the disputed question of the Portuguese 'politica de sigilo', the policy of secrecy.

There is a good deal in Morison's witty attack on the hypothesis that there was a definite, considered, and continuing policy of keeping discoveries secret until it was safe or necessary to reveal them: Jaime Cortesão may have a little more than the 'one undoubted fact' that Morison allows him, but the secrecy school undoubtedly heaps 'a mountain of inferences' on a very narrow base.[31] It is a little too convenient to be convincing: all the Top Secret documents were kept in the Casa da India, and then (conveniently again) destroyed in the Lisbon earthquake of 1755. As Morison points out, in some of the instances in which the existence of the policy is invoked to explain the non-existence of evidence, 'secrecy would have been no policy, but sheer imbecility', since Portugal had everything to gain by resolutely publishing her claims. In view of the constant multilateral traffic in pilots and experts, a rigid enforcement of the policy would have been unworkable and indeed self-stultifying. And the security system would have been very remarkable indeed to succeed in blotting out not only its subject matter, but all trace of its own existence—especially after 1580!

On the other hand, there are not a few clear hints—for example Ramusio's difficulty with the *Suma*—to what we might fairly expect: as much secrecy as it was possible to maintain concerning certain areas at certain times. The matter has been very fairly put by Damião Peres:

> In theory it is perfectly acceptable that the idea of keeping as secret as possible all knowledge which might favour the pretensions of rivals would spring to the minds of those directing Portuguese maritime enterprise. How far, however, can it be maintained that historical reality accords with this *a priori* supposition? . . . From all which has been here put forward, it must be concluded that there was no policy of secrecy, systematically organized and prosecuted during the golden century of the Discoveries, while it must be admitted that the State power, in certain periods and to differing degrees according to the circumstances, did exert itself to keep secret essential factors in the national task of overseas expansion.[32]

How far would the present case come under this very reasonable rule?

In assessing this, we must recall that it was just in 1522, the year after Mendonça began his voyage, that the *Vitoria* reached the Moluccas and the 'question' became most acute. Even after 1529, Spanish interest remained active: not only in 1536 but again in 1545, expeditions were sent across the Pacific from Spanish America to the Spice Islands.[33] Despite Saragoça, then, the question was only formally closed when Barros was writing Decada III of *Da Asia* in the fifties, and security was still probably important, or at least so regarded. Now Barros, though a fine and conscientious historian, was also the official historiographer; perhaps little more need be said! Denucé speaks of 'ses précieuses *Decadas da Asia*', but adds 'on ne doit l'utiliser qu'avec réserve pour toute la periode si embrouillée de la première occupation des Moluques'.[34]

Why then mention Cristovão de Mendonça at all? My guess is that in revising for publication the results of the voyage were suppressed—there is evidence even later of falsification on a bolder scale than this. But *Da Asia* is a large book, chronologically arranged, and it would be quite possible for the earlier references, probably several chapters back, to be inadvertently allowed to stand: a thing which has indeed happened with much shorter and simpler writings.*

There are perhaps other hints in the Portuguese literature, which certainly deserves more intensive study than it has received here; for instance Gabriel Rebello's remark:

> According to the information which we have of these Isles [of the Papuas], they run along a great land, which seems to be that imagined Southland, which on the east and west goes to the Strait of Magellan.[35]

But this might be a mere Ptolemaic memory—though very late for a Portuguese (Rebello was a rather limited man) —or it may refer to New Guinea itself, the insularity of which seems to have been known to or guessed by the Portuguese before Torres.

All this once more amounts to nothing beyond probability. Nevertheless, looking to all the circumstances, I am inclined to conclude with Armando Cortesão that 'the cumulative effect of all these considerations leads me to believe that there are serious grounds for giving credence to the discovery of Australia by the Portuguese in 1522'.[36] 'Serious grounds': no more than that, but no less.

---

* Even with a press cable: as a Military Press Censor of some standing, I can fairly say *experto crede*!

V. CONCLUSION: BEYOND THE PORTUGUESE?

There is far too much in this essay that is inferential, in the manner of *Osmunda Regalis*,* for any very firm conclusion to be drawn: the navigation is very tricky, full of shoals and reefs, and I am equipped only for reconnaissance, not for 'voyages of detailed and scientific survey'. Nevertheless, if the positive evidence for a pre-Dutch discovery of Australia lacks concreteness, I think it may be allowed that many of the negative arguments against it are not very well founded; that the question is more open than either Wood or Scott admitted. The object of this essay is simply to suggest the need for a new survey: 'if we would get rid of obscurantism', we should not regard open questions as *choses jugées*. If the question is regarded as of any interest or importance at all, there is a good deal of work to be done before we can legitimately be content with the traditional Wood-Scott position.

For one thing, there are the tantalizing possibilities of pre-Portuguese knowledge. This at least is not so very academic, since if Malays and Chinese knew of Australia, but did not think it worthwhile to put more than a few ephemeral fishing camps on it, Asians can hardly complain if, by their default, Europeans occupied the continent. I know from personal experience that this can be made the starting point of a rational defence of a restrictive immigration policy—if not so rigid as that which exists; a defence which can command respect in Asia, if not an acceptance which it might be unreasonable to expect.

On 1 April 1512 Afonso de Albuquerque wrote to the King of Portugal about a map taken from a Javanese pilot's

---

* 'We may therefore not unreasonably infer . . . that Osmunda Regalis, to call the abbess by a traditional name, the authenticity of which we shall discuss later, was probably born—assuming the passage we have quoted not to be an interpolation—in a smiling valley of one (though we should hardly be justified in saying which) of the loveliest counties of Anglo-Saxon Britain. Without prolonging a barren discussion . . . etc., etc., etc.' (see J. C. Squire (ed.), *Apes and Parrots*, London, 1928, pp. 167-70).

chart; the original with names in Javanese has been lost at sea, but he sends a copy with transliterations, and has discussed its meaning with the pilot himself: 'it seems to me, Senhor, the finest thing I have ever seen'—and in a flash we see Albuquerque, grand applied geographer that he was, bending eagerly over this treasure in the cabin of the *Frol de la Mar*.[37] There are other references, for example in Barros, do Couto, and the *Suma Oriental*, to the nautical and cartographical skill of the Arabs and the 'Jaos'; notably the account in Barros of the pilot of Melinde:

> Once he had discussed matters with him, Vasco da Gama was well satisfied of the competence of this pilot, especially when he showed him a chart of all the Indian coast laid out in the manner of the Moors, which is by meridians and parallels very close together, without wind-roses; since the grid of these meridians and parallels is very small, the coasts in the directions North-South and East-West is shown with much certainty, without the multiplication of wind- and compass-roses common in our chart. . . .[38]

There is a tremendous gap in our knowledge here. After all, for centuries Arabs, Chinese, and Malays had been sailing the seas of Insulindia: it seems scarcely possible that they never sighted Australia, and research into their navigational and cartographic techniques may yet give us a fairly definite answer to the question of pre-European knowledge of our continent. It may even be, as J. W. Forsyth has suggested (most unfortunately not in fully published form) that the Asian charts were the real sources of the Dieppe maps, and that the extraordinary protrusion of Cap de Fremose in the south-east of Jave la Grande is the result of an easily made draughting error in transferring the content of such a chart to a European projection.[39] Archaeology and anthropology too may have much to tell us, as is indicated by C. P. Fitzgerald's discussion of the Chinese image found at Darwin.[40]

Again, as Manning Clark has suggested, the more direct historical records of Indonesia need examination. Erédia, for example (and he was half Macassarese) reports Malay and Chinese voyages which have in common at least one thing—they were southwards from eastern Java, Flores, and Timor; and not all the details are fantastic. And we would give much for 'those verses and ballads and chronicles of the Empire of Mattaram, which tell of that ancient navigation'.[41]

Moreover it is a mistake to assume that even the European documentary material is exhausted. Portuguese quasi-contemporary works and secondary sources could well be re-examined; and within the last few years a complete manuscript volume of maps and drawings by Erédia (unluckily not relevant to our subject) has been discovered, in private archives, by Senhor Jorge Faro of Lisbon. It is thus still possible that more archival material may be found. At any rate the quest has still an abiding fascination, even though the last word may have to be with Camoes:

> Behold the spreading isles of Sunda, hid
> By a large zone towards the perilous South. . . .

Note: A good deal of the more detailed documentation of this essay has been omitted.

For assistance and/or critical discussion, I am greatly indebted to Senhor Jorge Faro of Lisbon, to Senhor Alexandre Marques Pereira of the Sociedade de Geográfia (Lisbon), and to Mr J. W. Forsyth of Sydney. Basic work was done mainly in London and Lisbon, on study leave from the Australian National University, and writing up in the Mitchell Library, to whose staff my thanks are also due.

References

The Compass of Geography

1 C. de Montesquieu, *De l'Esprit des Lois* (Paris, 1748), xiv, 12-13; E. Huntington, *Mainsprings of Civilization* (New York, 1945), p. 284.

2 W. A. Gauld, *Man, Nature and Time* (London, 1946), p. 124.

3 *La Maison du Berger*, III, stanzas 10-11.

Quantity and Quality in Geography

1 Ackerman: University of Chicago, Department of Geography Research Paper No. 53 (1958); Hartshorne: Rand McNally, for Association of American Geographers (Chicago, 1959).

2 J. Tricart, 'La Géomorphologie et la Pensée Marxiste', *La Pensée* (Paris), No. 69 (1956), pp. 3-24.

3 Preston James, 'The Field of Geography', in *American Geography: Inventory and Prospect* (Syracuse University Press, for Association of American Geographers, 1954), p. 15.

4 Cf. O. H. K. Spate, *India and Pakistan* (2nd ed.; London, Methuen; New York, Dutton, 1957), p. vii; J. E. Spencer, *Asia East by South* (New York, John Wiley; London, Chapman and Hall, 1954), p. vii; W. R. Thomas Jr., *Land, Man and Culture in Mainland Southeast Asia* (published by the author, 1957), *passim*.

5 Preston James, op. cit., p. 13.

6 G. H. T. Kimble, 'The Craft of the Geographer', *Canadian Geographical Journal*, 31 (1960), p. 257.

7 But cf. A. C. Montefiore and W. M. Williams, 'Determinism and Possibilism', *Geographical Studies*, 2, No. 1 (1955), pp. 1-11, and my comment in *Geographical Review*, 48, No. 2 (1958), pp. 280-3.

8 Derwent Whittlesey, 'The Regional Concept and the Regional Method', in *American Geography: Inventory and Prospect* (1954), pp. 37-40; cf. Hartshorne, op. cit., pp. 129-42, and Ackerman, op. cit., pp. 15-16, 28-30. Cf. J. F. Unstead's careful and potentially fruitful proposals in 'A System of Regional Geography', *Geography*, 18 (1933), pp. 175-87.

[9] Preston James, *Papers and Proceedings of the Regional Science Association*, 4 (1958), p. 26.

[10] These volumes, hereafter referred to as *Papers and Proceedings*, are published by the Regional Science Association, Wharton School, University of Pennsylvania, Philadelphia 4.

[11] *Papers and Proceedings*, 2 (1956), pp. 13-26 (Isard) and 27-39 (Garnsey). Text references to Isard are to this paper.

[12] Ibid., pp. 40-3; cf. R. A. Platt, ibid., pp. 46-8.

[13] Ibid., 4 (1958), p. 24.

[14] F. Lukermann, 'Geography: *de facto* or *de jure*'. Unpublished.

[15] *Location and Space Economy* (New York, John Wiley, and Technology Press, M.I.T., 1956), p. 182, n. 13.

[16] For a balanced view, see T. R. Smith, in *Papers and Proceedings*, 3 (1957), pp. 13-15, and the conclusion of Garnsey's paper cited above (3 (1956)), at p. 39. Significantly, Smith speaks of Garnsey's as the 'relaxed' conception of regional science, with presumably an implied contrast to Isard's.

[17] Cited, e.g. in Ackerman, op. cit., p. 12 (n. 22), and in the introduction to Leslie Curry's Auckland Ph.D. thesis, 'Climate and Livestock in New Zealand—A Functional Geography' (1958). I have seen, but cannot now place, a third very recent resurrection.

[18] 'Lord Kelvin Rides Again', *Economic Geography*, 36 (1960), guest editorial.

[19] Cf. B. J. L. Berry, 'Statistical Tests of Value in Grouping Geographical Phenomena', paper read at 1959 meeting of the Association of American Geographers, p. 1; P. R. Gould, 'The Geographical Application of Nearest Neighbor Theory' (unpublished MS., 1957), p. 1; M. F. Dacey, 'Analysis of Map Distribution by Nearest Neighbor Methods', University of Washington (Seattle), Department of Geography Paper No. 1 (1958), pp. 3-5; P. J. Clark, and F. C. Evans, 'Distance to Nearest Neighbor as a Measure of Spatial Relationships in Populations', *Ecology*, 35, No. 4 (1954), pp. 445-53. My attention was drawn to these papers, and indeed to the subject generally, by my student R. H. T. Smith.

[20] D. W. Goodall, 'Quantitative Aspects of Plant Distribution', *Biological Reviews*, 27 (1952), pp. 194-245 (at p. 195).

[21] D. W. Goodall, 'Vegetational Classification and Vegetational Continua', *Angewandte Pflanzensoziologie, Aichinger Festschrift*, No. 1 (1954), pp. 168-82.

[22] Samuel Butler, *Hudibras. The First Part* (1663), Canto I, lines 121-6.

23 B. J. L. Berry, 'Ribbon Developments in the Urban Business Pattern', *Annals Association of American Geographers*, 49 (1959), pp. 145-55.

24 W. L. Garrison (ed.), *Studies of Highway Development and Geographic Change* (Seattle, University of Washington Press, 1959).

25 In *Proceedings of the International Geographical Union Regional Conference in Japan 1957* (Tokyo: Science Council of Japan, 1959), pp. 302-9.

26 E. Van Cleef, 'Must Geographers Apologize?' *Annals Association of American Geographers*, 45 (1955), pp. 105-8. For succinct comment, see Hartshorne, op. cit., p. 128.

27 In *Geographical Review*, 48 (1958), pp. 167-84.

28 Cf. C. N. Forward and C. W. Raymond, 'Small-scale Land Use Mapping from Statistical Data', *Economic Geography*, 35 (1959), pp. 315-21.

29 Lukermann, op. cit., in n. 14; cf. also his 'Toward a More Geographic Economic Geography', *Professional Geographer*, 10, No. 4 (1958), pp. 2-10; P. W. Porter, 'Does Geography Need a Social Physic?' unpublished.

30 'Geography: *de facto* or *de jure*', ad fin.

31 J. A. La Nauze, 'The Study of Australian History, 1929-1959', *Australian Journal of Science*, 32, No. 6 (1959), pp. 227-34; also in *Historical Studies* (Melbourne), 9, No. 33 (1959), pp. 1-11.

32 *American Geography: Inventory and Prospect*, p. 15.

33 Collingwood, *The Idea of History* (Oxford, 1946), p. 163. 'Geographical' has been substituted for 'historical'.

34 Hartshorne, op. cit., p. 162.

35 *Papers and Proceedings*, 4 (1959), p. 26.

36 'Toynbee and Huntington: A Study in Determinism', pp. 211 below.

37 In introduction to D. H. Rawcliffe, *Illusions and Delusions of the Supernatural and the Occult* (New York, Dover Publications, 1959), p. 6.

Toynbee and Huntington

1 R. G. Collingwood, *The Idea of History* (Oxford, 1946), p. 177.

2 P. Geyl, 'Toynbee's System of Civilizations', *Journal of the History of Ideas*, 9 (1948), pp. 93-124.

[3] P. Gourou, 'Civilisations et malchance géographique', *Annales— Économies Sociétés Civilisations*, 4 (1959), pp. 445-50.

[4] D. Whittlesey, *The Earth and the State* (New York, 1939), p. 558.

[5] H. J. Mackinder, *Democratic Ideals and Reality* (Pelican ed., 1944), p. 30.

[6] R. Hartshorne, *The Nature of Geography* (Lancaster, Pa., 1939), p. 185.

[7] Collingwood, op. cit., p. 100; cf. L. Febvre, *A Geographical Introduction to History* (London, 1932), p. 225.

Reflections on A Study of History

[1] K. de B. Codrington, 'A Geographical Introduction to the History of Central Asia', *Geographical Journal*, 104 (1944), pp. 27-40, 73-91; L. Febvre, *A Geographical Introduction to History* (1932), pp. 261-86.

[2] P. Geyl, 'Toynbee's System of Civilizations', *Journal of the History of Ideas*, 9 (1948), pp. 93-124.

[3] P. Gourou, 'Civilisations et malchance géographique', *Annales— Économies Sociétés Civilisations*, 4 (1949), pp. 445-50.

Finis Coronat Opus?

[1] P. Geyl, 'Toynbee's Answer', *Med. der Kon. Nederlandse Akademie van Wetenschappen, afd. Letterkunde* (new series), 24 (1961), p. 7.

Terra Australis – Cognita?

[1] J. McAuley, 'The True Discovery of Australia', *Under Aldebaran* (Melbourne, 1946).

[2] *Australian Discovery by Sea* (London, 1929), p. xi.

[3] *A Short History of Australia*, p. 8.

[4] Wood, pp. 84-5; cf. ibid., p. 121.

[5] *Da Asia*, Decada III Liv. iii Cap. 4 (Vol. III*, pp. 351-2) (first published in 1563).

[6] Hydrographic Office, Admiralty, *Eastern Archipelago Pilot*, Vol. II, 5th ed., 1935, pp. 3, 134. Cf. also J. Horsburgh, *India Directory* (London, 3rd ed., 1826), p. 121.

[7] Wood, pp. 85-6; cf. pp. 42, 120.

References

[8] G. Ferrand, *L'Empire sumatranais de Çrivijaya* (Paris, 1922), pp. 185-97 (cited by J. Cortesao in D. Peres (ed.), *História de Portugal* (Barcelos, 1932), Vol. IV, p. 23). Cf. also A. Rainaud, *Le Continent austral* (Paris, 1893), p. 275, n.2.

[9] Barros, Dec. III Liv. iii Cap. 3 (Vol. II*, p. 269).

[10] For a general account of Erédia, see 'Manuel Godinho de Erédia: Quest for Australia' (p. 249, above); and for the boom and collapse of belief in his discovery the following (*inter alia*—all but the last in Mitchell Library): R. H. Major, *The Discovery of Australia by the Portuguese in 1601*; and *Further Facts relating to the Discovery of Australia* (London, 1873, with diverting *Supplementary Observations*—Pomposo eating his own words); A. T. Hamy, 'Le Descobridor Godinho de Erédia', in *Mémoires pour servir à l'Histoire des Découvertes . . . en Océanie* (Paris, 1878); C. Ruelens, introduction to L. Janssens (ed.) (with French translation) of *Erédia's Declaracam de Malaca* (Brussels, 1882); Rainaud, op. cit., pp. 350-6; Q. da Fonseca, 'A partiçipao dos portugueses . . . no descobrimento da Austrália', *Mem. da Acad. das Ciências de Lisboa* (Coimbra, 1937), pp. 399-417.

[11] J. E. T. Woods, *A History of the Discovery and Exploration of Australia* (London, 1865), Vol. I, p. 8.

[12] Wood, p. x.

[13] Reproductions of the main maps and opposing accounts will be found in Wood, pp. 113-29, and G. Collingridge, op. cit., pp. 166-94, *passim* (as well as numerous papers). Collingridge's discussion of their toponymy is the more careful, but distinctly *parti pris*. There is a recent discussion in M. Hervé, 'Australia: in French Geographical Documents of the Renaissance', *J. & P. R.A.H.S.*, 41, 1955, pp. 23-38, with important notes by J. W. Forsyth.

[14] *Cambridge History of the British Empire*, Vol. VII, pt. 1, 1933, pp. 32-3. Some account of Rotz will be found in E. G. R. Taylor, *Tudor Geography 1485-1583* (London, 1930), pp. 61-70.

[15] Hervé, op. cit. at pp. 26 and 23, and Forsyth's note 11.

[16] Wood, pp. 120, 126.

[17] *Australian Discovery by Sea*, p. xi.

[18] Ibid., pp. xi-xii; cf. *Short History*, p. 5; and for Wytfliet, Wood, pp. 11-12.

[19] Cf. Rainaud, pp. 274-6.

[20] Collingridge, pp. 169-70; Wood, pp. 125-6.

Let Me Enjoy

[21] Letter of Galvao cited in J. Denucé, *Magellan: La Question des Molluques et la Première Circumnavigation* (Brussels, 1911), p. 405, n. 2. Cf. J. A. Williamson (ed.), *The Observations of Sir Richard Hawkins* (London, 1913), pp. xvii-xix; J. Cortesao, in D. Peres, op. cit., Vol. IV, p. 66. Scott (by what one hopes is a fantastic slip) makes Galvao Spanish Governor of the Philippines!

[22] J. A. Williamson, loc. cit. (n. 33). On secrecy: Denucé, p. 401; Rainaud, pp. 263, 286; A. Cortesao, 'Espionagem dos Descobrimentos', *Vida Contemporânea* [sic!] 18, Lisbon, 1935, p. 2; and see below, n. 32.

[23] Any lingering doubts on this should be dispelled by E. G. R. Taylor, *Ideas on the Shape . . . of the Earth*, Historical Ass. Pamphlet No. 32 (London, 1943).

[24] Denucé, pp. 44-7.

[25] A. Cortesao, 'O Descobrimento da Australásia [i.e. Indonesia] e a "Questao das Molucas" ', Parte 3 Cap. X in A. Baiao *et al.* (eds.), *História da Expansao Portuguesa no Mundo*, Lisbon, 1937-41, Vol. II, pp. 130, 134-6; hereafter cited as 'Cortesao X'.

[26] Denucé, p. 371. The *Trinidad* was trying to sail to Central America.

[27] Denucé, p. 393; J. Cortesao, loc. cit.

[28] Almirante Gago Coutinho, *A Náutica dos Descobrimentos* (Lisbon, 1949), pp. 139-44, and A. Cortesao, 'A Expansao portuguesa através do Pacifico', Parte 3 Cap. XI in the *História da Expansao* (Vol. II, pp. 151-73; cited as 'Cortesao XI'). But cf. D. Peres, *História dos Descobrimentos Portugueses* (Oporto, 1943), pp. 479-82.

[29] Barros, Dec. III Liv. iii Cap. 3 (Vol. III*, pp. 269-70; discussed in Cortesao XI, pp. 156-9).

[30] Barros, Dec. III Liv. iv Cap. 3 (Vol. III*, p. 412); and Dec. III Liv. v Cap. 3 (Vol. III*, pp. 546-50) for the later reference.

[31] S. E. Morison, *Portuguese Voyages to America in the Fifteenth Century* (Harvard Historical Monographs XIV, 1940), pp. 76-86.

[32] 'Política de sigilo', Parte 3 Cap. III in *História da Expansao*, Vol. II, pp. 17-21.

[33] Galvao's letter (n. 21 above) and his *Discoveries of the World* (London, Hakluyt Society, 1862), pp. 238-9.

[34] Op. cit., pp. 31-2. For a good account of Barros and other Portuguese writers of the century, see B. Penrose, *Travel and Discovery in the Renaissance* (Harvard Univ. Press, 1952), pp. 277-90.

References

35 'Informaçao das Cousas de Maluca' (1569), in *Colleçao das Noticias . . . das Naçoes Ultramarinas* (Lisbon, Acad. Real das Sciencias, 1856), p. 187.

36 Cortesao X, p. 159.

37 Cortesao XI, p. 151; cf. his *Cartográfia e cartográfos portugueses dos séculos XV e XVI* (Lisbon, Seara Nova, 1935), Vol. II, pp. 126-8, for a discussion of some obscurities in the letter.

38 Dec. I Liv. iv Cap. 6 (Vol. I*, p. 319).

39 Note 16 in Hervé, loc. cit.

40 'A Chinese Discovery of Australia?' in T. Inglis Moore (ed.), *Australia Writes* (Melbourne, 1953), pp. 75-86; cf. P. M. Worsley, 'Early Asian Contacts with Australia', *Past and Present*, No. 8 (1955), pp. 1-11.

41 M. G. de Erédia, *Declaracam de Malaca*, Trat. II Cap. 1, p. 50 (MS., 1613; Brussels, 1882).

[It is regretted that the *til* is not available in the fount used for the above references.]